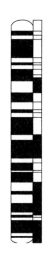

GUIDE TO
HUMA
GENOME
COMPUTING

G000055362

Edited by
MARTIN J BISHOP
MRC Molecular Genetics Unit
Cambridge, UK

ACADEMIC PRESS
Harcourt Brace & Company, Publishers
London   San Diego   New York
Boston   Sydney   Tokyo   Toronto

ACADEMIC PRESS LIMITED
24/28 Oval Road
London NW1 7DX

United States Edition published by
ACADEMIC PRESS INC.
San Diego, CA 92101

This book is printed on acid-free paper

A catalogue record for this book is available from
the British Library.

ISBN 0-12-102050-9

Printed and bound in Great Britain by
T.J. Press (Padstow) Ltd, Padstow, Cornwall.

Preface

Over the last 10 years or so, the growth of interest and activity in human genome mapping, and in genetics generally, has posed major organizational, administrative and managerial problems that have been unique in the history of biology. That is not to imply that, so far, the problems have been addressed globally (or even locally) with conspicuous success. But this timely book represents - taken at the most superficial level - one set of solutions to one set of such problems: those concerned with informing working scientists of the practicalities of making effective use of the power of computing to assist in the generating, processing, analysis and storage of data and the making of those data available, in as tractable a form as possible, as corporate resources to the whole community that now needs to use them. That such comprehensive computing facilities are now widely available is itself a substantial and creditable achievement. Even as recently as three years ago, it might have been possible for individuals or groups to have no link to external computing facilities and still to be credible forces in human genetics; that is no longer the case.

The book's overt didactic objective represents a substantial extension, both in scope and depth of detail, of the aims of the computing training courses that have been successfully run, over the last four years within the UK Human Genome Mapping Project and have made a major contribution to establishing a network of computer users in the UK. The book provides, for the first time, a comprehensive basis for "users" to make the most of what is available and, by informed feedback, to influence what is implemented. It should also help the dialogue - often non-existent - between users and their local computing services. Sorting out local failings is an expensive burden on central resources. Much of the necessary computing infrastructure often exists and has been paid for: making effective use of it should be accepted as a local responsibility. The book provides useful guidance on what additional local requirements will be implied, so that they can be properly budgeted for and expensive mistakes in procurement avoided. For those - whether in the UK or elsewhere - who need to argue a case for funding, there should be much useful material here.

What is less obvious - and merits spelling out - is that the book exemplifies a broad management philosophy that has been evolved, within the UK Project amongst others. This is a topic that has not engaged the interest of scientists: the use of the annual mass meetings of UK "users" to explore and ventilate these complicated and dense issues proved a failure; scientists want to talk about their own and each other's science and are bored by anything else. But, unless that reluctance is overcome, the Human Genome Project (with or without capital letters) is at risk. It is worth recalling that, when the bid for additional funding for a UK Human Genome Project was being planned, there was little enthusiasm amongst the (potential) user community in the UK. If that bid had not been made, the computing facilities now available through the Resource Centre would not currently be accessible to more than 1,000 users of the system. This book will be doubly valuable if, as scientists read it to help themselves with their science - and it will undoubtedly serve that purpose - they also think about the subtext: why are things the way they are now and where do we go from here and how?

Traditionally, human genome mapping data have been collated at the biennial Human Genome Mapping Workshops. In the late '80s it became clear that data were already accruing at a rate that required handling by computer, and after one shot by the group at Yale to solve the problem, a second venture - the Genome Database (GDB) was launched and the Human Genome Mapping meetings effectively became annual. The objective was to move to continuous data entry and to replace hard-copy distribution with on-line access. It is a moot point whether it is going to be practicable to follow this path and to broaden the scope of GDB (so far largely concerned primarily with genetic linkage data) to make it a unitary repository of all classes of human genome data. Essentially, GDB represents a classical management dilemma. An ill-defined problem arises and an inherently limited solution adopted; then as consequent (also ill-defined) problems arise that are not soluble within the management structure (how do people outside the US access the data and enter their own?) the existing investment becomes a compulsive reason for yet more investment. The question is when and how to grapple with the choice between ploughing on, or deciding to pull back and start again from the beginning, or accepting that the initial solution should be persevered with and refined but that new problems are to be solved in other ways. It is worth bearing in mind that GDB costs directly as much as the entire UK Project.

Irrespective of the practical politics of answering such questions and implementing the chosen solutions, anyone with a personal stake in genome mapping needs to ponder the reasons the problems arose in the first place.

The inevitable decision to computerize was a response to human genome mapping getting into a logarithmic phase of growth made possible initially by a whole series of technological developments and by individuals and groups moving into a fertile and promising field (bringing their resources and funding with them and shifting allocations within agency budgets). In the mid-1980s the idea of a systematic, rather than piecemeal, approach developed, and from that stemmed the various national and international programmes and initiatives that collectively represent the Human Genome Project (if such exists). However that concept was dressed up, it was driven by two implicit considerations: that to sustain further growth "new" money was needed that could no longer simply come from more-or-less informal reshuffling of existing resources; and that any new money had to be argued for (and stretched when won) by proposing to make the operation substantially more efficient and effective. That required some fundamental rethinking about the organization of research.

In the US (National Institutes of Health) initiative both these points were exemplified: by setting a major objective of complete sequencing of the human genome as a political play for more money, and by aiming to develop both collaboratively high-resolution physical maps as a framework for sequencing and, in parallel, less costly techniques for sequencing. That implies moving from "natural" logarithmic growth to a phased progress to an ambitious defined goal (with the implied expectation of funding to see the plan through over 20 years or so). Potential players then had a choice between joining that initiative, inevitably as minority shareholders, or of finding a complementary approach. The first option was simply not practical politics, either for most of the groups in the US or for other countries that wanted to be in the game. One reason is that, to be efficient and effective, mega-sequencing has to be a factory operation, partly because that is the nature of the operation and partly because individual groups will not be prepared to sequence with blinkers on: they will want to sequence what is interesting and pursue, in other ways, anything interesting that comes up.

With the exception of the US NIH programme, all corporate programmes (national and international) within the Human Genome Project are implicitly or explicitly offering new money, on a short-term basis, to their respective communities to improve efficiency and effectiveness and to justify further funding by delivery of the fruits. As demonstrated by the success of the existing sequence databases (whose importance and relevance extends far beyond genetics of course), computing is the stall on which those fruits will be displayed, whether to industry, to biologists or to clinicians. It is the value-adding activities of these latter groups of users that will be the political justification for continued funding for the Human Genome Project.

So far, computing has tended to lag, inevitably, behind the biology. That partly reflects the difficulty of specifying computing needs ahead of events. It also reflects the fact that the necessary funding for computing developments has had to be won by starting small and making a real case, by serving customer needs and giving them value for money, rather than putting forward grand prospectuses that compete blatantly for money that the scientists want for their immediate purposes. But any major increase in effectiveness and efficiency in the biology of human genetics, and in the application and exploitation of that biology, is now contingent on a major thrust of computing development. This book is an impressive illustration of the way in which fragmentary individual activities are now coming together and expanding.

It also argues a convincing case for a solution to the problem of ensuring that user needs are met. It is clear that software is best developed in day-to-day association with top-class scientific groups to satisfy local needs. Not only does that go a long way to ensuring that the software is what scientists want, but the development can usually be done on a shoe-string. Any douceur or additional funding should carry the obligation to make the software robust enough to be run and maintained from a central resource. The acknowledged success of the ACEDB system is a model.

For the same reasons, data are best kept by groups expert in the biology, and in databases designed to satisfy their own research needs, and as manageable subsets. The development of the Integrated Genomic Database (IGD) reflects the practical reconciliation of this philosophy with user need to be able to see all related and relevant data through a single window. All these activities have somehow to be managed.

Perhaps inevitably, large-scale national programmes generate a top-down management approach and tend to narrow the participating base to a few large groups. That may in practice be the only efficient way to do mega-sequencing. More generally, there is a natural tendency of peer-review committees to allocate funding to themselves and for "Task Forces" to get bogged down - if they move at all - in power politics. But the success, in political and public terms, of the Human Genome Project depends on its being pervasive. Interaction between the seats of power and the little people can be non-existent or restricted to beefing sessions at international meetings. Both the UK Project and the EC Genome Analysis Programme have been structured to favour distribution rather than concentration. That seems the right way to go. Paradoxically, unitary facilities are the key, because it is simply uneconomical to provide all groups with a complete repertoire of stand-alone facilities of their own. If both software development and database management are distributed, rather than concentrated, activities, there needs to be close coordination between the protagonists, and that coordination should be a bottom-up rather than top-down activity. The objective, which is made realizable by the existence of national and international networks and of systems centres like the UK HGMP Resource Centre's computing group, is for any individual user to be able to see what looks like a single system providing for all computing requirements. In reality, the system has many nodal components all accessed through a centre. The systems centre must provide services and not try to call the managerial shots. It can be the focus for dealings with the managements of national and international computing networks, to persuade them to respond to the growing needs of a community that has hitherto not loomed particularly large as users of networks. With the wisdom of hindsight it can be seen that the success of the UK Project has depended on having such a centre with those capacities.

The Human Genome Project raises major questions about intellectual property rights (or perhaps it would be more accurate to say that what should have been a non-issue was forced by the action of the US NIH in seeking patents rights over large collections of fragmentary sequences of randomly picked cDNAs). The data of the Human Genome Project do not themselves satisfy the requirements for patenting. And as, more and more, the generation of the data becomes a matter of routine, any lingering doubts on that score should disappear. The inventive step, the novelty and the utility - the prerequisites for patenting - will come from the exploitation of the data and resources. But by implication it illustrates clearly how dependent the Human Genome Project is on generosity and altruism in making complex software packages and data freely available. It will be easy for the pursuit of short-term profit and advantage to frustrate the larger purpose.

Dr Tony Vickers

Table of Contents

CHAPTER 3 Genetic Linkage Analysis 59

CHAPTER 1

The Computing Environment

Francis Rysavy

Clinical Research Centre, Watford Road, Harrow,
Middlesex HA1 3UJ, UK
Internet: frysavy@crc.ac.uk

A great deal has been written recently about molecular biology being in the midst of a major paradigm shift driven by the acquisition of nucleotide sequence information (Lander et al., 1991). To succeed in addressing major biological computational challenges such as sequence analysis, physical mapping, linkage analysis and protein structure prediction, considerable informational, computational, mathematical and statistical science is required. Today it seems unthinkable for a geneticist to work successfully without encountering a need to use computers. This chapter attempts to introduce readers to the basic concepts of a computing environment such as they may encounter during their research. Those interested in studying the topics discussed in more detail will find it useful to consult the bibliography.

1   Basic Computer Architecture Concepts

The computer is a device for transforming data. Data are unprocessed facts, e.g. quantities and values represented by numbers and words coded in formats acceptable for input to and processing by a computer (Brookshear, 1991). Today nearly all computers are digital and store and transmit data in the form of binary digits (bits) by the use of separate electrical signals denoting 0 and 1. Different patterns of bits are used to encode data into computer readable format. A number of code systems such as BCD (Binary Code Decimal), ASCII (American Standard Code for Information Interchange) or EBCDIC (Extended Binary Coded Decimal Interchange Code) are used.

Data originate from many different sources: the sequence of keystrokes during a word processing task, the intensities of light and colour at each point of a picture, the fluorescence readings of an electrophoretic column in a DNA sequencing machine, the stream of intensities of magnetization as data is read from a floppy disk, or indeed any device which can output numbers which measure the state of some physical quantity.

The basic interface between the user and the power of the computer to transform data is the keyboard and screen. A few keystrokes (or mouse clicks) initiate some application which will transform data into a form meaningful to the user. The application signals the success of the action by the appearance on-screen of the results of the processing. Between the initiation and the appearance of the results on-screen, the data has flowed between the computer's file-store, memory, processing unit, back to the file-store, onto the screen, and perhaps to other peripherals like a printer (Hayes, 1987; Stallings, 1987; Willis, 1987).

1.1 Processor

The processor, or more accurately the Central Processing Unit (CPU), is the central "engine" of a computer where the data transformation takes place. All the other parts of the computer merely feed data into it, or receive data back from it. All physical quantities can be represented by numbers. The power of computing stems from this fact, together with the ability of the CPU to compare numbers or to do arithmetic on them. All applications which transform data in useful ways are built up from these simple operations on numbers. The key element in the utility of the computer is the fact that the CPU can perform these simple operations millions of times per second.

Such is the importance of this speed of operation of the processor that it is governed by a "clock" which emits precise electronic pulses millions of times per second to time each elementary numerical operation of the processor. The higher the "clock rate" the faster data operations will be performed. To make CPUs faster and smaller is a major area of development for the manufacturers. Latest technological developments enable a complete CPU to be etched on a single silicon "chip" only a few square millimetres in size.

There are two current directions of processor development. The Complex Instruction Set Computer (CISC) attempts to gain overall advantage by offering more than just compare and simple arithmetic on its data, but this results in a restricted clock rate. The Reduced Instruction Set Computer (RISC) is designed to allow the fastest clock rates but does this by offering only a core set of elementary operations on numbers.

CPU chips are identified by their manufacturer's product numbers. For example the Intel 80486 CPU chip (a CISC) in current IBM compatible computers is one of a family of processor chips. The CPU chip in the Apple Macintosh is one from the Motorola 68000 family and is also a CISC. RISC processors called Sparc can be found in Sun, Alpha in DEC and MIPS in Silicon Graphics workstations.

1.2 Memory

The processor requires a large sequence of basic instructions of elementary numerical operations to perform useful data transformation for the user. This is called the application program. There are tens of thousands of these written for popular machines. The program has to be available to the processor at its clock rate so the program is stored in computer memory. Primary memory is made from electronic technology of the same kind as the CPU and can therefore "feed" the processor at the required rate. Primary memory is also used by the processor for fast access to the data which is being transformed. The more fast primary memory available to the processor the better. All memory is measured in units called bytes. A byte is electronic storage of any kind that can store a "character", that is, a single letter or digit. Usually it is a group of eight bits. A kilobyte (KB) is 2^{10} bytes or 1,024 bytes. A megabyte (MB) is 2^{20} bytes or roughly 1 million bytes. A page of this book can be stored in about 3 KB of memory.

1.3 File-store

In general, when the computer is switched off, the primary memory loses program and data - it is "volatile" memory. When not in primary memory, programs and data are held in secondary memory which is not volatile. Secondary memory is often known as the "file-store".

In current desktop computers the primary memory has storage for 4 to 32 MB and in many cases more. The file store has to be ten or more times larger than this so holds from 40 to 1,000 MB (1 gigabyte). Currently the most widely used technology for this level of storage is based on magnetic recording of data on magnetic disks and tapes. A magnetic disk can be either fixed or removable. The former, sometimes called the hard disk, with a capacity of at least 40 MB or more is built into the same enclosure as the CPU chip - the system unit. A removable disk, usually of smaller capacity such as the floppy disk, can be used to transfer data and programs between personal computers (PCs) of the same type. Magnetic tape is not so widely used for storage of data as in the past, having been largely superseded by disk storage. At present, magnetic tapes are primarily used for back-up of the magnetic disk, archival storage and data interchange purposes.

Optical data disks which use laser technology to pack large amounts of data (500 MB and more) onto a 5.25 inch disk are also becoming widely used. A CD ROM is an optical disk which already has information recorded on it by the manufacturer and it is only possible for information to be read from it. However, optical disks with both read and write capability are also available.

The storage space on a disk or a tape is organized into named units of storage called "files". A file is a named collection of bytes - a program or a collection of data bytes like the text of a document. The file system keeps a "directory" of file names and keeps track of the storage location of these on the magnetic disk. The user interacts with the file store solely through these named files, and the file system can show the user the directory of files stored as a list of names with each file size and other data such as date of creation.

This storage requires to be easily accessible for the user who needs to start application programs on the processor and indicate to the program which data to process and where to put the output results. A special program known as the "'operating system" performs this task (see Section 1.5). A central part of the operating system deals with the file-store organization - the file system.

1.4 Other Peripheral Devices

In addition to the main input device, the keyboard, and the main output device, the screen, other input and output devices can be connected to the computer. These are called peripherals.

A printer connected to the system unit can produce documents from any file or application program which produces text. Some printers, for example laser printers, can also produce graphical output - graphs and drawings and limited black and white pictures.

A mouse is an input device for pointing to items on the screen. A small plastic case is moved about on the desk and a pointer on the screen follows the movement. Two or three buttons when pressed initiate actions depending on where the pointer is on the screen.

A scanner allows pictures or documents to be entered to the appropriate application program and the picture saved as a file. This can then be processed as a picture rather than as text, and output via a printer with graphical capability.

The PC is also often found controlling and collecting data from laboratory equipment. The equipment can be connected to the PC by its low speed communications device - the "serial port". Other devices can be added to the PC by means of "expansion cards" which contain specialist electronics on small boards which are plugged into the system unit.

Expansion cards are available for sound input and output, video still and moving pictures, tape magnetic stores, digitizing tablets, or any device that can be controlled electronically.

1.5 Operating Systems

An operating system is a master control program which manages the function of the computer system as a whole and the running of application programs (Dietel, 1991; Tannenbaum, 1992). Not all computers use the same operating system. Some operating systems are adopted as "industry standards" and these normally have a good software base. There is application software designed to run only under the control of specific operating systems. In molecular biology and genetics computing the reader will most commonly encounter the following operating system names: Unix (various flavours) (Brown, 1984), PCDOS (Microsoft, 1992a), Macintosh OS, Windows NT, VMS, OS/2.

The operating system runs continually and is the means by which the user interacts with a computer and directs its actions. Application programs are started and terminated via commands to the operating system. Input and output to peripherals is controlled by user interaction with operating system internal programs. The status of the file store, the directory of files, is presented to the user by the operating system on demand. Some operating systems (e.g. Unix and VMS) allow several application and internal programs to run concurrently thus allowing, for example, printing one document, editing another and reading data from a DNA sequencing machine at the same time. Others (e.g. PCDOS and Macintosh OS) allow one to run a single program at a time.

Operating systems have undergone a revolution over the last few years in terms of the user interface. In the past, the user interacted with an operating system such as PC DOS or Unix with commands typed at the keyboard, and any responses were printed on the screen. Operating systems of this kind are called "command line" based. Command line operating systems require the user to remember a fair number of commands, and to initiate requests for the status of the system, the file directory for example. The command line operating system has been superseded by the graphical user interface (GUI) operating system. The Xerox operating system pioneered this approach and the Macintosh popularized it. Apple MacIntosh PCs never had a command line option and other operating systems have followed suite. The GUI is described further in Section 4.

2 Basic Computer Network Concepts

The promise of the information age is instant access to the sum of human knowledge from anywhere, at any time. The reality is a vast number of disconnected repositories of data and information, each with its own search engine, procedures and classification scheme. There is nothing more frustrating than knowing that the information you need is out of there and having no way to retrieve it.

2.1 What is a Computer Network? What are its Benefits?

Computer networks have been designed to help users out of this impasse. A computer network comprises two or more intelligent communicating devices (computer systems, workstations, PCs) linked in order to exchange information and share resources (Tannenbaum, 1988). A communicating device on a network is called a node. Some nodes are called hosts. A host is a network node that provides individual network users with various resources including processing power, information files, user applications and interconnections to different networks. Users access the networks from desktop devices which may be simple dumb terminals, PCs or sophisticated workstations.

From the perspective of individual users, the most apparent advantage of a network is that critical information, no matter where it is located, is available to them when they need it. From an organizational perspective the immediate advantages of a network are efficient use of information and cost-effective use of expensive resources.

A computer network can span a building, a University campus, a country or a continent. The terms local area networking and wide area networking primarily draw attention to the geographical area a network covers. Local Area Networks (LANs), usually privately owned, span a limited geographical area, such as a building or cluster of buildings (Martin, 1989). The maximum cable length is a few kilometres. Wide Area Networks (WANs) cover large geographical areas, extending across several cities, countries or even continents. Recent developments in LAN technology have vastly expanded the reach of LANs, thereby blurring the distinction between LANs and WANs. This is achieved by use of bridges, routers and gateways, devices that can link two or more widely separated LANs so that they appear to be one network spanning a large geographical area. The term Metropolitan Area Network (MAN) is used to describe the latest, high speed and long distance LANs. For the purpose of discussion, this chapter draws a distinction between LANs and WANs in terms of communication media and technology used. However, network users do not have to be aware of these distinctions. From their perspective a network should merely be a means of accessing critical information, regardless of whether this information resides in the next building or another city. The operation of networks can usually be separated into two main aspects. Firstly the physical medium of the networks and the method of placing the data on them, the protocols.

2.2   Physical Networks

Nodes communicate based on some combination of physical and logical connection. Physical connections are electronic, or in some cases still electromechanical, circuits between nodes, whether permanent or temporary. A logical connection implies that two nodes are able to communicate, whether or not they have a physical connection.

Currently the most common transmission media used to interconnect nodes in a LAN are:

- Twisted-pair wire, the original wire type used in telephone communications for low speed data transmission at speeds of 300 to 9.6 Kbps (9,600 data bits per second). Its higher specifications are used for faster data transmission today.

- Coaxial cable that supports higher data rates with high immunity to electrical interference and a low incidence of errors.

- Fibre optics made of plastics or glass that serve as a very high performance transmission medium not affected at all by electrical interference nor emitting radio-frequency noise, thus being inherently very secure.

Ethernet, based on so called Carrier Sense Multiple Access with Collision Detect (CSMA/CD) technology is most widely known type of LAN. It operates using a bus structure, that is, a single strand of cable to which all nodes connect. It uses baseband communication (i.e. only one signal can travel on the cable at one time) at 10 Mbps (10 megabits, 10,000,000 data bits per second). FDDI (Fibre Distributed Data Interface) based on another technology, the Token Ring, is another widely used LAN at present. It was developed by ANSI (American National Standards Institute), operates at 100 Mbps and can be up to 100 kilometres in length. Many manufacturers have developed proprietary LAN technologies specific to their own products such as AppleTalk, designed by Apple Computer, principally used with Macintosh systems, Datapoint Corporation's ArcNet and others. Protocols defining these LAN technologies are described below.

Once appropriate LAN cabling is in place it still needs computer systems, workstations, personal computers and dumb terminals to be connected to it to create the network. This can be achieved in a variety of ways the most common of which are:

- Special cards, for example an Ethernet card that connects workstations and personal computers directly to a LAN.

- Terminal Servers, devices which connect to a LAN and allow one or more terminals, which cannot directly support LAN protocols, to connect to it providing all necessary LAN support.

- Host Servers, which connect to a LAN and then allow a computer, which cannot directly support LAN protocols, to connect to it providing all necessary LAN support.

Nodes on a WAN may be linked by various types of communication media, owned usually by telecommunication companies (e.g. British Telecom, Mercury Communications in the UK), depending on the volume of data flowing between the nodes (Martin, 1990). Currently the most commonly used WAN communication media for transmission both nationally and internationally are:

- Public Switched Telephone Network (PSTN) dialup lines.
- Leased lines.
- Packet Switched Data Networks (PSDNs).
- Microwave links.

In principle a PSTN dialup line is similar to the connection the user gets when he/she picks up a phone and dials a number. When two nodes linked by a dialup line wish to communicate, the source node "dials" the destination and activates the line. At the end of the communication, both nodes "hang up" and the connection is severed. The user is charged for the length of time the nodes communicate and for the distance between them. Telephone networks are both extensive and available and, although computer and telephone signals are incompatible, adaptations and compromises were made to allow data communications over these lines. The PSTN was designed for transmission of the human voice, an analogue signal varying in frequency and volume. Special devices called modems (modulator-demodulators) convert digital data from a transmitting node into a form suitable for transmission to an analogue (voice) telephone channel. A second unit reconverts this signal to serial digital data for acceptance by the receiving node.

This does not apply to the forthcoming new public telephone system, the Integrated Services Digital Network (ISDN) which offers digital services for both voice and data. PSTN access at speeds up to 9,600 bps is available using modems supplied by a number of companies. From a price/performance point of view it offers users the least efficient physical network medium.

A leased line is a communication line that the customer leases or rents from a telecommunications organization. Whether or not the nodes are in a process of communicating with one another, the connection between them is permanently open. Thus a leased line makes economical sense only if the traffic between the nodes is heavy and continuous or when consistent level of service with low error rate is required.

Currently, leased lines and PSDNs offer a number of data transmission services at speeds up to 2.048 Mbps with much higher speeds to come in the very near future.

In the UK and elsewhere an independent third party can obtain a licence to offer users a range of services which are carried on circuits owned by local telecommunication organizations (e.g. British Telecom, Mercury Communications in the UK). The services include protocol conversion, store and forward message facility, and gateways to other networks. Such networks are called Value Added Networks (VANs). The UK

Joint Academic Network (JANET) is an example of such an undertaking. JANET provides its users with access to various other WANs in the UK and overseas including the EuropaNet (a WAN connecting some of the european academic research networks, EBONE (European Research Backbone IP Network), the German Wissenschaft Network (WIN), the French Academic Networks RENATER, the Italian network GARR, INTERNET, BITNET and others (LaQuey, 1990). These facilities give the scientific community access to national and international databases and centres of excellence in genome research and molecular biology worldwide.

Like radio waves, microwave links operate through the air. They are used for high speed data transmission services. A transmitting station or facility at the source converts the messages into microwaves, and a receiving station at the destination captures them and returns them to a form in which they can travel over physical lines. Usually a cable or other terrestrial line connects source and destination nodes to the transmitting and receiving stations, respectively.

2.3 Protocols

Just because it is possible to make an electrical connection does not mean that information can be exchanged among different nodes. All communications are governed by rules of procedure. In a networking context this means complex communication protocols, an agreed set of rules, both hardware and software, and formats for exchanging data between communicating devices. Each protocol has a distinctive name. In the not so distant past only proprietary protocols provided by individual manufacturers such as Digital Equipment's DECNet and IBM's Systems Network Architecture (SNA) were available. These made possible exchange of data within the product ranges of a single supplier whereas the products of different suppliers were usually incompatible. Such incompatibilities served to restrict the customer to the original supplier for further purchases.

It was against this background that the International Standards Organization (ISO) began work in 1979 on what is now known as the Open Systems Interconnection (OSI). The ultimate aim of OSI is to define standards for rules and formats for exchanging of data over networks which will enable computers from different manufacturers to communicate with each other economically and efficiently. To achieve this, the ISO has developed a definition of the way nodes on a network communicate - the seven layer Reference Model (Black, 1991). Note, that the Reference Model is not a communication protocol standard as such, but provides a structure into which internationally agreed protocol standards can be fitted. It describes the conceptual structure of communication systems.

This all sounds very complicated but the reader should not worry. From the user's point of view, use of any protocol on a PSDN is by and large transparent. Thus as an example, a geneticist who wishes to access from his/her desktop device any of the national and international genome or other molecular biology databases through private or public PSDNs in Europe will have to use, probably without knowing so, the so called X.25 protocol that fits the first three layers of the Reference Model. As has been said already, each protocol has its distinctive name. Computers of different manufacturers, provided they "talk" X.25, can connect to the same PSDN and exchange data among themselves. However, using X.25, PSDNs only transfer data among various nodes. Once data arrives at the destination node over the PSDN, another protocol, the software on that node and possibly some additional hardware must interpret the data to make it readable and comprehensive to users. Provided that the user's desktop device lacks suitable computer interfaces to access the PSDN, a packet assembler and disassembler (PAD) device will be required to carry out this task. Implementation of a PAD is based on a further set of OSI protocols, so called X.3, X.28, X.29 (often known as Triple X).

Other examples of OSI protocols are those defining the above mentioned LAN technologies, CSMA/CD and Token Ring. They also fit to the lower layers of the OSI Reference Model. The reader might have heard about a number of different OSI protocols covering all kinds of user services that are in various stages of development such as File Transfer (FTAM), Messaging (MHS-X.400 series), Terminal Support (VT), Directory Services (X.500 series), Management and Security Services.

However, for most applications the ISO protocol definitions are likely to take some time to fully emerge, reach the ratification stage and, what is from the user's point of view more important, be adopted, supplied and supported by the manufacturers. To bridge the gap in time scales, a set of other non-proprietary protocols is being used. In the UK, in both LAN and WAN environments, the following two sets of protocols are employed at present: the X.25 based UK Academic Coloured Books protocols, use of which is restricted to JANET (Joint Network Team, 1992), and the international Transmission Control Protocol/Internet Protocol (TCP/IP) operated worldwide. A number of proprietary communication protocols are also being widely used. Apart from the above mentioned DEC and IBM products, the better known include Netware, Xerox Networking Systems, Netbios and LAN Manager.

In the mid-1970s the US Defense Advanced Projects Agency (DARPA), whilst developing a wide area network ARPANET to link all its research centres, started work on internetworking technology which was to allow for open system interconnection. "Open system" because, unlike proprietary communication protocols available from a specific vendor, the specifications had to be publicly available. Thus anyone could build the hardware and software to make communication possible between nodes with diverse hardware architectures, to use almost any packet switched network hardware and to accommodate multiple computer operating systems. The result today is that TCP/IP is the de facto world networking standard (Comer, 1991). It has been adopted as a standard protocol within the UNIX operating system. TCP/IP includes a number of communication protocols which became widely used by network developers. The three below are a small selection of those available, but perhaps the most likely that the reader might encounter:

- TELNET - the standard protocol for remote connection service. It allows connection to remote hosts from another host or a terminal server.
- FTP (File Transfer Protocol) allows for transfer of files.
- SMTP (Simple Mail Transfer Protocol) allows user to user electronic mail (e-mail) to be transferred across the network.

INTERNET is a collection of many national, regional and site data networks worldwide that use the TCP/IP protocol suite functions and operates as a single international cooperative network. Currently it comprises more than 5,000 networks in 33 countries. The name also refers to the more than 500,000 connected computers and the people they serve - roughly 3 million strong. Since 1 November 1991 JANET has been part of the INTERNET and provides the IP service. This is of considerable importance to users of any up-to-date molecular biology and genetics computing facility and is likely to become more so in the future (Cooper et al., 1991; Reardon, 1989; Leebaert, 1991).

3 Network Services

The previous section described the networking infrastructure. Provided that the reader has access to such networks, a number of services are available there. The most important of these is e-mail, which is used for sending and receiving messages. Bulletin boards are used for sharing information and holding discussions in a public forum (Smith, 1992). The file transfer protocol (FTP) is used for transferring files across the network, especially from stores of large amounts of data and information. There are a number of aids to finding information on the networks including Gopher and WAIS.

3.1 Electronic Mail

e-mail is used in an analogous way to the postal system, and can be used for sending messages, or for transferring information to other places worldwide. It is, however, faster, with messages normally being delivered within a few minutes and copies can be sent to number of people simultaneously. Because of the wide availability of e-mail, it has been used to supply other services, including the provision of the answers from computer programs which take a long time to run, and as a means of sending small text files from one computer to another.

The main activities associated with e-mail include checking for new incoming mail, reading it, replying to it, saving or deleting it, and sending new mail. The implementation of e-mail programs (one of them, SMTP, has been mentioned in Section 2.3) vary a great deal, and on various computers, and there may also be different styles of e-mail programs used on the same computer. For details the reader is advised to study the local system.

It is useful to compare the features of an e-mail message with those of an ordinary letter. The letter consists of an envelope and the contents. The envelope bears the name of the recipient and the address in order that the letter may be delivered. It is also fairly common that the envelope gives the sender's name and address, and possibly bears some indication as to what the contents may be. The e-mail equivalent of the envelope is formed from a number of lines of text, referred to as the header, which include the name and address of the recipient, as well as that of the sender (Figure 1.1). The header also contains the date when it was sent, and may contain a subject line, to give the recipient some idea as to the contents of the message. Other pieces of information get added into the header, although these are often of more interest to the people who look after the mail systems than they are to the recipient.

```
>From tom_smith@uk.ac.cam.med Mon Feb 1 15:13:48 1993
To: fred_jones@uk.ac.crc
Subject: Linkage analysis workshop
Content-Length: 536
X-Lines: 29
The linkage analysis workshop will be held on March 31
at 10 am at the HGMP Resource Centre Harrow, Middx.
Lunch will be provided at 1.00 pm.
Kind Regards Tom
```

FIGURE 1.1 Example of an e-mail message.

The contents of an ordinary letter correspond to the body of the e-mail message. In the first e-mail systems the body consisted of a simple text message spread over a number of lines. Unfortunately some of these e-mail systems put a limit on the length of a line and/or on the number of lines. New systems are coming along, however, which will accept a number of body parts, where each of these parts may be of a different type. These types include simple text, as well as the formatted text from a word processor, digitized sound, digitized pictures and possibly even digitized video.

There are a number of different interconnected networks around the world, and it is necessary to approach the question of how to supply an address for the message, so that it may be delivered to the recipient. The original mailing systems required that the recipient's name and address had to be typed in at the keyboard. There is, however, a movement away from this approach, to one where the recipient is selected from a list. The user would have his/her own list of regular correspondents, while people not on the list would be pinned down via a number of hints supplied by the user. The mailing system would look up the name and address in a distributed directory system, and use the required information itself. The directory system currently being proposed is called X.500 and often linked with the e-mail system referred to as X.400. For the moment we will approach the question of how to address e-mail "manually".

If e-mail is being sent to another user of the same mailing system, then it is adequate to use the name of that person as they are known to that mailing system. This may be the name they use when they log onto the system. It is, however, becoming more common that the mailing systems also know a more obvious version of the user's names. There are two common conventions for doing this. One is to use the user's initial, followed by a dot, followed by his/her surname, the other is to use the user's first name, followed by a dot, followed by his/her surname. If it is not possible to work out what name to use, then it is usually possible to send e-mail to the person who looks after the user's mail system. This is done by addressing the message to "postmaster" with a message asking for help in discovering the name of the potential correspondent.

For the more general case of sending mail to another user elsewhere, the address is normally formed from some representation of the persons name, as described above, followed by a commercial "at" sign "@", followed by the name of the mail system. This latter is usually made up of several parts, separated by dots. The address is usually hierarchical, with a component corresponding to a country, or the name of a network, at one end of the address, and the name of the mail system at the other end. One complication is that the United Kingdom places these component parts in the opposite order from the rest of the world.

As an example, a fictitious user of the HGMP-RC (the UK Human Genome Mapping Project Resource Centre, currently located in Northwick Park Hospital, Harrow, Middlesex) computing facilities, Frances Mary Goldingay, would be able to receive e-mail from the UK addressed to:

```
F.Goldingay@uk.ac.crc
```

whilst from the rest of the world it would be addressed to:

```
F.Goldingay@crc.ac.uk
```

The "uk" corresponding to the country, "ac" to the academic community, and "crc" to the Clinical Research Centre, which operates one unified mail system for the HGMP-RC at present. The European countries, and many others, tend to use the standard two letter abbreviations for their country name, e.g. "fr" for France and "de" for Germany. The Americans tend to omit the country from their addresses and use three letter component parts such as "edu" for educational establishments and "com" for commercial ones. The networks which appear in e-mail addresses include "uucp", "earn" and "bit-net". UUCP is the name used for an early network consisting of a number of Unix computers. EARN and BITNET are technically the same network, originally based on large IBM computers, EARN being the European part (the European Academic and Research Network) and BITNET the American part.

3.2 Bulletin Boards

e-mail was originally set up to provide communication between two people. It has, however, been used to send messages to lists of people, which has lead to its use as a means of conferring among a group of people. Unfortunately this can lead to users' e-mail being congested with circulated messages and hiding urgent messages. Bulletin boards were developed as a better way for groups of people to discuss ideas. Network News (sometimes referred to as Usenet) is such a system. It allows for the easy and rapid dissemination of ideas, conjectures, polemics, cries for help, musings and general chit-chat. Whereas e-mail is used to send messages to individual people, network news articles are circulated among sites. At such sites the news articles are stored centrally where they may be read by the users. This mechanism does not stop the user from saving a copy of an especially useful article in his/her own file space.

Network News can be compared to bulletin boards made of chipboard and green baize. Anyone can put a message on the bulletin board. It will remain there for some time before being removed by the departmental secretary. Anyone can stop by the board and read the messages posted there at any time. Anyone can put replies to the messages on the board, or can contact the postee directly. Different boards are devoted to specific topics and people get annoyed if a message advertising a car for sale is put on the board devoted to forthcoming seminars.

Network News articles are also divided by subject matter. These news groups are arranged in a hierarchical manner with the names formed from parts separated by dots. Thus biological matters are grouped under "bionet" and there are several subdivisions including "molbio" and "software", each with a number of newsgroups, e.g. "bionet.-software" or "bionet.molbio.gene-linkage". There is a method for starting new news groups, involving voting. This has lead to there being nearly 2,000 groups at present with more starting every week.

Network News works by people posting messages to selected news groups. These messages are then disseminated to all participating sites comprising many thousands of universities and institutes around the world. Anyone at a participating site may then choose to start reading Network News. Generally, users will have a small subset of news groups to read, as there is too much for anybody try to read all of the news groups. These articles are not usually stored indefinitely, but the rate at which expired articles are removed depends on the site and the news group. Thus at the HGMP-RC the biological and scientific news groups are generally expired after a month, while most of the other groups are expired after a week. Anyone may reply to a message (Figure 1.2) by posting his/her own message on the same news group to start a public discussion, or choose to contact the original sender directly by using e-mail, telephone or physical postage.

```
Article: 732 of bionet.molbio.genbank
Path: mrccrc!daresbury!biosci!NET.BIO.NET!kristoff
From: kristoff@NET.BIO.NET (David Kristofferson)
Newsgroups: bionet.molbio.genbank
Subject: BIOSCI/bionet Frequently Asked Questions
Message-ID: <9301151000.AA07240@net.bio.net>
Date: Fri, 15 Jan 93 10:00:03 GMT
Sender: kristoff@net.bio.net
Distribution: bionet
Lines: 16
New users of BIOSCI/bionet may want to read the "Fre-
quently Asked Questions" or "FAQ" sheet for BIOSCI. The
FAQ provides details on how to participate in these
forums and is available for anonymous FTP from net.bi-
o.net [134.172.2.69] in pub/BIOSCI/biosci2.FAQ. It may
also be requested by sending e-mail to biosci@net.bio.-
net (use plain English for your request). The FAQ is
also posted on the first of each month to the newsgroup
BIONEWS/bionet.announce immediately following the
posting of the BIOSCI information sheet.
Sincerely,
Dave Kristofferson BIOSCI/bionet Manager
kristoff@net.bio.net
```

FIGURE 1.2 Example of Network News.

The main activity associated with using Network News is reading articles and submitting or posting articles, but there are other activities which the user needs to be aware of. There are a number of news handling programs, and they vary greatly in their appearance, not only between different computers, but also between different programs on the same computer. To discuss all these individual programs in detail is outside the scope of this book. The interested reader might find a great deal more in the appropriate literature.

3.3 FTP Servers

FTP, as already mentioned in Section 2.3, is the file transfer protocol which is used for copying files between computers which are connected to the INTERNET. The manner in which files are stored varies between computers, and FTP ensures that a file will be correctly stored on the recipient machine. The protocol includes a mechanism for identifying the user, so that checks can be made as to which files the user is allowed to access. This follows the common approach of a user name and password.

There are many sources of information available on the international networks. Such information includes data of general interest, instructions on how to do something, and computer programs. The machines which make such a body of information available via FTP are referred to as "FTP Servers". Due to the very large number of people interested in this information, and the large number of different sources, it is not practical for these people to all have a valid user name and password on each of these repositories. In order to circumvent this problem, the use of anonymous FTP was developed.

Those machines which provide an anonymous FTP service have a user name set up called "anonymous", which will allow a wide range of passwords. It is conventional to ask people to enter their electronic mail address as the password, so that the providers of the service have some idea as to who is using it. Once a user has been identified as anonymous, they have access to a selected set of files, which have been made available by the service provider. Generally such users will be interested in copying files from such a service, but there may be occasions where the user is allowed to send files to the service.

The file transfer protocol is usually available as a program called "ftp". The program usually has a very similar appearance when used in a command line style of operation, even on different types of computers. When a graphical user interface is used, this may tend to vary with computer.

An example will be given of retrieving information from the HGMP-RC Computing Handbook stored on an anonymous FTP server at the HGMP-RC computing facilities. In this example the user is sitting at a PC, although it would look very similar from most other types of desktop computers or terminals.

In this example (Figure 1.3) the user runs the FTP program under the PC DOS operating system, giving the name of the computer which is running an anonymous FTP service, in this case "ftp.crc.ac.uk". The FTP program can be seen making contact with this server, and asking the user to provide a user name. As it is desired to use the anonymous facility, the name "anonymous" is entered at this prompt. The user is then prompted for a password. The password is not displayed on the screen as it is entered, and it is usual for the user to supply his/her electronic mail address as the password. The "dir" command is used to obtain a listing of the files. At this point a number of directories are visible, with the names displayed on the right, and a group of letters on the left, with the "d" indicating that this line refers to a directory. To facilitate access to the files in the directory called "manual", the user gives the command "cd manual", so that future commands refer to files in this directory. A "dir" command then provides a list of the files which are of real interest, being the individual chapters of the manual. The command "get" is used in order to transfer the desired file (chapter2 in this case) to the disk on the user's PC. Finally the "quit" command is used to leave the ftp program.

```
C:\MARY> ftp ftp.crc.ac.uk
Connected to dna1.crc.ac.uk.
220 dna1 FTP server (SunOS 4.1) ready.
Name (ftp.crc.ac.uk:fgolding): anonymous
331 Guest login ok, send ident as password.
Password:
230 Guest login ok, access restrictions apply.
ftp> dir
200 PORT command successful.
150 ASCII data connection for /bin/ls (192.68.153.79,3258) (0 bytes).
total 6
dr-xr-xr-x  2 0         1              512 Jul 22 15:56 bin
dr-xr-xr-x  2 0         1              512 Jul 22 16:09 dev
dr-xr-xr-x  2 0         1              512 Jul 22 16:03 etc
dr-xr-xr-x  2 0         1              512 Oct 27 09:02 manual
drwxrwxrwx  2 ftp       ftp            512 Oct  5 11:17 pub
dr-xr-xr-x  3 0         1              512 Jul 22 15:57 usr
226 ASCII Transfer complete.
366 bytes received in 0.83 seconds (0.43 Kbytes/s)
ftp> cd manual
250 CWD command successful.
ftp> dir
200 PORT command successful.
150 ASCII data connection for /bin/ls (192.68.153.79,3259) (0 bytes).
total 154
-rw-r--r--  1 0         1            28017 Oct 27 08:59 chapter1
-rw-r--r--  1 0         1            27381 Oct 27 09:00 chapter2
-rw-r--r--  1 0         1            17261 Oct 27 09:00 chapter3
-rw-r--r--  1 0         1            10839 Oct 27 09:00 chapter5
-rw-r--r--  1 0         1            29855 Oct 27 09:00 chapter6
-rw-r--r--  1 0         1            35046 Oct 27 09:00 chapter7
226 ASCII Transfer complete.
459 bytes received in 0.093 seconds (4.8 Kbytes/s)
ftp> get chapter2
200 PORT command successful.
150 ASCII data connection for chapter2 (192.68.153.79,3260) (27381
bytes).
226 ASCII Transfer complete.
```

```
local: chapter2 remote: chapter2
27885 bytes received in 0.41 seconds (66 Kbytes/s)
ftp> quit
221 Goodbye.
C:\MARY>
```

FIGURE 1.3 An example of an anonymous ftp session.

3.4 Gopher and WAIS

There is a large amount of information of a diverse nature available on the INTER-NET, much of which may be copied to a local computer using the anonymous FTP mechanism described above. However, there does remain the problem of locating this information (Conner, 1987). Information systems, such as Gopher and WAIS, are available to assist in this area, and also to provide means for transferring the information to a local computer which are more convenient than using FTP.

Gopher was originally developed by the University of Minnesota Microcomputer, Workstation, Networks Centre to help its campus find answers to computer questions. It has since grown into a full-fledged world-wide information system used by a large number of sites in the world. It is designed to deliver documents to the user from a large number of servers distributed around the world at centres which cooperate in providing this service. It allows access to these various types of data residing on multiple hosts in a straightforward manner, without the user having to make connections to different servers. This is accomplished by presenting the user with a hierarchical arrangement of documents, and by using a client-server communications model (see Section 6 below). Hence the user communicates with a friendly program running locally, which sends requests across the network to the cooperating servers and receives back documents or lists of documents. In effect the information around the world appears as one very large file system with a simple browsing mechanism for exploring it. In addition to browsing through hierarchies of documents, users can submit queries for Gopher to search servers. The search servers typically have full-text indexes for a set of Gopher documents, the response to a query being a list of documents that matched the search criteria.

The appearance of Gopher on the screen of the user's desktop device will depend a little on whether it is a version for character style displays (the command line interface in Section 1.5), or whether it is designed for a graphical user interface (discussed in Section 4.2). However, the general idea is that the user is presented with a list on the screen. Each item of the list may be one of several types, but the most important are directories and text files. The user will select an item from the list. If the item were a directory, then the contents of that directory would be listed. If it were a text file then the contents of that file would be displayed on the screen, with the possibility of saving the file being offered to the user. The type of item in a list is identified by its "exten-sion".

/	Item is a directory.
.	Item is a text file.
<?>	Item is a search index.
<CSO>	Item is a CSO phone book.
<TEL>	Item is a telnet session.
<)	Item is a sound (symbol looks like a speaker)

With a character style display, items are selected by moving a pointer up or down with the arrow keys on the keyboard, and using the right arrow key to activate an item, and the left arrow key to return back up the hierarchy. The graphical user interface versions use the mouse for these actions (Figure 1.4).

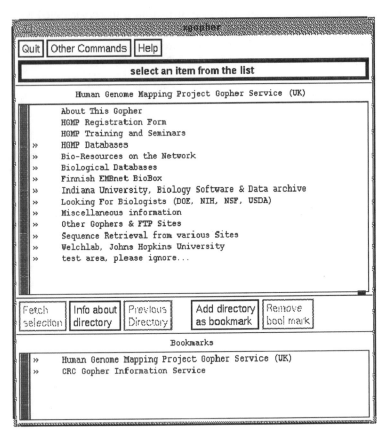

FIGURE 1.4 An example of a graphical interface Screen, the initial display showing the information available in the top level directory of the UK HGMP Gopher.

Programs which facilitate user access to the worldwide Gopher information system, the so called Gopher clients, are available for a number of operating systems, including Unix, Macintosh and DOS. They can be obtained using the anonymous FTP service from a server called boombox.micro.umn.edu in the directory /pub/gopher.

WAIS (Wide Area Information Server) approaches the problem of locating information differently from Gopher. Instead of providing facilities to browse around hierarchically referenced documents, WAIS provides a searching facility for the electronic libraries of information around the world, but more specifically it searches the contents of the documents. Once the desired documents have been found, the contents may be perused. These documents are physically located on many different servers or "sources" and it is necessary to specify which source or sources are to be queried before making a search.

The WAIS information system was built around two concepts: first, the user should be able to provide feedback to assist or retarget the search; and, second, that the best way to search for articles (or any other documents) is to search from a good example, not just from one or two keywords. The user can provide feedback, by seeing what the search has produced, and providing further information, to home into the information required. It is also possible to make the search more general, so as to widen the area of search. It is also possible that in a search for subject A, an article with information on subject B emerges, which is also of interest to the user. In this case it is possible to use that article as a model for another search. It is also possible to branch off into a new search without losing track of the original search.

The information which is held by the sources is being updated constantly, and a facility is provided for the user to save the data from a search, so that it can be repeated at selected intervals. This can be performed either automatically, say, overnight, or manually, whenever a fresh answer is desired.

The appearance of the system will vary depending on the implementation and style of operation (Figure 1.5), and the description given here will be a generic one. When the user wishes to conduct a search they will be offered a list of sources, from which any number may be selected. Keywords may then be entered for the search. After a while a list will be displayed of the articles which have produced a match. The quality of the match is measured, and the list is ordered with the best match at the top, and the poorest at the bottom. The contents of the article can then be retrieved for displaying and/or saving.

However, using keywords alone is often insufficient to produce a good enough answer and it is therefore useful to select some documents (or some sections of some documents) from the first part of a search to guide the next part of a search using the "similar to" feature of WAIS.

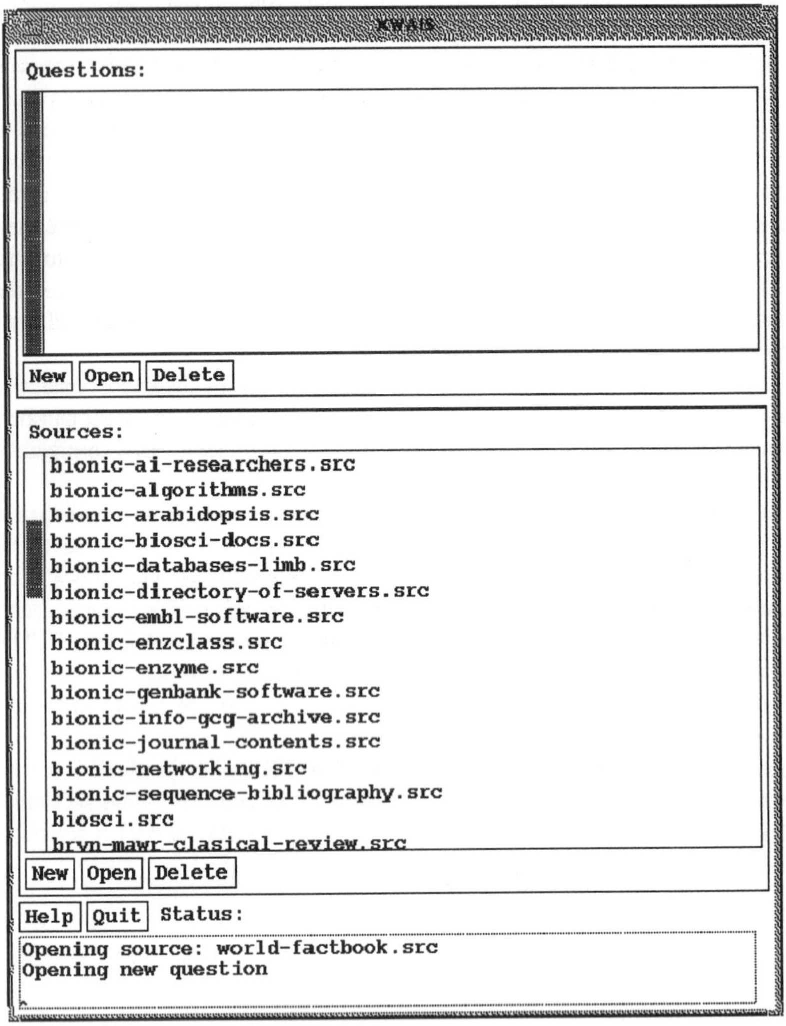

```
┌──────────────────────────────────────────────────┐
│                       KWAIS                        │
│ ┌────────────────────────────────────────────────┐ │
│ │ Questions:                                      │ │
│ │ ┌───────────────────────────────────────────┐  │ │
│ │ │                                           │  │ │
│ │ │                                           │  │ │
│ │ │                                           │  │ │
│ │ │                                           │  │ │
│ │ │                                           │  │ │
│ │ └───────────────────────────────────────────┘  │ │
│ │ [New] [Open] [Delete]                          │ │
│ ├────────────────────────────────────────────────┤ │
│ │ Sources:                                        │ │
│ │ ┌───────────────────────────────────────────┐  │ │
│ │ │ bionic-ai-researchers.src                 │  │ │
│ │ │ bionic-algorithms.src                     │  │ │
│ │ │ bionic-arabidopsis.src                    │  │ │
│ │ │ bionic-biosci-docs.src                    │  │ │
│ │ │ bionic-databases-limb.src                 │  │ │
│ │ │ bionic-directory-of-servers.src           │  │ │
│ │ │ bionic-embl-software.src                  │  │ │
│ │ │ bionic-enzclass.src                       │  │ │
│ │ │ bionic-enzyme.src                         │  │ │
│ │ │ bionic-genbank-software.src               │  │ │
│ │ │ bionic-info-gcg-archive.src               │  │ │
│ │ │ bionic-journal-contents.src               │  │ │
│ │ │ bionic-networking.src                     │  │ │
│ │ │ bionic-sequence-bibliography.src          │  │ │
│ │ │ biosci.src                                │  │ │
│ │ │ bryn-mawr-clasical-review.src             │  │ │
│ │ └───────────────────────────────────────────┘  │ │
│ │ [New] [Open] [Delete]                          │ │
│ │ [Help] [Quit] Status:                          │ │
│ │ Opening source: world-factbook.src             │ │
│ │ Opening new question                           │ │
│ └────────────────────────────────────────────────┘ │
└──────────────────────────────────────────────────┘
```

FIGURE 1.5 An example of a graphical interface screen, the main window to the WAIS.

4 Graphical User Interface

Human beings have very a great ability to understand graphically presented information. Meaningful patterns can be recognized and interpreted almost instantaneously.

High quality graphical user interfaces (GUIs, pronounced "gooeys") are in many ways the "last frontier" in providing computing to a wider variety of users (Peddie, 1991). The early emphasis in computing was to optimize the scarce hardware resources, computer time and memory to run programs efficiently. With today's plummeting hardware costs and increasingly powerful graphics oriented personal computing environments, emphasis is being placed on optimizing efficiency for users, to produce quality interfaces that increases productivity and satisfaction. The quality of the user interface often determines whether users enjoy or despise an application or a computer, whether it is praised or damned. Success and total acceptance by the genome research community of GUIs provided by e.g. ACeDB (the nematode database) and the Encyclopedia of the Mouse Genome indicates that the work increasingly requires interactive graphics facilities.

4.1   User Interface Concepts

A user interface requires some input devices to enter information into the computer system. This is formally known as the man-machine interface. Input devices are those pieces of hardware which the user employs to enter information into a computer system or an application, namely, a keyboard, mouse, trackball, light pen, joysticks, tablets, buttons/dials, gloves and many other devices. There are many ways to use the input devices to enter information into a computer. These are known as interaction techniques and tasks that help built an efficient dialogue between the user and the computer. The form and style of the dialogue is said to be the user interface. User interface design is regarded as an art and it varies from computer system to computer system.

The key goals in user interface design are increase in speed of learning, and in speed of use, reduction of error rate, encouragement of rapid understanding of how to use the interface, and increase in attractiveness to potential users (Larson, 1992). The reader will generally find that a user interface cannot be both easy to learn and fast to use. It rarely meets all the above objectives. There are unfortunately few absolutes in user interfaces, the matter is subjective. Appropriate choices depend on many different factors, including user requirements, the environment of use, available of hardware and software resources, and budgets.

There are several primary interaction styles for a user interfaces which include menu selection, form fill in, natural language dialogue, question and answer dialogue, command languages (the command line interface in Section 1.5) and direct manipulation (primarily GUIs, Section 4.2). None of these styles is mutually exclusive; successful interfaces often meld elements of several styles to meet program design objectives not readily met by one.

Menus are widely used in both graphical and non-graphical user interfaces and applications. In either case, however, the fundamental advantages of menus is that the user can work with what is called 'recognition memory', where visual images (textual or iconic, pull-down menu items) are associated with already familiar words or meanings. This avoids the users having to recall commands from memory in order to enter information into the computer. It is very attractive to novices. Menus, along with form fill in, allow selections to be indicated visually, further reducing the user's memory load and also allowing rapid input if the current selection is desired.

Use of the command language is the traditional way to interact with a computer. The command line interface, that well known A> (or similar) prompt offers little assistance and even less encouragement to users of the computer and is very unhelpful to novices. Learning commands is a major liability, with the need for appreciable typing skills. Errors are more likely to occur from typing incorrect commands.

Natural language dialogue is often proposed as the ultimate objective for interacting with a computer. If computers could understand our commands, typed or spoken in everyday English, then everyone would be able to use them. Unfortunately, this technology is still very much in its infancy.

Question and answer dialogue is computer initiated; the user response is constrained to a set of expected answers. Using the keyboard for input, the user can give any answer. A common failing of instances of this dialogue form is the inability to go back several steps to correct an answer. With a form fill in, by contrast, the user can see all the items of data entered, and so can quickly tell, for instance, an incorrect data item and thus navigate to the data and amend it.

4.2   WIMPS User Interfaces

Direct manipulation is the primary GUI (discussed in Section 1.5). Here objects, attributes, or relations which can be operated on, are represented visually (Lalande and Pugh, 1991). Operations are invoked by actions performed on the visual representations, typically using a mouse. These visual representation of objects are known as "icons". The GUI approach uses the whole of the screen of a desktop device or a terminal as an area of interaction with the user (Figure 1.6). Much more of the status of the used computer system is held on screen - application programs are shown as "icons", small postage stamp sized pictures related to the application's function. Files are drawn as icons of documents. The mouse pointing device is used by the user to point at an icon and press one of the mouse buttons ("click"). This initiates the application which creates a "window" overlaying a rectangular part of the existing display. The user then interacts with the application program within this window. When the application is terminated, the previously obscured parts of the screen reappear. Many of these windows can be present on the screen at one time, the more recent overlapping earlier invocations. Text and pictures can be moved between windows, so that several applications can be run simultaneously.

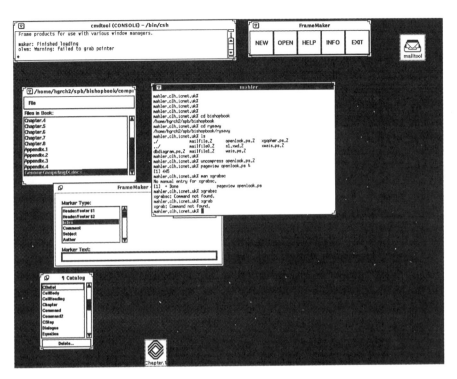

FIGURE 1.6 An example of a WIMPS screen.

Work on the GUI systems started in Xerox's Palo Alto Research Centre (PARC) in the 1970s, seeding the computer world with the now ubiquitous windows, icons, mouse, pull-down menus user interfaces (WIMPS) (Preece and Keller, 1990). This work lead to the Apple Macintosh GUI which made use of Apple PCs more intuitive and therefore easier. The Macintosh operating system has always been a GUI and Macintoshes do not have a command line option. The GUI approach gained wide acceptance in the user community. GUI based operating systems started supplanting the old command line type and today a variety of GUI systems such as Microsoft Windows (Microsoft, 1992b), Presentation Manager, NextStep to name just a few are available for PCs. The application which produces the display must run on the same system that actually supports it. In other words each dot (called a pixel, or picture element) of a graphical image on the PC's screen is directly mapped from the same PC's memory where this picture element corresponds to one or more bits.

The Massachusetts Institute of Technology (MIT) X Window System (X11), is used to implement two well known GUIs, OpenLook and Motif, which supersede the UNIX command line, and has been designed as a network oriented windowing system (O-Reilly, 1992). An application need not be running on the same system that actually supports the display. Applications producing graphical images may execute on other computer nodes, sending requests across networks (both LANs and WANs) to a particular display, and receiving keyboard and pointer events from the system controlling the display. The X Window System is based on a client-server model. The process or program that controls the graphic display is known as the server, the applications are known as clients (more about the client-server model in Section 6). Multimedia and visualization technologies are the future steps in graphical user interface developments (Earnshaw and Wiseman, 1992).

GUI systems require desktop devices, workstations, PCs or terminals, available from a number of manufacturers, equipped with appropriate networking and graphical facilities, with sophisticated displays and user interface features for information management and presentation. These devices have to be smoothly and controllably integrated into the network and database architectures. The reader will find details in Appendix 3.

5   Database Concepts

Increasingly sophisticated and affordable IT tools are becoming available to the researcher which enable volumes of genomic research data to be generated, collected, analysed and mapped. Genetic research requires more and more data to be easily accessible. Computing methods that allow the efficient and accurate processing of experimentally gathered data are playing a crucial role in almost all genomic research. It was suggested that sequence databases are likely to become "the profound research tools of biologists over the next decade" (Lander et al., 1991).

A database project usually consists of three components (Bowers, 1990; Date, 1990; Ullman, 1988):

- Development of a database structure that allows for storage and maintenance of the required data.

- Data entry, maintenance and management.

- Retrieval of the data by end users equipped with suitable analysis and display tools addressed in detail elsewhere in this book.

The most important part of database application design is identification of the pertinent data to be stored to satisfy all applications, i.e. molecular biology or genetics application software programs accessing the database after it has been implemented. Traditionally, the process consists of two separate stages. First all available data are analysed to discover what has to be represented in the database to produce satisfactory results. Then the data are modelled to define how the data will actually be internally stored and externally represented. However under certain circumstances the process might be reversed, the user might want to identify the external data representation first and only then the database designer may investigate from where and how the data can be collected and stored.

To distribute the contents of repository databases that consist of discrete collections of facts, e.g. the EMBL (European Molecular Biology Laboratory) nucleic acid sequence database and the SwissProt protein sequence database, traditional file processing techniques may be used. In the file processing environment all the data required for a particular application are usually stored in a single data file or possible in a set of separate data files. The data are usually kept in the files as a collection of alphanumeric characters represented in ASCII format (see Section 1), i.e. each character as a single integer in the range 0-127. In multiple applications, each requires its own file of data. This can often lead to considerable redundancy in stored data with resultant waste of storage space. This technology does not easily allow data to be shared between different applications (Bowers, 1990). It becomes less than adequate when the facts stored in various datasets are interrelated and information must be related in such a way that meaningful knowledge can be extracted. More advanced database technology, a database management system (DBMS), has to be employed. This is a programming system, a piece of software which has the ability to manage persistent data and access and manipulate large amounts of data efficiently. The architecture of a such a system is divided into three levels: conceptual, external and internal. Note that neither do all available databases fit neatly into this particular framework nor does this architecture provide the only possible framework.

The goal of the initial data analysis and modelling is to produce a conceptual view of a database, i.e. as complete as possible a definition of all of the information which is required by the project for which the database is being built. This is called the conceptual schema of the database. It is independent of the way the data will be physically stored and it may or may not be different from the way the data are going to be viewed by a particular user. It is intended to be a view of the data free from any computer hardware and software constraints. The conceptual schema is a logical description of the data in the database.

The user is presented with the external view of the data. This is defined by an external schema. As already mentioned above, the external view and the conceptual schema may be rather similar if not identical. However, whilst there is a single conceptual view, there in most cases will be many external views. The external schema can, apart from the data items in the conceptual schema, consist of data items derived from the conceptual schema data items. There can be several external schemata or one per application or user using only some of the data items from the conceptual schema. These are called user views or sub-schemata.

The internal level is the closest to physical storage (magnetic and optical disks, magnetic tapes) and is concerned with the way in which the data are actually stored. The details of how the data are physically stored is usually hidden from the general user.

The database users are either application programmers or general users of any degree of sophistication. Users are provided with a tool, a language, to define or manipulate the data in the database system. In database textbooks these are called conceptual, external or internal data definition language and data manipulation languages (DDL, DML). Thus as an example, to define a conceptual schema the application programmer would use a special DDL provided by the DBMS.

5.1 SQL

To interrogate a database, the user will have available in most cases a standard query language (SQL) that a DBMS provides to retrieve and represent the required data (van den Lans, 1988; Date and Darwen, 1989). SQL was formerly known as SEQUEL, a language developed by IBM, originally used in the experimental database known as System R. The language has both data definition and data manipulation capabilities and is now used in a number of commercial database systems. In some cases, the entire database is marketed under the name SQL. Often manipulation of a database is done by an application program. Such programs are commonly written in any conventional programming language (host language) such as C or COBOL that invokes commands of a DML. The latter is called a declarative language. One can use it to express what one wants, without explaining exactly how the desired result is to be computed. Such languages are very good at manipulating the database. However if the query requires that computational tasks be performed at the same time, procedural languages such as C or COBOL have to be used.

5.2 Database Models

A database is a collection of data elements used by applications of some particular project such as the Human Genome Data Base (GDB), mouse backcross or cDNA sequences. Genes, alleles, clones, papers, journals and other are the basic entities about which data are recorded in these databases. The term entity is widely used in the database to mean any object, event, activity or association that is to be represented in the database. Attributes are facts about entities also to be stored there. In general there will be relationships that link the entities in the database together. It can be said that a relationship is merely a special kind of entity. A data structure is a set of all data elements of a conceptual or external schema, namely entity types, attributes and relation types. It can be graphically represented by a data structure diagram. Figure 1.7 shows a simple data structure diagram with three entity sets AUTHORS, PUBLICATIONS, and JOUR-

NALS. The first two are related by the relationship WRITTEN_BY and the second and third are related by PUBLISHED_IN. Three attributes, NAME, AGE, ADDRESS are shown for AUTHORS. PUBLICATIONS has the attributes NAME and SUBJECT while JOURNALS has only one attribute, NAME.

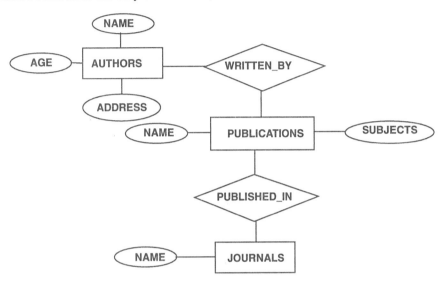

FIGURE 1.7 An example of a simple data structure diagram.

The range of data structures supported at the external or conceptual user level and the way in which the available tools (languages and others) permit the user to view and manipulate the data relationships allows for a categorization of a database system into one of several basic models: relational, network and hierarchical. These are often called the second generation of databases. Relational databases such as Ingres, Sybase and Oracle are the most popular commercial databases used to store genome data at present. As has been already stated above, none of these technologies meets the needs of storing the genome data in full. The models of the future are the object oriented (Gray et al., 1992), the knowledge based and deductive database systems. Others form the subject of research. To describe all these individual models in detail and analyse the differences between them is outside the scope of this chapter. The interested reader might find a great deal more in the appropriate literature.

5.3 Database Administration

The database administrator (DBA) is a person, a group of persons or a whole depart-ment responsible for overall control of database systems. The DBA is usually not only answerable for the design of the database, but also for choice of the DBMS used, its implementation and training of all involved in the database running and use. The most complicated job is that of physical entering of the data in the database. Once the data is entered, it has to be maintained and kept up to date. Its integrity, security and recovery present formidable challenges to a DBA.

- Database Integrity - The major issue for the database management is to ensure that the data in the database is accurate, correct, valid and consistent. Any inconsistency between two or more entries that represent the same entity demonstrates lack of integrity. Database technology cannot do very much to protect users against data errors made in the outside world before the data has been entered in the system. However, certain safety measures can be built into a database to ensure that errors within the system are minimized.

- Database Security - The DBA has to ensure that adequate security measures are taken to prevent unauthorized disclosure, alteration or destruction of both the data within the database and the database software itself. A password and a list of privileges attached to it are most commonly used to control user access rights to database information.

- Database Recovery - The process of recovery involves restoring a database to a state which is known to be correct following some kind of failure. The technique of redundancy is used in the sense that it has to be possible to recover the database to its "'correct'" state from information available some-where else in the system. The most common way to achieve this is to "dump" the contents of the database with a defined frequency on another medium, magnetic tape or optical disk, which is then stored in a safe place.

6 Client-Server Computing

The client-server computing model of systems as a method of centralizing shared resources such as databases (Salemi, 1993), while localizing the processing and graph-ics resources, has become the computing environment of the 1990s. Client computers and server computers (which respond to client requests) are geographically dispersed although linked together by LANs and WANs. These arrangements result in end user operated, distributed computing facilities providing support for all those connected to the network and seamless access nationally and internationally. Users can therefore interact with a number of local and remote systems and are no longer confined to communicating with a single computer (Berson, 1992, Inmon and Kaplan, 1992). The network is the computer.

In a conventional application a single program or process running on a computer does all the work. For example, in a conventional database application the program accepts a user's request for data, searches the database for requested data, sorts the data, and displays it for the user. In a client-server application there are two independent processes rather than a single integrated process running on one or more computers. In the case of the database, the client process accepts request for data and displays it on a user's desktop device, whilst the server process searches the database and sorts the data on another computer. The client asks for the data and the server provides it. The computing workload can be spread across a number of computers on the network specializing in what they do best such as database servers, file servers, graphical workstations, and communication servers (Sloman and Kramer, 1987).

The components of a client-server system include:

- Local Network and Internetwork Technology to interface existing and new systems as discussed in Section 2. The system design must allow for choice of heterogeneous hardware, the best for a defined research programme, but the user interface must be homogeneous to speed up learning and minimize the training costs.

- Desktop Devices (workstations, personal computers and graphics terminals) capable of providing a graphical user interface for information management and presentation. The emphasis is on the graphical presentation of data as a primary tool. Graphical displays are based on X window technology as discussed in Section 4. An application program as a client process requests that the X terminal, the server, displays images and sends the user's keystrokes or mouse movements back to the client application. The X window protocol is used for communication. Such applications require sufficient memory to run both the client and the server processes. The server computer has to be powerful enough to run this application efficiently. These devices have to be smoothly and controllably integrated into the network and database architectures.

- Database Technologies and Architectures to make available to the users common shareable data in the network and mechanisms to provide on-line access to selected databases around the world at high speeds.

A widely used technology is the NFS (Network File System) based distributed file system. It provides centralized control of local databases on a particular site and high speed access mechanisms from that site to programs and data in other computers on various LANs and WANs. In an NFS file system, the client process, an application or a user, requests that the remote file system, the server process, sends it part of the contents of a file. The RPC (Remote Procedure Call) technique is used for communication between client and server processes. To run the NFS efficiently a dedicated fileserver with plenty of memory and disk space, fast disks and intelligent Ethernet controllers to process NFS requests are required. Also, the NFS software has to be properly tuned.

An SQL based database, such as the GDB in the Johns Hopkins University, Baltimore, USA, and its UK, German, French, Japanese and Australian nodes, is an example of a client-server system. A process on the client Unix workstation converts the user data requests into SQL messages and then sends them to the database server process, which finds the appropriate data and returns them to the client. As the extra overhead of receiving and decoding SQL queries is incurred the database server hardware must be sufficiently powerful to handle this.

7 Molecular Biology And Genetics Computing Network

7.1 Design Philosophy

This is not a rigid description of the way the computing environment that supports the genome research is progressing, but a snapshot of what is, and will continue to be, a rapidly evolving, loosely organized web of molecular biology and genetics computing centres (Bleasby et al., 1992). Many of the them actually perform two or more of the functions described below and the boundaries are often blurred, but the general picture is as follows. Various centres or nodes, specializing in some aspect of the use of computers in molecular biology and genetics, are linked together by computer networks in such a way as to provide a service to the customer, namely the research worker.

Such an environment encompasses the following nodes:

- User Nodes - these are the computing facilities directly available to the worker on the local site. Access from a user node to the rest of the world is provided by the networks.

- Service Nodes - usually computing centres funded by national research bodies to provide a centralized specialist service to users in a research field. There are usually one or two of these in a country.

- Database Nodes - centres which collect data and programs and distribute them to service nodes who make them available to the users. The service nodes remove the need for the users to worry about obtaining the latest databases and setting up the required software. They shield the database nodes from having to provide the computing power to do search requests for the users.

- Research Nodes - computing sites that devise new and better ways of collecting, analysing and presenting data.

- Specialized Computing Nodes - these possess unusual or unique computing hardware or allow for those who do not wish a local database or program to be run offsite but who are happy for users to use their service.

This 'de facto' specialization of the various nodes will probably continue in the future, producing something like specialist agencies and public libraries, providing expertise and services to the users.

7.2 User Nodes

Local computing facilities should consist of desktop devices and terminals as discussed in Section 4 above. Character based dumb terminals are a minimal requirement, but X windows graphics devices should be set up if possible, either as hardware, or as emulation software running on PCs or Macintoshes. The desktop devices should be connected in a LAN to a server providing local services such as disk space, WAN connection, network services, printers, plotters, digitizer pads and others. The connections to the outside world have been discussed in Section 2.2. At present, access to networks from many user nodes is often patchy and the speed of the connection to the network is sometimes less than optimal.

Typically there is at least one person whose job it is, either by design or by default, to look after the computing needs of the local users. This function may be performed by either a local computing centre or a designated person whose job it is to look after the laboratory's computers or may simply be the person in the laboratory who knows most about computers and who has been dragooned into performing this function.

7.3 Service Nodes

The service node will typically provide additional computing facilities to users who access them over the WANs. They provide high powered computers (often computers that are on the verge of being described as "supercomputers", although this is a very fluid term, as the power of computers doubles every two years or so). They make available many more programs than the user nodes could afford to support. They maintain immediate access to data and programs obtained from the database nodes which they will update frequently (often daily or weekly). They will attempt to provide a comprehensive user support for the services they provide.

Typically the service nodes will not only supply their own services to users, but also services of other service nodes or of specialist nodes. The details of access to these other service nodes or specialist nodes are often hidden from the users and it may not be obvious to the user that they are using services that are situated in sites other than on the service node that they had connected to.

Some client-server programs make the transition from one node to another so easily that the user can be completely unaware that they are using resources on many different machines across the international networks. This can be apparent only when there is a major fault on the networks.

This trend towards providing services from different sites in a seamless fashion is one of the fastest developing trends in research computing at present, but it leaves many questions unresolved, such as who should pay for the services that are provided to the users on the network when the users could be from many different countries.

Some service nodes and contact names at the time of writing are listed in Appendix 2.

7.4   Database Nodes

Database nodes collect and collate data from various sources, sometimes producing a unique database which they produce, maintain and distribute, often with some software to search and manipulate it. They often hold collections of useful and public domain (free) software. They distribute the data and software by means of CD-ROM and magnetic tape or by FTP or by some form of mail server. They commonly do not attempt to provide an interactive service to users, preferring to leave this up to the service nodes, so people usually cannot run the stored software and databases on the database nodes.

Mail servers are systems where the user can obtain data from a site by sending a mail message to an address at that site containing command words which cause the system to search for the required data and to return it to the person to sent the mail. The most useful command to get going with using mailservers is "HELP". Mailservers are becoming less common with the increase in speed of the networks and the consequent improvement in performance of interactive programs like FTP.

So much data are available via FTP from database nodes that a system has been written to find the required files. Archie is a database which allows users to find which sites hold the programs or database files that they are interested in.

To use Archie, telnet into one of the database nodes given in Table 1.1.

When you are connected, give the log-in name "archie" and then give the command "help".

TABLE 1.1 Archie database nodes

IP name	IP number	Area served	Site
archie.doc.ic.ac.uk	[146.169.11.3]	UK/European	Imperial, London, UK
archie.funet.fi	[128.214.6.100]	European	FUnet, Helsinki, Finland
archie.au	[139.130.4.6]	Australian	Deakin, Geelong, Australia
archiecs.huji.ac.il	[132.65.6.15]	Israel	Israel
archie.sura.net	[128.167.254.179]	World	SURAnet, Maryland, USA
archie.rutgers.edu	[128.6.18.15]	World	Rutgers, New Jersey, USA
archie.unl.edu	[129.93.1.14]	World	Lincoln, Nebraska, USA
archie.ans.net	[147.225.1.2]	World	ANS, New York, USA
archie.mcgill.ca	[132.206.2.3]	World	McGill, Montreal, Canada

Almost every service node provides some data or programs that can be obtained by Anonymous FTP, but some provide such a wealth of data that they deserve to be classed as database nodes. Amongst these are the following:

```
CSC, Finland, Rob Harper, FTP to nic.funet.fi or 128.214.6.100
IUBIO, Indiana, Don Gilbert, FTP to iubio.bio.indiana.edu or 129.79.1.101
NCBI, Maryland, Dennis Benson, FTP to ncbi.nlm.nih.gov or 130.14.25.1
EMBL, Germany, FTP to ftp.embl-heidelberg.de or 192.54.41.33
```

There are many sites that produce databases of some form or other. The LiMB database (Listing of Molecular Biology databases - obtainable from most biological database nodes) lists some 100 known databases. Some of the most notable are listed in Appendix 2.

8   Research Nodes

These research into more efficient or faster methods of collecting, analysing and presenting data. This is done both by large nationally-funded research centres such as NCBI (USA), Genethon (France), MRC Laboratory of Molecular Biology, Cambridge (UK), and others and by many university departments. The results of this research are evaluated and made available to the user by the service nodes.

8.1   Specialized Computing Nodes

These sites specialize in use of the most advanced computer hardware including high performance parallel or other computers and neural-net machines which they make available to users over WANs. These sites may also hold databases which they do not wish to be run off site but which they are happy for users to access directly (sometimes for a fee). Often e-mail services are provided to run complex database searching tasks quickly. Also, frequently research is carried out into more efficient or faster methods of performing computing jobs in biology on high performance computers.

9   References

Berson A (1992). "Client Server Architecture" McGraw-Hill, New York.

Black UD (1991). "OSI: A Model for Communication Standards". Prentice-Hall, Engelwood Cliffs, NJ.

Bleasby AJ, Griffiths P, Harper R, Hines D, Hoover K, Kristofferson D, Marshall S, O'Reilly N and Sundvall M (1992). Electronic communication and the new biology. Nucleic Acids Res. 20, 4127-4128.

Bowers DS (1990). "From Data to Database". Chapman and Hall, London.

Brookshear JG (1991). "Computer Science; An Overview". Benjamin/Cummings, Menlo Park, CA.

Brown P (1984). "Starting with UNIX". Addison-Wesley, Reading, MA.

Comer DE (1991). "Internetworking With TCP/IP", Vols I and II. Prentice-Hall, Engelwood Cliffs, NJ.

Connor M (1987). "Computers and Computing Information Resources". Gale Research Co.

Cooper, R, Hutton, JS, Smith, IL (1991). From JANET to SuperJANET. Proceedings of a Symposium on High Speed Networking for Research in Europe. Computer Networks ISDN Syst. 21, 347-351.

Date CJ (1990). "An Introduction to Database Systems", 5th edn. Addison-Wesley, Reading, MA.

Date CJ and Darwen H (1989). "Guide to the SQL Standard", 2nd edn. Addison-Wesley, Reading, MA.

Dietel HM (1991). "An Introduction to Operating Systems", 2nd edn. Addison-Wesley, Reading, MA.

Earnshaw RA and Wiseman N (1992). "An Introductory Guide to Scientific Visualisation". Springer-Verlag, Berlin.

Gray PMD, Kulkarni KG and Patton NW (1992). "Object Oriented Databases". Prentice-Hall, London.

Hayes JP (1987). "Computer Architecture and Organisation". McGraw-Hill, New York.

Inmon WH and Caplan JH (1992). "Information Systems Architecture; Development in the 90's". QED Information Sciences, Wellesley, MA.

Joint Network Team (1992). "JANET Starter Pack. Introductory Information about JANET for Computing Services". Joint Network Team, Rutherford Appleton Laboratory.

Lalande WR and Pugh JR (1991). "Inside Smalltalk", Vols I and II. Prentice-Hall, Engelwood Cliffs, NJ.

Lander ES, Langridge R and Saccocio DM (1991). Mapping and interpreting biological information. Commun. ACM 34, 33-39.

LaQuey TL (1990). "User's Directory of Computer Networks". Digital Press, Bedford, MA.

Larson JA (1992). "Interactive Software; Interactive User Interfaces Building Tools". Prentice-Hall, Engelwood Cliffs, NJ.

Leebaert D (1991). "Technology 2001; The Future of Computing and Communications". MIT Press, Cambridge, MA.

Martin J (1989). "Local Area Networks, Architectures and Implementations". Prentice-Hall, Engelwood Cliffs, NJ.

Martin J (1990). "Telecommunications and the Computer". Prentice-Hall, Engelwood Cliffs, NJ.

Microsoft (1992a). "Microsoft MS-DOS 5.0 User's Guide and Reference". Microsoft Corporation, Redmont, WA.

Microsoft (1992b). "Microsoft Windows User Guide". Microsoft Corporation, Redmont, WA.

Peddie C (1991). "Graphical User Interfaces and Graphics Standards". McGraw-Hill, New York.

Preece J and Keller L (eds) (1990). "Human Computer Interaction". Prentice-Hall, London.

Reardon R (ed.) (1989). "Future Networks, New Developments, New Opportunities". Blenheim, London.

Salemi J (1993). "Guide to Client Server Databases". Ziff-Davis Press, Emeryville, CA.

Sloman J and Kramer J (1987). "Distributed Systens and Computer Networks". Prentice-Hall, Engelwood Cliffs, NJ.

Smith B (1992). "UNIX Desktop Guide to Mail and News". Hayden.

Stallings W (1987). "Computer Organization and Architecture". Macmillan, New York.

Tannenbaum AS (1988). "Computer Networks". Prentice-Hall, Engelwood Cliffs, NJ.

Tannenbaum AS (1992). "Modern operating systems". Prentice-Hall, Engelwood Cliffs, NJ.

Ullman JD (1988). "Principles of Database and Knowledge-Base Systems". Computer Science Press, Rockville, MD.

van den Lans RF (1988). "Introduction to SQL". Addison-Wesley, Reading, MA.

Willis N (1987). "Computer Architecture and Communication" Blackwell , Oxford.

O'Reilly (1992). "X-Window System Series", Vols 1-8. O'Reilly , Sebastopol, CA.

CHAPTER 2

Experimental Materials Databases

Gabrielle Fisher

Human Genome Mapping Project Resource Centre,
Watford Road, Harrow, Middlesex HA1 3UJ, UK
Internet: gfisher@crc.ac.uk

1 Introduction

Scientists working on the Human Genome Mapping Project (HGMP) are generating a wide range of resources to help them in their studies. To know what resources are available and how one gets hold of them can be a daunting task. Anyone new to the field, or in a newly established molecular genetics laboratory without outside experience to draw on, would find it a problem. There are several possible solutions. One solution would be to investigate commercial supplies by reading through catalogues of the numerous biotechnology companies who supply a wide variety of common basic resources, such as cloning vectors, sequencing primers, restriction endonucleases, cell lines, etc. A disadvantage of this approach is that catalogues are often updated only once a year, although the supply of resources is constantly changing as research progresses and demands change. Demand for primer banks and sequencing data has increased as scientists have changed from hybridization mapping methods using clones, to mapping by the polymerase chain reaction (PCR) using oligonucleotide primers (Weissenbach et al., 1992). New biotechnology products are mostly publicized through advertisements in popular weekly journals such as "Science", "Nature" and "New Scientist". Scientists may be targeted by individual companies if they happen to be on their

GUIDE TO HUMAN GENOME COMPUTING
ISBN 0-12-102050-9

mailing list for example through personal registration at commercial laboratory exhibitions or through the sale of their society membership list to the company. These established scientists are often sent information directly about new and forthcoming products. The new scientist, however, is less fortunate.

An alternative solution is to make use of one of the several large non-profit making centres which supply reliable and well characterized resources and services to workers on the Human Genome Project. Some of the major centres include the American Type Culture Collection (ATCC) and the Coriell Institute, in the USA, and in the UK the purpose built Human Genome Mapping Project Resource Centre (HGMP-RC) (for addresses see Appendix 2).

The ATCC is a private, non-profit making organization which maintains and distributes a collection of human and mouse probes, primers and libraries in addition to its world renowned collection of micro-organisms (bacteriophages and bacteria, protozoa and algae) and banks of cell lines and hybridomas. Catalogue databases for each of these collections are available for on-line search and are described in Section 4.1.5.

The Coriell Institute is a biomedical research institute which houses the largest collection of human cell lines relating to human genetic mutations, aging, and mental disease. Human/rodent somatic cell hybrids are available as cultures and a mapping panel is available as purified DNA. The Institute also offers DNA from monochromosomal hybrids and from hybrids retaining three or fewer human chromosomes in a variety of combinations. Unfortunately, at the time of writing, no database appears to be publicly available.

The UK HGMP-RC supplies specialist materials (cDNAs, probes, primers, yeast artificial chromosomes (YACs) and cell lines), information and services (oligonucleotide synthesis, fluorescent in situ hybridization (FISH) mapping, cell transformation and computing). Registration is open to scientists worldwide whose work is relevant to the HGMP. At the current time, registration is free to academic workers but a fee is payable by non-academic users. The supply of resources is restricted to registered users who by registering have signified their agreement to certain terms and conditions including a willingness to return data. Resources and services are supplied free of charge to UK academic users in exchange for materials and data generated through their use (non-UK users have free access to computing and to materials for a nominal charge). The aim is to promote the sharing of resources and improve the flow of information. The centre accumulates the information, stores it in databases and redistributes data to other users via the HGMP-RC computing facilities (see Section 3.1). For example the original Primer Database holds information about the sequences of the oligonucleotides kept in the Primer Bank. Further information about how they were used, for example PCR amplification conditions, is added to the database as soon as it is returned by the user. Full details are made available via the on-line database and the HGMP-RC menu (Figure 2.1).

Perhaps the best solution and most efficient way to find out what resources are available and how one gets hold of them is to gain access to the public databases of these major centres. Some of these are described later.

2 Listings of Molecular Biology Databases and Files

A comprehensive search of what is available will need to include the many smaller centres, as well as the major centres. Details of their resources can be found in databases and files, which are publicly accessible through international computer networks, as described in Chapter 1. Two databases, Archie and LiMB, can provide a very useful start to a search.

2.1 Archie

This is a database for finding out what files of interest are available, for example sequence files, and where they are. The information given allows users to transfer those files back to their own directory using the file transfer protocol (FTP); a fuller description is given in Chapter 1.

2.2 LiMB

A list of molecular biology databases (LiMB) exists as a database in its own right (Appendix 2). It provides a useful starting point for anyone trying to find out what is available. From the main HGMP-RC menu (Figure 2.1) the option "Other Molecular Data" provides direct access. The database contains information about contents of many databases related to molecular biology and details of how they are maintained and distributed. The data has been gathered from questionnaires and journals. Each record includes information about how to contact the database (network address, names and addresses, etc.) and also gives information about other databases to which the given database is cross-referenced. Some of these databases are considered in this chapter.

3 Useful Networks

Different databases have different methods of direct access, via different networks. Data stored in one database can also be accessed indirectly by being cross-referenced in another database. For example, clone data in The Integrated Genomic Database (IGD) may be the same information in the GDB, ATCC Database for the Repository of

Human and Mouse Probes and Libraries (DRHPL) or the UK Probe Database. Similarly, mapping data for the mouse genome from several databases (Genetic Strains and Variants of the Laboratory Mouse and The Mouse in Biomedical Research, GBASE: The Genomic Database of the Mouse, The Chromosome Atlas, and The Mouse Locus Catalogue) have been collected together in the Encyclopedia of the Mouse Genome. A single database can be accessed in several different ways. For example, the UK Probe Bank can be accessed through the HGMP-RC service node and the Imperial Cancer Research Fund (ICRF) network. The European Collection of Animal Cell Cultures (ECACC) database can be accessed on-line from the Microbial Strain Data Network (MSDN), via the HGMP-RC and the Deutsches Institut für Medizinische Dokumantation und Information (DIMDI). Three computing facilities the UK HGMP-RC, MSDN and Interlab (Ansaldo) provide access to some major experimental materials databases which are considered here. The main menu for each is shown in Figures 2.1, 2.3, and 2.4. Access to a network requires authorization, registration and password/account. Once on the network further access to the databases is normally free.

3.1 UK Human Genome Mapping Project Resource Centre (UK HGMP-RC)

Access to a variety of databases has been made easier through the UK HGMP-RC. The HGMP-RC computer facilities provide registered users with a simple way to access a wide range of genetics and molecular biology software packages and databases (IGD, GDB, OMIM, sequencing databases, etc.). To access databases through this computing service, each user is provided with all the necessary files and permissions, disk space for personal data, a user account name and a password. Users should preferably be equipped with a personal computer, workstation, or X-terminal which can support X applications and is linked to the Internet network for example through use of the Joint Academic Network Internet Protocol (JIPS) (see Chapter 1). When logging onto the system, users are presented with a screen showing a menu of selections (Figure 2.1) which open up many of the relevant databases.

```
MOLECULAR BIOLOGY SOFTWARE FOR THE HGMP-RC

MAIN MENU

>>>>>>>>>> You Have NEW MAIL. Choose Option 2

        0) Help
        1) Exit

        2) Electronic Mail
        3) BIOSCI/Network News (Biologist's Bulletin Boards
        4) Information Services
        5) Analysis and Manipulation of Sequences
        6) Sequence Database searching
        7) Genome Data
        8) Linkage Analysis
        9) Cell Lines, Clones & Probes Database
        10) Other Molecular Data
        11) Utilities (File Transfer & Management)
        12) UNIX Operating System
        13) Miscellaneous ("How to..." etc.)
        14) Queries, Suggestions and Comments to User Support

                Enter a number >
```

FIGURE 2.1 The HGMP-RC menu system.

From the main HGMP-RC menu the option "Cell Lines, Clones and Probes Menu" (Figure 2.2) allows further access to a number of experimental materials databases.

```
        CELL LINES, CLONES AND PROBES MENU

        0) Exit
        1) Return to Previous Menu

        2) UK DNA PROBE DATABASE
        3) UK HGMP PRIMER DATABASE
        4) cDNA DATABASE
        5) European Human Cell Bank
        6) Wessex Register of Chromosome Abnormalities
        7) Chromosome Abnormality Database
        8) RLDB
```

FIGURE 2.2 Cell Lines, Clones and Probes Menu.

3.2   Microbial Strain Data Network (MSDN)

This is an international network set up to establish pathways of communication concerning collections of data on microbial strains and cell lines held in culture collections and to provide a means for locating strains with specific properties. For human genome scientists several useful databases including the European Collection of Animal Cell

Cultures, ATCC Cell Lines Catalogue, Hybridoma Data Bank, and ATCC Collection Recombinant Clones and Libraries Catalogue can be accessed through this network (Appendix 2). For UK HGMP-RC registered users who have an MSDN account, the connection is simplified via the menu option "Information Services". After signing onto the main MSDN network, "CODATA" displays the main menu service (Figure 2.3).

```
              CODATA/MSDN Services Menu
      ENTER "QUIT" TO LEAVE CODATA/MSDN SERVICES MENU


           CODE    SERVICE

           *1      ACCESS CODATA/MSDN NEWS
           *2      USE ELECTRONIC MAIL
           *3      SEARCH A DATABASE
           *4      ACCESS A BULLETIN BOARD CONFERENCE
           *5      SIGN OFF CODATA/MSDN SERVICES
```

FIGURE 2.3 CODATA/MSDN services menu.

Option 3 accesses the database menu (Figure 2.4).

```
      *1 HYBRIDOMA DATA BANK DIRECTORY
      *2 MICROBIAL STRAIN DATA NETWORK DATABASE
      *3 AMERICAN TYPE CULTURE COLLECTION DATABASES
      *4 NCYC & NCFB ONLINE SERVICES
      *5 EUROPEAN COLLECTION ANIMAL CELL LINES DATABASE
      *6 INFORMATION CENTRE FOR EUROPEAN CULTURE COLLECTIONS
      *7 DEUTSCHE SAMMLUNG VON MIKROORGANISMEN DATABASE
      *8 CAB INTERNATIONAL MYCOLOGICAL INSTITUTE DATABASE
      *9 NETHERLANDS CULTURE COLLECTION DATABASES(CBS/NCC)
      *0 RETURN TO CODATA/MSDN SERVICES MENU
```

FIGURE 2.4 CODATA/MSDN database services.

Options 1, 3, and 5 are considered later.

3.3   Interlab/Ansaldo

The Ansaldo network hosts the Interlab Project databases: Cell Lines, HLA typed B cell lines and Molecular Probes. They can be accessed by means of the Interlab/Ansaldo network, via Internet. Telnet to istge.ist.inige.it (130.251.201.2). After logging in to the Interlab network the main menu screen presents databases or system activities options (Figure 2.5).

```
        ====INTERLAB MENU===

Databases                    System activities
1. Cell lines                10. Mailbox
2. HLA typed B cell lines    11. Password

        0. Exit  Enter your choice

              Char Mode: Replace
```

FIGURE 2.5 Interlab services menu.

Options 1, 2 and 3 are considered later.

4   Materials Databases

4.1   Human Cell Lines

The starting point for many human genome studies will be a collection of human DNA, for example DNA from families with an inherited disease. Cell lines provide an important renewable source for extensive or long term studies and a means to archive DNA from deceased subjects or those with a very rare inherited disease. Several data-bases may prove useful.

4.1.1   European Collection of Animal Cell Cultures (ECACC) Database

This database stores information on over 1,000 cell lines from a variety of species including the human and mouse. There is also an extensive collection of hybridomas and T-cell clones. It can be accessed in several ways: through the MSDN, via the HGMP-RC (in part) and via DIMDI.

4.1.2   European Human Cell Bank (EHCB)

This is an additional specialized collection to the ECACC, funded by the UK HGMP. Cells have been collected mainly from laboratories throughout the UK and also the Netherlands. Many of the cells are stored as untransformed peripheral blood lym-phocytes and are transformed on request. From the HGMP-RC menu (Figure 2.1), the option Cell Lines, Clones and Probes Menu (Figure 2.2) gives access to the EHCB data-base. This stores information about human cell lines maintained as part of the ECACC. The first database prompt offers help and an option to view a catalogue listing the iden-tity number, sex, phenotype, pedigree number, diagnosis and some remarks about the source of the cells. It contains over 6,000 records of cells mostly derived from patients and their families with genetic disorders and chromosome abnormalities. They also include a specific collection of HLA defined lymphoblastoid cell lines, many of them homozygous for the various class I and II antigens and a panel of cell lines from random donors. The second prompt gives users the opportunity to search the database with suitable key words, for example a search for "prader" (relating to the Prader-Willi syndrome) will find some 20 records. Each gives, in addition to the catalogued information, details about the age and race of the patient, the MIM (Mendelian Inheritance in Man) number which can be used to search the OMIM (see later) database for further information, pedigree number, cell type, availability and/or restrictions to access, and some additional clinical remarks. A number of cell lines in this collection are cross-referenced in the Interlab Project Cell Lines database. The cells listed can be obtained directly from EHCB (see Appendix 2).

4.1.3 Wessex Register of Chromosome Abnormalities

The Wessex Register of Chromosome Abnormalities can be accessed through the HGMP-RC menu and the optional Cell Lines, Clones and Probes Menu (Figure 2.2). It stores information about over 4,000 sources of cells with a wide variety of cytogenetic abnormalities. An introduction defines the fields and explains the abbreviations used. A catalogue is available in response to the first prompt and lists ID number, sex, chromosome, abnormality, ascertainment and karyotype fields. Individual records include details of laboratory number, the reason for referral, type of abnormality, chromosomes affected, breakpoints involved, parental origin of abnormality, and for those cells which have been submitted to the European Human Cell Bank for transformation and establishment of a cell line then the Human Cell Bank ID number is given (Figure 2.6). The database can be searched using one or more key words to select specific records. In addition to the catalogue as an excellent source of key words, any likely words will do, as for example a search using the key word "prader" (for the Prader-Willi syndrome) will find over a dozen records relating to this disease. Cells can be obtained directly from the Human Cell Bank for those records which include a Cell Bank ID number, otherwise the Wessex Regional Genetics Laboratory will help to obtain the necessary material to establish a cell line.

```
ID: 911367
Sex: F
DOB: 03/07/85
Ascertainment: ? PRADER WILLI
Abnormality: Deletion
Chromosome: 15
Breakpoint:
Breakpoint: 15q11/15q13
Karyotype: 46,XX.del (15) (q11q13) de novo
Pedigree No: 865861
Porton Cell Line ID: AW/DD233/L
Maternal DOB:
Paternal DOB: 09/06/54
```

FIGURE 2.6 Example of Wessex database record.

4.1.4 Chromosome Abnormality Database

The Cell Lines, Clones and Probes Menu option (Figure 2.2) from the HGMP-RC menu also gives access to the Chromosome Abnormality Database. This stores similar information to the Wessex database about acquired and constitutional abnormalities. Acquired abnormalities are detected in bone marrow and other tissues in the study of leukaemia and other neoplastic conditions. Constitutional abnormalities are usually diagnosed from samples of patient's blood or by prenatal study of abnormalities of foetal origin. Data is submitted from a number of UK cytogenetic laboratories, in a non-standard format, and editing is kept to the minimum such that some interpretation may be required, for example date of birth may refer to that of the mother in one laboratory or that of the baby in another. The database can be searched for either acquired or constitutional abnormalities either by viewing the catalogue or by using one or more key words to search for specific records. The catalogue gives information about the laboratory No., pedigree No., ascertainment and karyotype. Again a good source of key words for a search is the catalogue itself, but any likely word(s) will suffice and all records containing those word(s) will be selected, for example a search for "Angelmans" will find the record shown in Figure 2.7.

```
Sex:unknown
DOB: //
Pedigree no.: 9079
Ascertainment: SB
Laboratory: Duncan Guthrie Institute of Medical Genetics
            Yorkhill
            Glasgow, G3 8SJ
Lab ID (quote in any correspondence): 901690
Received by local lab: //
Tissue: Blood
Referral category: CL
Karyotypes:
ANGELMANS
Site at which stored materials are kept: see Lab. address
ID no.for sample (quote in any correspondence): (Lab ID)
Date added to this database: 24/07/1992
```

FIGURE 2.7 Example of Chromosome Abnormality Database record.

In these records: "sex" is the phenotypic sex of the patient; "DOB" is the date of birth of the patient, but may be of the mother or baby; "pedigree number" is the number which links samples from the same individual or from other members of the same pedigree; "ascertainment" is the reason the sample was taken (e.g. stillbirth (SB)); "referral category" (only for records in the constitutional register) may be used instead of tissue type or ascertainment to determine which samples were for prenatal diagnosis, checks for constitutional abnormalities, etc.; "karyotype" is a description of the chromosomal constitution of the cells and, in the case of acquired abnormalities, may only be partial detailing only the abnormalities and not the complete chromosome constitution; "number of cells analysed for each karyotype" is as given and "confirmation", for records in the acquired register, is an indication of whether the diagnosis given in the ascertainment field was confirmed. The data are freely available, but have been provided on condition that the laboratory from which records have been collected is consulted and gives permission prior to the use of its data in any further publication. Cells are available for those records which give an address, e.g. "site at which stored materials are kept", and an identity number, e.g. "ID number for stored sample", and may be obtained by contacting the local laboratory directly.

4.1.5 ATCC Cell Lines Database

From the CODATA/MSDN main menu (Figure 2.3), option 3 reveals a further option (1) to select the ATCC databases. The Cell Lines database is available as an on-line catalogue. The database stores information on some 3,100 cell lines and hybridomas maintained by the ATCC. They are derived from approximately 75 species from both human and animal origin. Each record contains information about the ATCC No. and patent details, name and aliases, tissue or organ source, pathologic description, diseases present in donor, species, age, sex, race, originator or depositor of cell line, date of accession, animal strain or breed, receptors present in or on cells, whether HeLa markers are present or not, viruses to which the cells are susceptible or resistant, tumori-genicity, reverse transcriptase (+/-); karyology, (karyotype, modal numbers, range, morphology (fibroblast, epithelial, lymphoblast), isoenzymes (or isotype for hybridomas), histocompatibility antigen (HLA, ABO, H-2, etc.) and differentiation antigens (Ly, CD, etc.), products produced and or secreted, mode of growth, notes and comments about references, growth media, contaminants, etc. Cell lines can be obtained by sending orders electronically to the ATCC (see Appendix 2).

4.1.6 Hybridoma Data Bank (HDB)

From the CODATA/MSDN main menu (Figure 2.3), option 3 then option 1 gives access to this international data bank on cloned cell lines and their immunoreactive products. The on-line directory contains excerpts from data records describing hybridomas, monoclonal antibodies, and other products of immunoclones known to be available from developers and/or commercial distributors. The database is owned and copyrighted by CODATA. Access is strictly limited to internal distribution by subscribing individuals and/or organizations. Each record provides information about reactants, cross reactants, distributor of cell line or product, designation of individual cell line or product, immunocyte donor, immortal partner, type and classification of product, availability restrictions or special conditions, comments and literature references.

4.1.7 Cell Line Database (CLDB)

The Cell Line Database includes data on >2,500 human and animal cell lines available from many Italian laboratories and some European cell culture collections including the ECACC (see Section 4.1.1), the German Collection of Microorganisms and Cell Cultures (DSM, Braunschweig), Institute "Giannina Gaslini" (Genova, Italy) - a collection from patients affected by inherited metabolic diseases, the Institute of Cytology (St Petersburg, Russia) and these include human somatic cells from patients with hereditary disease and a collection from the Biochemistry Dept, Pavia, Italy - a collection of dermal fibroblasts from patients affected by inherited connective tissue disorders. This database is available via the Interlab/Ansaldo network and the Interlab menu (Figure 2.5). Data is stored on identification (name, typology, karyology, etc.), origin (species, tissue, tumour, pathology, transforming agent, etc.), specific functions and applications, preservation and culture characteristics, retrieval sources (bibliographic references, catalogue codes etc.). Data on individual cell lines can be retrieved on the basis of most features such as for example name, catalogue, origin, transformation or specific functions.

4.1.8 B Line Data Base (BLDB)

This database is also accessed via the Interlab/Ansaldo network and the Interlab menu (Figure 2.5) It relates to HLA typed human lymphoblastoid cell lines, mainly from families with HLA linked/associated diseases. Information is stored on identification (name, histocompatibility workshop No., etc.), extended HLA typing, ethnic origin, related pathology, family pedigree (including a semi-graphic representation) and retrieval sources such as, for example, bibliographic references and catalogue codes.

Whilst undoubtedly many other valuable collections exist (for example a set of chromosome specific somatic cell hybrids is available from the Coriell Institute for Medical Research, Camden, USA) their catalogues are unfortunately not available on-line.

4.2 Oligonucleotide Primers, Clones and Libraries

These provide renewable sources of characterized fragments of DNA, i.e. reference markers which can be used to map "unknown" DNA.

4.2.1 UK HGMP Primer Database

This database can be accessed through the HGMP-RC menu. The Cell Lines, Clones and Probes Menu (Figure 2.2) gives access to the UK HGMP Primer Database. Data include information about the bank of over 1,500 oligonucleotides which has been created at the HGMP-RC through an oligonucleotide synthesis service. The bank includes a set of mouse chromosome specific microsatellite primers (Love et al.,1990), primers relating to specific human diseases for example Duchenne's Muscular Dystrophy, Neurofibromatosis, Alzheimer's and Batten's, and mapping markers for the human genome including many of the HGM11 reference markers and Mfd primers, i.e. those devised by Dr J. Weber (Marshfield Medical Research Collection). The composition of the bank changes frequently with demand. It currently includes over 1,500 oligonucleotides for the human, and just over 180 for mouse and other rodent species. Oligonucleotides are synthesized on request in return for information about the sequences and how they are used. The majority (80%) of the synthesis is banked and can subsequently be requested by other users, again in return for information generated through its use. The data is collated and stored in the Primer Database which is available to others through the HGMP-RC network. In this way the Resource Centre builds up information about the bank. On accessing the database, the first prompt offers a catalogue listing the oligonucleotides in chromosomal order and giving the Identity Number (ID), brief details of their use and information about the species, chromosome and locus they were designed for. By querying the database using key words gleaned from the catalogue, users may view specific records which give complete details of the ID, originator, sequence, species, locus, chromosome, regional assignment, associated disease, paired oligo ID, PCR amplification data (i.e. cycle conditions, primer concentration, DNA concentration, magnesium ion concentration, etc.), PCR product size, comments and results including associated probes and YACs. For example a search for "prader" will find two records of oligonucleotides which have been used in linkage studies of the Prader-Willi region. Each time the oligonucleotide is requested, information about its use is accumulated and added to the database record. The oligonucleotides can be obtained from the Resource Centre and are available free to UK users and to others for a nominal charge.

Some 50 Mfd mapping primer pairs are also available from the ATCC DRHPL (see 4.2.5).

4.2.2 Molecular Probe Data Base (MPDB)

This database stores information about synthetic oligonucleotides and is available on-line via the Interlab/Ansaldo network and the Interlab menu (Figure 2.5). The information is extracted from the literature and includes identification (name, nucleotide sequence, related amino-acid sequence, etc.), target gene (name, EMBL/GENBANK sequence accession number, map location, allelic variants recognized, etc.), technical data (melting temperature, NaCl molarity, etc.), applications and retrieval sources (bibliographic references, distributors, catalogue code). The database can be searched for individual oligonucleotides on the basis of most features (name, distributor, nucleotide sequence, target gene or application).

4.2.3 EMBL Data Library and GENBANK (Genetic Sequence Database)

These two sequence databases can be obtained in numerous ways including anonymous file transfer protocol (see Chapter 1), from GOPHER, WAIS, the Staden package, or through the GCG package available through the HGMP-RC menu (Figure 2.1). They store nucleic acid sequence data for most published sequences and provide a rich source of sequences for potential oligonucleotide primers. A search of these databases for repetitive elements within sequences can provide a basis for the development of useful sets of microsatellite PCR mapping markers (Beckmann and Weber, 1992; Hearne et al., 1991). There are many programs designed to aid in primer design. The "Primer" software package, for example, simplifies the design of oligonucleotide primers for a given target sequence.

The PRIMER software program automatically selects PCR primers and is available in several ways including from the Internet via anonymous ftp or directly from the Whitehead Institute (see Appendix 2 or e-mail "primer@genome.wi.edu") and is available through the HGMP-RC menu from the "Analysis & Manipulation of Sequences" option. The program will select primers from cloned and sequenced genomic DNAs useful for PCR amplification, sequencing and hybridization reactions. The sequence to be analysed must be designed/edited carefully so that it appears in the correct format, i.e. by typing ***sequence: <file name>**. The text file must appear exactly as in Figure 2.8.

```
*sequence: seq1
*target: []   (if the target is to be specified)
TACGTACGCC GATCGTGCAG TAGCAAAAGC CACACGTGCA GACTGACGTC
GACTCTG[CAC CACACACACA CACACACACA CACACA]GTAC TTTGCAGTCC
CATGCGTACG ACTGCGCATG CAGC
```

FIGURE 2.8 Input to the PRIMER program.

On entering the Primer program, the first prompt requests the file. Typing the <file name> (i.e. seq1 for the example given) opens the file to analysis. Users can opt either for (a) automatic analysis or (b) manual testing. For automatic analysis, one can specify the target sequence to be amplified and the size of the PCR product, the length of the primer and the PCR reaction conditions as for example annealing temperature. The program analyses which of the possible flanking primers fulfil the user's criteria and also pre-set conditions including the avoidance of repeat regions (e.g. Alu repeats in humans), ambiguous bases and self complementarity. Pairs of forward and reverse primers are automatically tested for pairwise complementarity (those which complement would lead to the problem of primer-heterodimer formation) and similarity of annealing temperatures. Recommended pairs are listed in the output file (i.e. `seq1.pcr` for the given example). Individual primer pairs can also be tested manually and any given pair can be tested against specified conditions without reference to the target sequence.

4.2.4 UK DNA Probe Bank

This database can be accessed in several ways, including through the HGMP-RC menu, the ICRF network and indirectly as part of the IGD, described later (Section 4.3.1). From the HGMP-RC menu, the Cell Lines, Clones and Probes Menu (Figure 2.2) gives access to the UK DNA Probe Bank. An initial prompt offers access to the catalogue listing over 800 clones maintained at the UK HGMP-RC. The database is compiled and new clones accessed at the Imperial Cancer Research Fund (ICRF), Clare Hall Laboratories (see Appendix 2). Probes have been collected from laboratories throughout the world and include some from the DRHPL collection. They consist mainly of human DNA clones with just a few mouse, mitochondrial and others and cover all the chromosomes. The catalogue includes details of each clone's identity number, species, HGM symbol, map position, clone name, vector, type and brief description. Clones are listed in order of cytogenetic location and give good coverage of both arms of most chromosomes with the exception of 13p, 14p, 15p and 21p. Users can scroll through the complete listing, but a more efficient way to search for an individual probe is to query the database. Words used in the catalogue can be useful key words. A more specific way to search would be to enter the precise clone name, for example pCAT, but since this level of detail may not be possible in practice, the more usual way is to use a word or string of words which are likely to partly describe the probe for example "minisatellite" or "T-cell receptor" or to use the locus name for example "APP". All records fulfilling the given criteria will be selected and the total number displayed. Individual records can be viewed and printed out. Each record then gives full details of the probe, namely the ID number, official HGM symbol, clone name, map location, type species, polymorphism, availability, description, excision data (vector resistance, site and size of insert), polymorphism data (enzyme, allele, frequency and size), originator (name and address) and appropriate references. Maps and reports can be printed out and graphical displays showing the chromosomal and regional assignment are possible through the IGD database. After listing the probes the user is invited to store the files in his or her directory to be printed out as and when required. The probes themselves can be obtained by sending a standard order form to the HGMP-RC (see Appendix 2). At the current time there is no charge for these to UK users, but for users elsewhere there is a nominal charge.

4.2.5 The Database for the Repository of Human and Mouse Probes and Libraries (DRHPL)

This database is of special interest to human genome scientists and is available separately from the ATCC on-line. International connections can be made through British Telecom's Tymnet and the US Telenet and also through the Microbial Strain Database Network. This probe database holds information about over 1,200 human and over 100 mouse genomic and cDNA clones, some 50 oligonucleotide primer pairs which detect polymorphisms at specific loci (largely derived from the collection of Dr J. Weber, Marshfield Medical Research Foundation), some 60 human chromosome specific genomic libraries and 16 primate or murine cDNA and genomic libraries maintained by the repository (Maglott and Nierman, 1991), at the ATCC. Gene probe records list information about probe name, gene name, ATCC numbers, depositor information, construction summary, locus abbreviation (HGM), map position, references and enzymes detecting restriction fragment length polymorphisms (RFLPs). Data is held on the chromosomal assignment, RFLPs, literature references, distribution lists and cross-references for some 270 clones and 55 libraries. The information about the probes has been obtained from the depositors, literature and the former Human Gene Mapping Library (HGML) database at Yale. The data is cross-referenced to other databases, and the same data can now be accessed through GDB. Oligonucleotide records show the ATCC No., locus, designated name, sequence, heterozygosity (%), polymorphism information content (PIC) value, number of alleles, size range (bp) and references. Records for the ATCC genomic library list details of its construction (insert size, vector, cloning site), its coverage, depositor, references and some additional information. Authorized customers can place orders for clones, oligonucleotides and libraries by electronic mail.

4.2.6 Genome Data Base (GDB)

The central database is held at Johns Hopkins University (Baltimore, USA), but read-only copies are available at other centres including DKFZ (Germany) and the HGMP-RC (UK). From the HGMP-RC menu (Figure 2.1), for example, the option Genome Data gives access to the combined databases GDB/OMIM. These databases are well known to most human genome mappers. OMIM stores text information about inherited diseases and is an on-line version of the book "Mendelian Inheritance in Man" by Victor McKusick plus the McKusick Human Gene Map and Molecular Defects List. GDB stores gene mapping information including primer sequences and allele frequencies for a large set of over 800 human microsatellite mapping markers which have recently been developed (Weissenbach et al., 1992). The data do not relate to any one central repository, but enough information is provided to enable users to obtain the material resources mentioned. Information in GDB can be cross-referenced to OMIM (On-line Mendelian Inheritance in Man) because of the direct searching link, via chromosome location and MIM numbers which appear in both GDB and OMIM databases. The information in GDB is organized into 5 categories: loci (genes, fragile sites, anonymous DNA segments), polymorphisms (including alleles and haplotypes), probes (clones, PCR primers, allele specific oligonucleotide (ASO)), contacts (for probes and GDB/OMIM users), references (journals, books, etc.). The database can be searched within each category, for example one can search amongst all the probes (c. 22,000) for human PCR primers for polymorphic genes by "call"-ing and selecting the "probe manager" then filling in the search table with the requirements to be met. Thus by selecting "PCR" for Type, "Genomic" and polymorphic "+", then commanding a "retrieve and sort" and opting for "probe" by which to order the list, after a pause, over 1,000 records which have met the given criteria are retrieved and a recommendation made to refine the search. By adding the search criterion location "22" then commanding a "retrieve and sort", 14 records are found. Individual records can be highlighted and "viewed" for full "table details" giving the primer name, sequence of each oligonucleotide with its length and orientation, locus (indicating polymorphic nature), whether it is an STS (sequence tagged site), amplified product size, gene position (e.g. exon), GENBANK accession number and annotated details for example relationship to other possibly nested primers. A "call" to the "locus manager" can retrieve further information specific to the probe in this individual record and allows the option to view any mouse homology, likewise a "call" to the "polymorphism manager" will show any polymorphic information which might be associated with the probe, a "call" to the "map manager" will give an ordered list of the probe relative to probes in the same region and a "call" to the "source manager" will identify a contact source of the probe. A summary of all the information for a single locus is available and gives the number of genes, fragile sites, DNA segments, breakpoints, restriction sites, map sets, etc. (this may take 15-20 minutes). Using the sequence information one can then synthesize the required pair of oligonucleotide primers. Similarly, one can search the database for clones for mapping by hybridization studies and find the names of the clones and the name and address of the person to contact to obtain the clone or the sequences necessary to synthesize the primers, the PCR product size and the gene position for example exon and codon information.

4.2.7 cDNA Database

This database is available through the HGMP-RC menu and the Cell Lines, Clones and Probes Menu option. The cDNA database stores information about cDNA clones and libraries available from the Resource Centre. The same data can be accessed in several different ways within the database. The cDNA database main menu allows users to search either for cDNA sequences or for library details. A query screen invites the user to define parameters for a search and a list of valid options can be displayed. For example, choosing to search for libraries brings up a table inviting details of a laboratory code (where the library was made e.g. HGMP-RC) and library code (the code for a bone marrow library). Commanding a search retrieves details of how the library was made, as for example the cloning vector used (e.g. gt11), the restriction enzyme (e.g. EcoR1), host bacteria (e.g. *Escherichia coli*), pfu titre, etc. Details (species, age, etc.) of the tissue or cell line from which the library was made can be found by commanding "origin!". The name and address to contact to get the cDNA clones is found by commanding "Lab Contact!". From the main cDNA database menu one can opt to see "statistics" for each "laboratory", "library" and microtitre "plate". From the submenu, "plate statistics" gives details of the number of entries in the database for each microtitre plate well, e.g. plate number 1 of the bone marrow library has 22 clones, i.e. wells with sequences in the database. From the same submenu one can choose library statistics to see the number of plates, clones and sequences in the database for each library, the average length of the sequences, matches to known sequences either nucleic acid or protein, and matches to cDNAs in both the chosen and all cDNA libraries. Again from the same submenu, each laboratory's results can be summarized and analysed, for example by choosing to see data for the HGMP-RC laboratory shows the number of libraries available (e.g. 17), the number of clones (e.g. 1691), the number of sequences (e.g. 1825), the average length (e.g. 201 bases) and results of their matches to known sequences, either nucleic acid or protein. Details of individual clones can be retrieved by choosing from the cDNA database main menu to "search for cDNA sequences" having specified the laboratory code, library code and plate number. Table details include its Entry ID: e.g. AAAAUJS, its "clone" identity, e.g. H-1-A05, the laboratory and library names and remarks about its database match, e.g. good match to mitochondrial sequences. Using this information the "sequence" can be viewed after having specified the "Entry ID". Each sequence can then be compared to other databases (GENBANK, Swissprot and other cDNAs in the same database) and the "alignment" checked for individual base mismatches. Information can be extracted and "output" to a file for storage and /or printing out, but the entry is logged for the records. Individual cDNA clones can be obtained from the Resource Centre using the "clone" information as an identity. Clones are also distributed as an array on filters. "Interesting" clones can be identified by hybridization studies and subsequently requested from the Resource Centre.

4.2.8 Other cDNA Files

Some cDNA sequences have been deposited in public files and can be accessed by anonymous file transfer protocol. Archie (see Chapter 1) can provide a useful way to find them. One source is the US National Centre for Biotechnology Information (NCBI) file server. This can be accessed using FTP to ncbi.nlm.nih.gov., using "anonymous" as "name" and an e-mail address as the "password". The command "dir" gives a list of available directories. ncbi-genbank/gbest.seq.Z is the cDNA sequence file. The .Z after a file indicates that it is a binary file and the command "bin" must be given before transfer. Some of these files are extremely large and are usually transferred as compressed files. The command "uncompress" must be given before they can be read, but it is important to ensure that there is enough disk space to accommodate a file which may be over ten times the compressed size. These files may also be deposited in GENBANK and EMBL. All cDNA fragments submitted to EMBL and GENBANK are included in the "EST" section of GENBANK.

4.2.9 RLDB (ICRF Reference Library Database)

One way to access this database is through the HGMP-RC menu. The Cell Lines, Clones and Probes Menu gives access to the RLDB (Reference Library Database). This database stores mapping information about cosmid libraries and the probes which have been mapped to them. Chromosome specific cosmid libraries for chromosomes X, 11, 17, 21 and 22 are included. The mapping information has been gathered from several laboratories who have received libraries (usually in the form of high density filter grids), screened them with probes of interest and returned information on the identified clones as well as on the probes they used. This database is currently being extended to include information derived from a similar exercise with YAC libraries. A list of probes, their hybridization results, chromosome location and sender is available from the RLDB. An up-to-date list can also be obtained by e-mail from the RLDB or by anonymous FTP from the repository at NCBI. The database runs under software from the US Welch laboratories information retrieval experiment (IRX) and can be questioned in plain English. A search will find all records which contain the main words of the question and rank them in order of most likely relevance. For example, entering the question "yac" will find a number of probes. To read information about each, an arrow cursor is first moved up or down in the left margin to align with a document title and that document may then be printed or read on-line. Thus the first of the documents gives further details about the species and chromosome location (Human X q28-) and the sender's name and address. In other instances, for example probe CF56A, a list of 13 associated cosmid clones is also given. The libraries and the clones used to screen them are available from the RLDB (see Appendix 2).

4.3 Integrated Databases

4.3.1 Integrated Genomic Database

Several of the experimental materials databases are integrated into one database, the Integrated Genomic Database (IGD). This can be accessed through the HGMP-RC menu option Genome Data. The current data held is displayed at the outset and lists contents and sources of data. The database makes it easier to select related information, for example one can select a chromosome and see a list ("key set") of possible loci associated, then view a picture of that chromosome showing the chromosome bands, HGM symbols for genes and map positions of the loci (from information in GDB), associated probes (from information in GDB, UK DNA Probe Bank and RLDB) cosmid clones (from RLDB), sequences (from EMBL - primates only, SwissProt, etc.) Clinical information from the OMIM database is also cross-referenced by the MIM number. This database is in the early developmental stage but is likely to become a major source of information on human mapping data and resources as more and more databases are integrated.

4.3.2 The Encyclopedia of the Mouse Genome

This integrated database provides a comprehensive collection of mouse genetic information, from sources such as for example Genetic Strains and Variants of the Laboratory Mouse, The Biology of the Laboratory Mouse and The Mouse in Biomedical Research, GBase (also available from the menu as an independent option), The Chromosome Atlas and The Mouse Locus Catalogue. It operates in a similar way to IGD and provides graphical displays of the mouse chromosomes with lists of known mouse genes including mutant alleles, recombination distances from the centromere and chromosomal assignments and the chromosomal assignment of their human homologue. A recent addition to this database has been the sequences of a large mapping set of mouse microsatellite primers (Dietrich et al., 1992) used extensively in studies of the mouse genome.

4.4 Restriction Enzymes

Restriction enzymes for cutting DNA at specific sites are essential for most molecular biology work. REBASE is a restriction enzymes database and can be accessed in many ways including by anonymous ftp from the NCBI and EMBL file servers and from the UK HGMP-RC menu option "Other Molecular Data". REBASE stores information about the name, prototype, recognition sequence, methylation site, references and commercial source for a wide variety of restriction enzymes and methylases. The database is developed and maintained by New England Biolabs but includes data from many other commercial sources including Amersham, BRL, Stratagene, Fermentas, Appligene, American Allied, IBI, Northumbria Biologicals, Boehringer Mannheim, Toyobo, PL-Pharmacia-LKB, Molecular Biology Resources, Promega Corporation, Sigma, USB, Serva, ILS and New York Biolabs. Enzymes can be ordered from the appropriate source.

5   References

Beckmann JS and Weber JL (1992). Survey of human and rat microsatellites. Genomics 12, 627-631.

Dietrich W, Katz, H, Lincoln, SE, Shin H-S, Friedman J, Dracopoli NC and Lander ES (1992). A genetic map of the mouse suitable for typing intraspecific crosses. Genetics 131, 423-47.

Hearne CM, McAleer MA, Love JM, Aitman TJ, Cornall RJ, Ghosh S, Knight A, Prins JB and Todd JA (1991). Additional microsatellites for mouse genome mapping. Mammalian Genome 1, 273-282.

Love JM, Knight AM, McAleer MA and Todd JA (1990). Towards construction of a high resolution map of the mouse genome using PCR-analysed microsatellites. Nucleic Acids Res. 18, 4123-4130.

Maglott DR and Nierman WC (1991). Mammalian probes and libraries at the ATCC. Mammalian Genome 1, 59-64.

Weissenbach J, Gyapay G, Dib C, Vigna A, Morissette J, Millasseau P, Vaysseix G and Lathrop M (1992). A second-generation linkage map of the human genome. Nature 359, 794-801.

CHAPTER 3 | # Genetic Linkage Analysis

Stephen P. Bryant

Imperial Cancer Research Fund, Human Genetic
Resources Laboratory, South Mimms, Potters Bar,
Hertfordshire EN6 3LD, UK
Internet: spb@mahler.clh.icnet.uk

1   Introduction

Human genetic linkage analysis is primarily concerned with the mapping of genes
by the analysis of traits segregating in human pedigrees (Ott, 1991). The process
requires the ability to compute probabilities on pedigrees and make inferences about
order and distance between loci. In the simplest case, it is possible to directly score
recombination events and it can be shown that this provides a robust estimate of the
recombination fraction, and hence the genetic distance, between loci. In organisms such
as the mouse *Mus musculus*, mating systems can be set up such that all offspring are
scored in this way and haplotypes can be easily constructed. Ordering of loci can be a
simple matter of minimizing the number of recombination events in the data set, since
double recombinants are expected to be rare over short intervals (Chapter 5). In human
analyses, mating types where recombination events can be scored with sufficient certainty are uncommon (Figure 3.1).

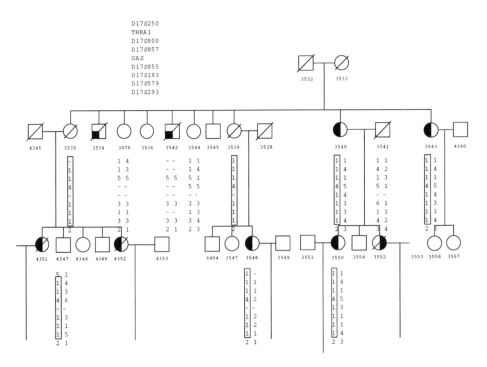

FIGURE 3.1 Breast cancer and nine DNA marker systems co-segregating in a large family. The legend at the top shows the names of the loci on chromosome 17 for which typing was obtained. Note that some people, particularly spouses, are untyped, and that several of the crosses are uninformative. The illustration was created from XShell (Section 2.3) using the Pedigree/Draw output option, and retouched using MacDrawPro on an Apple Macintosh.

Human data are complicated by phase ambiguity and it is necessary to resort to other methods of estimation. These methods draw heavily on the concept of *maximum likelihood*. For a set of phenotypic observations on a pedigree, the exact probability can be expressed as

$$\sum_{genocoms} \left[\prod_{founders} P(gen) \right] \cdot \left[\prod_{nonfounders} P(gen|\,pargen) \right] \cdot \left[\prod_{observed} P(phen|\,gen) \right] \qquad \textbf{(EQ 3.1)}$$

where

> $genocoms$ = all genotype combinations,
> gen = genotype,
> $phen$ = phenotype, and
> $pargen$ = parental genotype (Thompson, 1986).

Equation 3.1 can be applied directly to a single segregating phenotype, but can also be modified to handle the multilocus case by incorporating the recombination fraction(s) as additional parameter(s). The equation is rarely implemented directly in the form shown, since the number of permutations rapidly becomes prohibitive. Instead, full likelihood computations are usually based on the algorithm of Elston and Stewart (1971) with modifications by Lange and Elston (1975) and later by Canningset al. (1978) to handle complex pedigrees. Some parameters may be known and fixed, and others may be unknown and allowed to vary within bounds. A particular set of hypothetical values will often lead to a different probability conditional on the hypothesized values being true. The way in which the probability of the observed outcome changes can be exploited using the proportionality

$$L(H|D) \propto P(D|H) \qquad \textbf{(EQ 3.2)}$$

which should be read as "the likelihood of the hypothesis under consideration, conditional on the observed data, is proportional to the probability of the data conditional on the hypothesis". What this means is that a greater degree of belief is placed upon hypotheses which would make the observed outcome more likely (Edwards, 1972). The hypothesis could be a particular value of a single continuous parameter, such as the recombination fraction between two loci, or a discrete hypothesis, such as the chromosomal order of a set of loci.

For any parameter being estimated, the value which maximizes the exact probability of the observed data is called the Maximum Likelihood Estimate (MLE). Whereas absolute probabilities can indicate the MLE of a parameter (or hypothesis), they say nothing about the *relative* degree of belief which can be associated with that hypothesis *compared* with any other. A measure of support for a particular hypothesis compared with an alternative can be given as the ratio of two likelihoods, expressed as

$$\frac{L(H_1)}{L(H_2)} \qquad \textbf{(EQ 3.3)}$$

which provides the odds in favour of H_1 over H_2. The properties of this ratio are such that the results from different data sets can be mutiplicatively combined to provide an overall measure of support. Equation 3.3 is more usually given as the log of the ratio,

$$\log\left(\frac{L(H_1)}{L(H_2)}\right) \qquad \textbf{(EQ 3.4)}$$

which is equivalent to

$$\log L(H_1) - \log L(H_2) \qquad \textbf{(EQ 3.5)}$$

and which can be summed across equivalent data sets. In a linkage analysis, hypotheses which are often compared are those where H_2:θ=0.5 and H_1:θ=<some other value> where θ is the recombination fraction between two loci. This measure of support, $Z(\theta)$, where logs are taken to the base 10, is the well-known log-of-odds ratio, or lod score for linkage (Equation 3.6).

$$Z(\theta) \ = \ \log\left(\frac{L(\theta)}{L(0.5)}\right)$$ (EQ 3.6)

Morton (1955) promoted the idea of mapping using lod scores since it offered an elegant solution to the problem of combining data from experiments conducted in different laboratories, even when the primary data were unavailable. Lod scores can be combined from published tables, or from other groups working on different families, until a threshold is reached whereupon linkage is either accepted or rejected. For two autosomal loci, a lod score of 3 is necessary to exclude non-linkage. For two X-linked loci, a lod score of 2 is sufficient. Similarly, a lod score of -2 is sufficient to exclude linkage for a certain distance from a marker. As was hinted previously, several parameters may be estimated simultaneously using this method. These could be a set of recombination fractions in a multilocus map, or the penetrance and allele frequency of a dominant trait. Also, there is no reason why hypotheses should not be discrete, and the method of support is heavily used to discriminate between different orders of a set of loci.

Depending on which hypotheses are under consideration, differing thresholds of the lod score are regarded as significant. For example, where there are two alternative orders of a multilocus map, orders which are supported by lod scores of at least 3, against all alternative orders obtained by inverting adjacent loci, are referred to as *framework orders*. It should be noted that if more than one parameter is being estimated, the type I error rate for comparing, say, linkage against non-linkage will increase if the significance threshold remains at 3.0. I return to this problem in a later section.

Another common technique is to compute the likelihood at several unknown positions of a marker against a fixed, known map. These plots commonly use $\log_e$ on the ordinate and are referred to as location scores to distinguish them from lod scores. To get the equivalent lod score, divide the location score by 4.6. Logs to the base e have a close relationship to a chi-square distribution.

Most current linkage methods are based on the above fundamental principles. The approach has led to the mapping of traits such as: malignant hyperthermia (Ball et al., 1993); familial adenomatous polyposis (Bodmer et al., 1987); cystic fibrosis (Bowcock et al., 1986); multiple endocrine neoplasia type I (Larsson et al., 1988); nasopharyngeal carcinoma susceptibility (Lu et al., 1990); ataxia telangectasia (McConville et al., 1990) and breast cancer susceptibility (Porter et al., 1993); as well as the construction of reference linkage maps of the entire genome (Donis-Keller et al., 1987; Weissenbach et al., 1992).

The seminal volume for students of human genetic linkage analysis is the revised edition of Ott (1991). I aim to avoid a detailed discussion of the theoretical background that is effectively covered there but instead concentrate on practical computational issues that face any linkage practitioner and which have not been covered in depth elsewhere. Short reviews of various aspects of linkage analysis have appeared in Ott (1987) and Lander(1987). I have been selective in the sense that I have only attempted to survey in detail those programs of which I have direct experience. Brief treatment or omission of any program should not necessarily be deemed a reflection of quality. Genetic linkage analysis is a rapidly evolving field and I have summarized information about bulletin boards, newsletters and contacts in the final sections of the chapter. There is no general route for distribution of software within the field and so I have provided contact names or anonymous ftp addresses within the text where appropriate.

Full postal addresses, where available, can be found in Appendix 2 or the contact manager component of the Genome Data Base (GDB, see Chapter 5). Most software described here is freely available from the originator or in some cases from third parties or by anonymous ftp. However, this is not always the case and readers are advised to contact the program author in the first instance.

Since I last reviewed some of the computing issues confronting linkage analysts (Bryant, 1991), there have been a number of significant advances. These include the almost universal adoption of the UNIX operating system as a platform for analytical software, and the X Window protocol as a basis for user interface design. UNIX and X issues are covered elsewhere in this volume (see Chapter 1). The initiatives which take advantage of these new technical developments are still very much research topics (Peter Cartwright, personal communication) but are expected to yield great benefits in the coming years. At the present time, some software is only usable under DOS on personal computers and most groups will perform data management on these machines.

I continue immediately below with a discussion of data management issues and follow this with a practical treatment of estimating the recombination fraction between two loci and constructing a lod score table. I examine how dominant and recessive traits are modelled and how partial penetrance can be incorporated into an analysis. I briefly cover the practical issue of heterogeneity and show how data sets of more than two loci can be explored, including the construction of large reference maps. I explore the technique of placing an unmapped locus on a fixed reference map, and discuss how to approach tackling traits which do not show a clear, monogenic pattern of inheritance, or even where no clear Mendelian pattern of segregation can be ascertained. I consider how maps from diverse sources of data can be integrated and discuss the possibilities for data presentation and pedigree display. I finish with a pot-pourri of information resources, such as relevant newsletters, bulletin boards, resource centres, contacts and training courses.

2 Data Management

A linkage analysis requires large amounts of information to be stored and translated between various electronic formats. For this reason, an effective strategy for data management is essential. It would be ideal to be able to point the researcher to a freely-accessible, X-based client program, probably running under UNIX, which could be connected via the Internet to a robust data server which embodied translators for all available packages for display and analysis. The closest that current work comes to this is that being carried on at Salt Lake City under the direction of Peter Cartwright. However, this has yet to reach the stage where the products are available to the community at large, and most implemented solutions are a hybrid of X and VT based systems with a mixture of analytical software bolted together with a variety of utilities, usually written by different groups.

At the moment, the researcher has little choice between UNIX and DOS-based systems with which to manage data. The one UNIX system which is based on X Windows (GENBASE) uses standard Sybase X clients, but the end result is still very much a traditional forms-based system (see Section 2.1). Another system, XShell (Section 2.3), uses Oracle under UNIX and can use the Oracle X Client Software, but again the results are unexciting. It appears that the toolkits provided by the database vendors fall far short of the quality expected by users and system developers. The situation is improving, with toolkits appearing that make it more feasible to produce high quality interfaces. In this section I examine these two UNIX systems, along with one purely DOS-based system.

2.1 GENBASE

GENBASE has been written to support the software requirements of the European Community funded EUROGEM project which has the task of doubling the density of the Centre d'Etude du Polymorphisme Humaine (CEPH) reference maps by the end of 1995. The CEPH family panel of DNA is widely know and used by a large number of laboratories (Dausset et al., 1990).

With the agreement of the CEPH in Paris, GENBASE is being made available to the UK genome community via the Human Genome Mapping Project Resource Centre (HGMP-RC) at Northwick Park. It is hoped that European and international availability will follow with service delivery via genome centres in Heidelberg, the United States and elsewhere.

2.1.1 Features

The data model within GENBASE follows the CEPH format closely, although GEN-BASE does not restrict families to be of the 3-generation CEPH type and can be used to model extended pedigrees and other kinds of genetic system, such as affection status and quantitative trait loci.

One notable feature of GENBASE is the ability to historically record genotypes assigned to individuals. This provides a convenient way of showing which typings have changed and how these differ from the originals.

GENBASE supports the creation of LINKAGE files. These LINKAGE files can be converted into CRI-Map or MAPMAKER data sets by utilities written by John Attwood (Sections 7 and 8). A Pedigree/Draw interface is also incorporated (Section 9.1) and it is also possible to import and export data between GENBASE and the DOS CEPH database programs.

2.1.2 The User Interface

As mentioned above, GENBASE uses the Sybase X and VT client facilities to present a point and click interface to the user. The layout of the various forms and menus follows a fairly standard Sybase format (Figure 3.2),

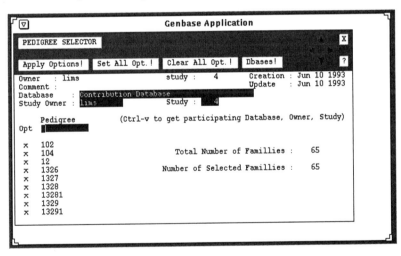

FIGURE 3.2 Editing information within GENBASE. If the user has access to an X terminal, the mouse can be used to quickly navigate through the application. In this window, pedigrees are being tagged for inclusion within a "study", a term used by GENBASE to denote a collection of programs and marker systems which are treated as a unit for management and transfer to other programs.

and users of the GDB should experience little problem in adjusting to this system. Some of the behaviour of GENBASE is a little idiosyncratic, but the software is subject to regular review and these problems are sure to be resolved in the near future.

2.2 LINKSYS

LINKSYS (Attwood and Bryant, 1988) is a DOS-based system for the management of genealogical data for analysis by LIPED and LINKAGE. It is obtainable by sending 2×1.2 MB or 4×360 KB formatted diskettes to John Attwood.

2.2.1 Features

LINKSYS organizes data on allele frequency, phenotype-genotype relationships, family structure and phenotypes. It is possible to produce quite sophisticated LINKAGE and LIPED data files including liability classes and incomplete penetrance. LINKSYS data files can be used as input to PEDRAW (Section 9.2) and CYRILLIC (Section 9.5).

2.2.2 The User Interface

A Turbo Pascal toolbox was used to construct LINKSYS and so it is controlled, like much DOS software, entirely from the keyboard with single keystrokes. As keyboard interfaces go, it is above average.

2.3 XShell

XShell is a data management aid for LINKAGE that has been built around the Oracle Relational Database Management System (RDBMS). In order to use XShell, an Oracle run-time licence is required. Oracle is available for DOS machines as well as UNIX and VMS, though the price varies widely. It is worth pointing out, however, that C++ has been heavily used to write some of the utilities. The GNU C++ compiler (g++) has been used on the SPARC platform, and a compatible compiler will be needed should any other operating system be chosen. g++ is available for DOS systems.

2.3.1 Features

XShell manages pedigrees of arbitrary size and structure, and keeps track of projects by organizing families and markers into "groups", which are used as a handle for export to LINKAGE and other programs. A great deal of ancillary information can also be recorded. For typing purposes, it can model both Numbered Allele and Affection Status types of system, including the facility to define liability classes with a range of penetrances. It also includes an interface to LIPED and KIN, which are less often used.

2.3.2 The User Interface

Much of the system is constructed using SQL*Forms and SQL*Menu, which are standard Oracle 4GL tools (Figure 3.3). The most useful way of configuring the system is to mount it on a SUN server (which need not be large) and to access using VT emulation from an Apple Macintosh or IBM Personal Computer (PC). X Windows versions of the Oracle client tools are available but initial experience has been disappointing and they cannot be recommended at present. XShell can be obtained from the author.

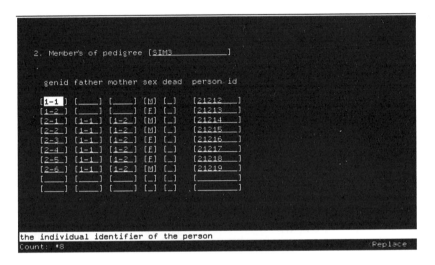

FIGURE 3.3 Editing pedigree information in XShell. Here the members of family SIM3 are being set up. Each person has a unique identifier (person id) across the whole database, as well as an identifier (genid) within the pedigree. Pointers to parents and a symbol to indicate sex are also included. XShell is multiuser, which means that several people could be updating (different areas of) the database simultaneously.

A SUN IPC is sufficiently powerful to provide good interactive response for at least six users. Pedigrees and markers are organized into groups of arbitrary size. Any marker or pedigree can be assigned to more than one group, so this offers a convenient handle with which to flag a set of families for analysis. The LINKAGE files are suitable for use with LCP and correctly format the penetrances of each liability class as well as assigning the phenotypes of each. Sophisticated output to Pedigree/Draw (Section 9.1) is possible using phenotypic information to mark family members as affected and to display typing and ancillary information beneath each member (see Figure 3.14).

2.4 Choosing a System

Any of the three systems described above will provide the basic functionality required to manage pedigree data for linkage analysis. GENBASE and XShell require a UNIX system whereas LINKSYS can be used on a DOS system or instead used via DOS emulation under UNIX. There is no software currently available for the Apple Macintosh which offers anything like the facilities provided by that described in this section. However, there is an excellent application for pedigree display, described in Section 9.1. GENBASE and XShell offer an export facility to this package. Text files can be easily transferred from a UNIX box to a Macintosh using ftp client software such as NCSA Telnet (available from many ftp sites). Many laboratories are still restricted to a DOS environment, and LINKSYS should be the software of choice. It is possible to run LINKSYS using the DOS emulation software on both SUN and Apple machines. Problems were experienced with early versions of the SUN software, but these have hopefully been largely resolved with the adoption of SoftPC on both platforms.

3 Generating Lod Score Tables

In this section I discuss the software that is available to assist the researcher in constructing lod score tables. This kind of analysis can easily be performed on a small DOS system (the old 640 KB systems were perfectly adequate) in reasonable time, though UNIX versions of the same software are readily available, and of course are much faster.

3.1 LIPED

The software package LIPED (Ott, 1974) is preferred by many people over LINKAGE for two-point analysis because of the style of presentation as well as the various processing options, which can be simply chosen.

It uses a penetrance matrix to represent phenotype-genotype relationships which can be used to encode codominant RFLPs or PCR formatted markers and dominant/recessive traits. It can cope with various permutations of age-dependent penetrance and the division of people into liability classes. LIPED is distributed as FORTRAN source code and executables for DOS. It is very easy to port to other operating systems, including UNIX. It is provided along with many other useful utilities for linkage from Professor Jurg Ott, on the anonymous ftp server york.ccc.columbia.edu.

3.1.1 Input Format

Data files can be generated from LINKSYS or XShell. An example of a LIPED input file is shown in Figure 3.4.

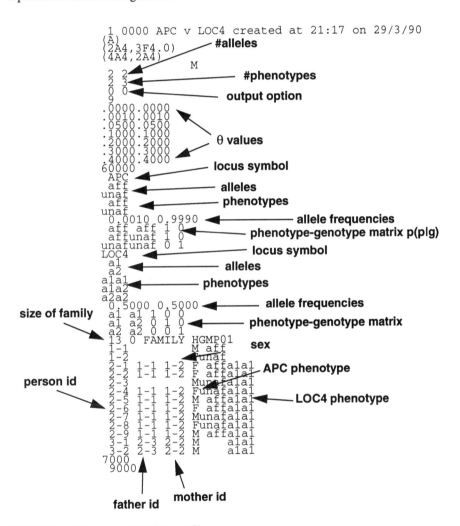

FIGURE 3.4 Part of a LIPED input file.

The LIPED program itself can be run on a local PC or else on a remote UNIX server. The command to invoke the program is almost identical. On UNIX, the command would typically be

liped myinput myresults

which would provide a result file similar to that in Figure 3.5.

```
Program LIPED Version for VAX VMS Nov. 1987 J. Ott modified by S. Bryant
Copyright (c) Jurg Ott 1987. All rights reserved
-----------------------------------------------------------------

Date = 29-MAR-90

PROBLEM 1 APC v LOC4 created at 21:17 on 29/3/90
**********
(autosomal linkage)

Pedigree 1 FAMILY HGMP01
-----------
13 individuals

LOCUS 0 APC VS. LOCUS 1 LOC4
-----------------------------------------

GENE FREQUENCIES FOR 0 APC 0.0010 0.9990
GENE FREQUENCIES FOR 1 LOC4 0.5000 0.5000

R MALE  R FEM.  LOG10[L(R)]  LOD-SCORE
0.5000  0.5000  -6.90880     0.000
0.0000  0.0000  -6.91218    -0.003
0.0010  0.0010  -6.91218    -0.003
0.0500  0.0500  -6.91214    -0.003
0.1000  0.1000  -6.91192    -0.003
0.2000  0.2000  -6.91097    -0.002
0.3000  0.3000  -6.90986    -0.001
0.4000  0.4000  -6.90907     0.000
```

Table summarizing lodscores for this family for each pair of male and female θ values

```
Pedigree 2 FAMILY HGMP02
-----------
6 individuals

LOCUS 0 APC VS. LOCUS 1 LOC4
-----------------------------------------

R MALE  R FEM.  LOG10[L(R)]  LOD-SCORE
0.5000  0.5000  -5.10851     0.000
0.0000  0.0000  -5.10851     0.000
0.0010  0.0010  -5.10851     0.000
0.0500  0.0500  -5.10851     0.000
0.1000  0.1000  -5.10851     0.000
0.2000  0.2000  -5.10851     0.000
0.3000  0.3000  -5.10851     0.000
0.4000  0.4000  -5.10851     0.000
```

SUMMARY   { more results go here }

Summation of lods over families

```
R MALE  R FEM.  SUM OF LODS
0.0000  0.0000  -96.65254
0.0010  0.0010   1.92349
0.0500  0.0500   3.10987
0.1000  0.1000   2.86150
0.2000  0.2000   2.05226
0.3000  0.3000   1.19320
0.4000  0.4000   0.46464
```

best estimate of θ

FIGURE 3.5 Part of a LIPED output file.

These results may be summarized by observation into the tabular form of Table 3.1, which shows a two-point analysis between Adenomatous Polyposis Coli (APC) and some markers on chromosome 5.

TABLE 3.1 Two-point linkage analysis of APC v LOC1-LOC5 using LIPED

APC v	0.0	0.001	0.05	0.10	0.20	0.30	0.40	$\hat{\theta}$
LOC2	-inf	-1.43	4.49	4.79	3.90	2.31	0.69	0.1
LOC3	-inf	-5.65	-0.84	-0.15	0.22	0.18	0.05	0.2
LOC4	-inf	1.92	3.11	2.86	2.05	1.19	0.46	0.05
LOC5	2.93	2.92	2.63	2.34	1.77	1.15	0.49	0.0

Lod scores are summed over all pedigrees. This tabular form provides a rough guide as to the shape of the likelihood curve and hence to the MLE of θ.

The best estimate of θ between APC and LOC4 appears to be at 5% with a lod score of 3.11. This is statistically significant. The analysis has also averaged out the difference between the sexes, although sexes-separate estimates of the recombination fraction are recommended and desirable. The way in which these are obtained differs according to the software package used. In LIPED, likelihoods can be computed with any pair of recombination fractions (θ_m, θ_f). The likelihood function can then best be represented by a surface, the third dimension of which is the lod score. The pair (θ_m, θ_f) which maximizes the likelihood of the data can then be found by observation. To get a better estimate with LIPED, increase the number of θ estimates.

A support interval for θ can be obtained by using the range $Z_{max} \pm 1$ lod. Figure 3.6 shows the shape of the lod score curve for APC v LOC4. The 1-unit support interval for θ can be seen to lie in the range approximately 0.02 - 0.18.

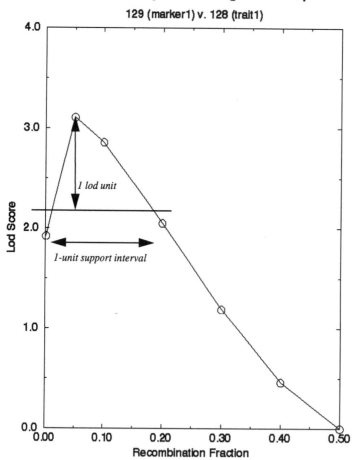

Lod Score Analysis - Pedigree Group APC
129 (marker1) v. 128 (trait1)

FIGURE 3.6 The lod score curve associated with the APC v LOC4 data from Table 3.1. A 1-unit support interval has been constructed for the recombination fraction by dropping a line 1 lod unit down from the peak. The graph was drawn directly from XShell using the public domain ACE/gr package.

3.2 LINKAGE Program Package (LPP)

LINKAGE (Lathrop and Lalouel, 1984) is a general-purpose package for multipoint linkage analysis. It can be used as a flexible self-contained system but most practitioners prefer to run it in conjunction with one of the available data management packages (principally LINKSYS).

Markers are divided into several types which are sufficient to handle most genetic systems which may be encountered. These include codominant RFLP, VNTR or microsatellite PCR markers, affection status markers including dominant-recessive systems with partial penetrance and quantitative trait loci.

Efficient versions exist for large map work using CEPH-style families. LPP is distributed in Pascal and C source code for a variety of operating systems, and contains several modules of interest (Table 3.2).

TABLE 3.2 LINKAGE modules

Option	Function
LINKMAP	Locus placement in a fixed map
ILINK	Iterative estimation of the recombination fraction
MLINK	Two-point tables
LODSCORE	Iterative two-point
CMAP	Locus placement in a fixed map - nuclear families
CILINK	Iterative estimation of the recombination fraction - nuclear families

LINKAGE is primarily distributed by Mark Lathrop from the CEPH in Paris. The current version is 5.2. In order to obtain the Paris version of LINKAGE, send a fax to Pascale Denayrouse, specifying the media (3.5 inch, 5.25 inch, TK50 tape, 60 MB QIC tape) and operating system (DOS, Ultrix, VMS, SunOS) you require.

A version of LINKAGE for DOS based on 5.2 is available from the anonymous ftp server `york.ccc.columbia.edu`, managed by Jurg Ott.

There have been problems in compiling LINKAGE on SUN machines using the new version 3.0 of the Pascal compiler, with the optimization flags set. It is currently believed to be a bug in the compiler for which a fix is available. The general warning is be extremely careful when recompiling LINKAGE at the moment, with untested compilers. There are a number of versions of the LINKAGE software in circulation which have been created using the Pascal to C translation utility (`p2c`). This utility is available via anonymous ftp from many sites (e.g. `src.doc.ic.ac.uk`) and it is recommended that interested researchers acquire their own copy and make their own translated set (which is fairly automatic). Alternatively, a C version of LINKAGE, which has been produced by p2c and heavily optimized, is available by anonymous ftp from gc.bcm.tmc.edu in directory fastlink.51. There are several problems at the moment with LINKAGE existing in several distinct versions but it is hoped that the situation will improve.

LINKAGE data files are most often created by an auxiliary program, such as those described in Section 2. LINKSYS offers this facility (see Section 2.2), as does XShell (Section 2.3) and GENBASE (Section 2.1). Occasionally, it is still necessary to edit the files by hand, since these ancillary programs do not support all of the features of LINK-AGE, such as liability classes and reduced penetrance. With care, it is perfectly possible to create LINKAGE data sets with any editor that can create ASCII text files.

3.2.1 Input Format

The data set is divided into a pair of files, the parameter file (Figure 3.7) and the pedigree file (Figure 3.8).

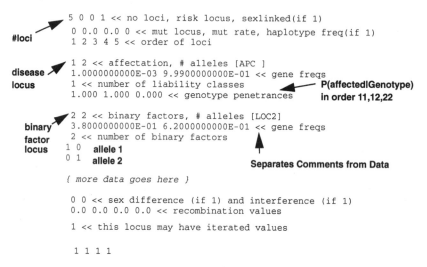

FIGURE 3.7 Part of a LINKAGE parameter file.

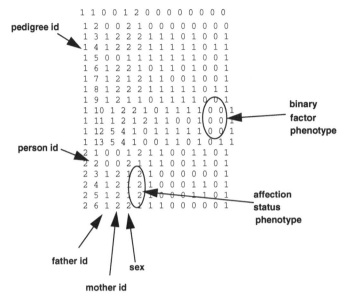

```
        1  1  0  0  1  2  0  0  0  0  0  0  0  0
pedigree id  1  2  0  0  2  1  0  0  0  0  0  0  0  0
        1  3  1  2  2  2  1  1  1  0  1  0  0  1
        1  4  1  2  2  2  1  1  1  1  1  0  1  1
        1  5  0  0  1  1  1  1  1  1  1  0  0  1
        1  6  1  2  2  1  0  1  1  0  1  0  0  1
        1  7  1  2  1  2  1  1  0  0  1  0  0  1
        1  8  1  2  2  2  1  1  1  1  1  0  1  1
        1  9  1  2  1  1  0  1  1  1  1  0  0  1
        1 10  1  2  2  1  0  1  1  1  1  0  0  1
        1 11  1  2  1  2  1  1  0  0  1  0  0  1
        1 12  5  4  1  0  1  1  1  1  1  0  0  1
        1 13  5  4  1  0  0  1  1  0  1  0  1  1
person id  2  1  0  0  1  2  1  1  0  0  1  1  0  1
        2  2  0  0  2  1  1  1  0  0  1  1  0  1
        2  3  1  2  1  2  1  0  0  0  0  0  0  1
        2  4  1  2  1  2  1  0  0  0  1  1  0  1
        2  5  1  2  1  2  1  0  0  0  1  1  0  1
        2  6  1  2  2  1  1  1  0  0  0  0  0  1
```

binary
factor
phenotype

affection
status
phenotype

father id

sex

mother id

FIGURE 3.8 Part of a LINKAGE pedigree file.

If input files are created with LINKSYS or XShell they need be processed with the MAKEPED utility. If they are created from GENBASE, they do not. MAKEPED is a program for preprocessing the pedigree file to include more information on the pedigree structure for use by the algorithms that perform the likelihood calculations. It can be run interactively with

<code>makeped</code>

or in batch mode using the syntax

<code>makeped <inputfile> <outputfile> [Y|N]</code>

If an N is included at the end of the command line, MAKEPED assumes that there are no loops present and will continue without user intervention. If your families do not contain any inbreeding loops, when MAKEPED asks Does your pedigree file contain any loops? reply **N[RETURN]** and to Do you want probands selected automatically? reply **Y[RETURN]**.

LINKAGE data files must in addition be processed by the Linkage Control Program (LCP) which sets up temporary data files for a particular analysis and also creates a batch file for the appropriate operating system.

LCP has a command structure based on the control (**[CTRL]**) key. The most important are **[CTRL-U]** which clears a field and **[CTRL-N]** which moves on to the next screen. The cursor keys move up and down the fields. **[CTRL-Z]** closes the output file. Please note that t here is a slight complication in that LCP refers to markers as *p1...pn* where the order is as given in the locus data file (hgmp.par), and not by the symbols they may have had within the management system being used. The module which is of use in constructing a two-point table is MLINK. MLINK allows the user to produce a two-point table of lod scores similar to that in Table 3.1. Sex-separate lod scores should be presented whenever possible (Keats et al., 1990).

The script file (by default often called pedin) can be executed either interactively or in the background. The output is collected into two files, typically final.out and stream.out, but these can be renamed. The final.out file can be examined directly but it is more usual to parse the stream.out file using the Linkage Report Program (LRP) into a more readable form (Figure 3.9).

```
                                    mahler
                        L O D   T A B L E   R E P O R T

File: stream.out                                    Screen:   1 of 1

Order     0.0   0.001   0.05    0.1    0.2    0.3    0.4
-----   ------  ------  ------  -----  -----  -----  -----
1=2     -infini  -1.43   4.49   4.80   3.91   2.31   0.70  a
1=3     -infini  -5.65  -0.84  -0.15   0.23   0.19   0.06  a
1=4     -infini   1.92   3.11   2.86   2.05   1.19   0.46  a
1=5       2.93    2.92   2.64   2.34   1.77   1.15   0.50  a

= = Test Interval
a = LOD Scores                          (LOG 10)
b = LOG 10 Likelihoods                  (LOG 10)




                    Enter Command : []

        CTRL/A - Abort  CTRL/H - Help  CTRL/Z - Exit  CTRL/R - Return
```

FIGURE 3.9 Part of the output from an MLINK analysis. The loci have been given the identifiers 1-5 to correspond with APC, LOC2-LOC5, the order in the parameter file. Lod scores have been computed for a range of recombination fractions, selectable within LCP.

4 Iterative Estimation of the Recombination Fraction

A useful corollary to a lod table is an MLE of the recombination fraction (θ). This is usually ascertained by iterative estimation. The LODSCORE module of LINKAGE is used for this. It is always necessary to construct a table as an adjunct to this kind of analysis and not to rely on LODSCORE alone. MLINK will indicate the precision of the estimate, which will depend on the amount of information in the sample. It is particularly important to filter out those estimates which terminate due to a flat likelihood curve, rather than due to a well-supported peak. The recombination fraction can be converted into a linear distance measure (centimorgan or cM) with an appropriate mapping function (Pascoe and Morton, 1987). There is also an equivalent program (CLODSCORE) which is used for 2 or 3 generation CEPH-style families.

The starting value of θ is the point at which the iterative algorithm will start. If there is some prior information on the actual MLE of θ, it may be more efficient to use this value rather than the default (0.1). To generate a table of MLE values for a dataset containing several loci, a dialogue similar to the following should be used. In this example, the MLE of the recombination fraction between APC and the markers in Table 3.1 are computed. The reports from LRP are very readable (Figure 3.10).

```
┌─▽──────────────────────── mahler ─────────────────────────┐
│           T W O - P O I N T   L O D S C O R E   R E P O R T │
│                                                             │
│ File: stream.out                          Screen:  1 of 1   │
│                                                             │
│ Order    Recomb  Lodscore                                   │
│ ────────────────────────                                    │
│   1-2    0.0930    4.80                                      │
│   1-3    0.2330    0.24                                      │
│   1-4    0.0410    3.12                                      │
│   1-5    0.0010    2.93                                      │
│                                                             │
│                                                             │
│                                                             │
│                                                             │
│                                                             │
│                   Enter Command : █                         │
│     CTRL/A - Abort  CTRL/H - Help  CTRL/Z - Exit  CTRL/R - Return │
└─────────────────────────────────────────────────────────────┘
```

FIGURE 3.10 Part of the output from the LODSCORE analysis. The loci have been recoded as in Figure 3.8. The value of the recombination fraction is the point at which the iterative algorithm terminated due to successive estimates being sufficiently close together. The lod scores indicate that there is significant linkage between APC(1) and LOC2(2) and LOC4(4).

Compare these results with Table 3.1.

5   Modelling Genetic Systems in LINKAGE

In this section I indicate how different genetic systems can be set up within the parameter and pedigree files of LINKAGE.

5.1   Codominant

In the parameter file, loci are coded either as binary factor union systems, as
```
2 2 << binary factors, # alleles [BINARY FACTOR SYSTEM]
 0.5 0.5 << gene freqs
 2 << number of binary factors
1 0
0 1
```
with the phenotypes as a set of zeros and ones
```
2 1 0 0 1 1 1
2 2 0 0 2 1 1
2 3 1 2 1 1 0
2 4 1 2 1 1 0
2 5 1 2 1 1 0
2 6 1 2 2 1 1
```
or as numbered allele systems, as
```
3 4 << cri-236 Numbered Alleles, #alleles [NUMBERED ALLELE SYSTEM]
0.2500 0.2500 0.2500 0.25 << gene frequencies
```
with phenotypes given as a pair of integers
```
1316 18369 18367 18368 1 4
1316 18370 18367 18368 1 4
1316 20649 18367 18368 1 4
1316 20651 18367 18368 1 4
1316 20652 18367 18368 1 4
1316 20653 18367 18368 1 4
1316 20654 18367 18368 1 3
1316 20655 18367 18368 2 4
```

5.2   Dominant

For a fully penetrant, autosomal dominant trait, the entry in the parameter file should look like this:
```
1 2 << affectation, # alleles [DOMINANT TRAIT]
1.0000000000E-03 9.9900000000E-01 << gene freqs
1 << number of liability classes
1.000 1.000 0.000 << genotype penetrances
```
Note that the penetrances are given for each genotype in the order (1, 1), (1, 2), (2, 2) where 1 and 2 reflect the order of alleles in the gene frequencies line of the parame-

ter file. Phenotypes in the pedigree file are scored as **2** for affected, **1** for unaffected, **0** for unknown.

```
1 1 0 0 1 2
1 2 0 0 2 1
1 3 1 2 2 2
1 4 1 2 2 2
1 5 0 0 1 1
1 6 1 2 2 1
1 7 1 2 1 0
1 8 1 2 2 2
1 9 1 2 1 1
```

5.3 Recessive

For a fully penetrant, autosomal recessive trait, the entry in the parameter file should look like this:

```
1 2 << affectation, # alleles [RECESSIVE TRAIT]
1.0000000000E-03 9.9900000000E-01 << gene freqs
1 << number of liability classes
1.000 0.000 0.000 << genotype penetrances
```

Phenotypes in the pedigree file are scored exactly as for dominant affection status systems.

5.4 Partial Penetrance

This is simply encoded by specifying values other than 0.0 or 1.0 in the penetrance matrix within the parameter file. No change is necessary to the pedigree file. An example is given below, where the penetrance for the homozygous genotype has been reduced to 80%.

```
1 2 << affectation, # alleles [DOMINANT TRAIT - PARTIAL PENETRANCE]
1.0000000000E-03 9.9900000000E-01 << gene freqs
1 << number of liability classes
0.800 0.000 0.000 << genotype penetrances
```

5.5 Liability Classes

These are coded as separate penetrance matrices, one on each line.

```
1 2 << affectation, # alleles [RECESSIVE TRAIT - WITH LIABILITY CLASSES]
1.0000000000E-03 9.9900000000E-01 << gene freqs
3 << number of liability classes
0.600 0.000 0.000
0.800 0.000 0.000
1.000 0.000 0.000 << genotype penetrances
```

In the phenotype file, an additional column after the phenotype code shows to which liability class a person has been assigned.

```
1 1 0 0 1 2 1
1 2 0 0 2 1 1
1 3 1 2 2 2 1
1 4 1 2 2 2 1
1 5 0 0 1 1 2
1 6 1 2 2 1 3
```

5.6   X Linkage

For X linkage analyses, hemizygous males can be scored as homozygous which simplifies coding with LINKSYS. The first line of the parameter file must be flagged to indicated that the data set is X linked (see below). Also, if affection status phenotypes are included, for each liability class the female and male penetrances need to be present, first the female corresponding to the $n(n+1)/2$ possible genotypes and then the male, corresponding to the n alleles.

```
2 0 1 1 << No. Loci, Risk Locus, Sexlinked (if 1), ILINK
0 0.0 0.0 0 << Mutation Locus, Mutation Rate, Sexlinked (if 1)
1 2

3 2 << test1 Numbered Alleles, #alleles
 0.50000 0.50000 << gene frequencies

1 2 << mr Affection Status, #alleles
 0.00100 0.99900 << gene frequencies
 1 << No. of liability classes
 1.00000E+00 1.00000E+00 0.00000E+00
 1.00000E+00 0.00000E+00 << female followed by male penetrances

0 0 << sex difference (if 1) and interference (if 1)
0.1 << recombination values in males
1 << This locus may have...
1
```

6   Heterogeneity

Heterogeneity is a problem that is possible in any study (Cavalli-Sforza and King, 1986), and has been a particular problem in the study of diseases such as tuberous sclerosis (Povey et al., 1991). It is also likely to be a problem in diseases such as the common cancers, where there are a proportion of early-onset cases that have a distinct genetic component, and a proportion of late-onset cases that do not. The various permutations of admixture tests are best tackled using a program such as HOMOG, available from Professor Jurg Ott. Alternatively, Maclean et al. (1992) describe a method, implemented in a program, which has high power for detecting linkage in the presence of heterogeneity, which is a common problem in mapping "complex" traits.

7   Multipoint Analysis

It is often necessary to deal with data from multiple loci, such as when constructing large maps from reference families (e.g. the CEPH families) and also when trying to place an unknown marker (often an affection status locus) on a map of known markers. It is desirable to be able to jointly estimate the recombination fraction between all loci simultaneously, without relying on being able to reconstruct the values from an examination of the two-point scores. The MLINK module of LINKAGE could be used to compute the likelihood of a particular map (fixing the order and distances) with the ILINK module used for iteratively estimating the distances for a fixed order or a whole range of possible orders. The method of maximum likelihood can be used to compare competing hypotheses such as different orders of the same set of loci, as well as the evaluation of marker-marker distance by computing likelihoods based on the data from several markers (Lathrop et al., 1985).

Following on from the examples in previous sections, the problem might now be to find the order of the linked markers around the APC locus. Examination of the two-point lod scores and θ estimates may give us some clues as to the most likely order. There are several ways to proceed. One is to use the ILINK component of LINKAGE on the disease families to find linked triplets and to enlarge the map gradually using the LINKMAP module (Section 7.2.1). An alternative approach is to generate RFLP or PCR data on the linked loci in nuclear families and construct a reference map. This map could then be used as a template on which to place the disease locus, using LINKMAP as before.

Since the construction of reference maps is such an important, specialized area, I consider it in detail below.

7.1   Construction of Reference Maps

The discovery of the RFLP made it possible to consider constructing maps of the entire human genome using abundant, anonymous DNA markers (Botstein et al., 1980). Concomitant with the computation of the likelihood is the efficient discovery of the MLE by iteration. Recent developments with the Expectation-Maximization (EM) algorithm (Lander and Green, 1987) have meant that the distances between all markers in multilocus maps can be jointly estimated with a small number of iterations (typically less than 10). This has made it feasible to use the method of maximum likelihood to construct large maps of chromosomes 1 (Dracopoli et al., 1991) and 2 (Spurr et al., 1992), and others.

The software described in this section is almost always run on UNIX machines. MAPMAKER behaviour under VMS is somewhat antisocial and cannot be recommended on VAX platforms that are intensively used by other people.

An alternative to multipoint analysis is the combination of information from multiple two-point analyses. This approach, developed in the MAP package (Morton and Andrews, 1989) leads to a greatly improved throughput in the map-building process, and is also exploited in the FASTMAP program of Curtis and Gurling (1993).

In this section I discuss MAPMAKER, CRI-Map, MAP and FASTMAP.

7.1.1 MAPMAKER

Eric Lander and Phil Green have produced an interactive package for genetic map building called MAPMAKER (Lander et al., 1987). It is exclusively applied to codominant markers and is particularly useful in constructing a dense marker map around the area of a putative disease locus. MAPMAKER is written in the language C which is available on both UNIX and VMS. The current version is 3.0 and is available via anonymous ftp from `genome.wi.mit.edu` in `/distribution/mapmaker3`. It is available in UNIX, VMS and MS-DOS formats and can also be obtained direct from Dr Eric Lander's Laboratory.

It is designed for CEPH-like families or F2 crosses. It cannot be used for mapping non-codominant traits, nor can it exploit data from extended families. But it is a very useful tool for exploring a CEPH-style data set up to whole chromosome (> 100 markers) in size. An example of the input file format is shown in Figure 3.11. This is best created using a utility such as link2map from John Attwood.

```
                                                            person
     *FAMILY LIST:                                          ids
 family id
     *1326 1326-A 1326-B 1326-C 1326-D 1326-2 1326-1 1326-3
      1326-4 1326-5 1326-6 1326-7 1326-8 1326-9
     *1327 1327-11 1327-10 1327-9 1327-12 1327-2 1327-1 1327-3
      1327-4 1327-5 1327-6 1327-7 1327-8
     *1328 1328-A 1328-B 1328-C 1328-D 1328-2 1328-1 1328-3
      1328-4 1328-5 1328-6 1328-7 1328-8 1328-9 1328-10
      1328-11
     *13281 13281-9 13281-8 13281-7 13281-6 13281-2 13281-1 13281-3
      13281-4 13281-5
     *1329 1329-A 1329-B 1329-C 1329-D 1329-2 1329-1 1329-3
      1329-4 1329-5 1329-6
     *13291 13291-13 13291-12 13291-11 13291-10 13291-2 13291-1 13291-3
      13291-4 13291-5 13291-6 13291-7 13291-8 13291-9

     *LOCUS NAME: Locus1
     *ABBREVIATION: LOC1
     *GENETICS: CD           codominant
     *COMMENTS: Inferred phenotypes excluded.

     *DATA:                                                 indicates
     *1326 0/0 0/0 0/0 0/0 0/0 0/0 0/0 0/0 0/0 0/0  0/0     missing
      0/0 0/0                                               data
     *1327 0/0 0/0 0/0 0/0 0/0 0/0 0/0 0/0 0/0 0/0 0/0
      0/0
     *1328 0/0 0/0 0/0 0/0 0/0 0/0 0/0 0/0 0/0 0/0 0/0
      0/0 0/0 0/0 0/0
     *13281 0/0 0/0 0/0 0/0 0/0 0/0 0/0 0/0 0/0
     *1329 0/0 0/0 0/0 0/0 0/0 0/0 0/0 0/0 0/0 0/0 0/0
     *13291 1/2 1/2 1/1 1/1 1/2 1/1 1/1 1/1 1/2 1/1 1/2
      1/1 1/1
     *END


     *LOCUS NAME: Locus2
     *ABBREVIATION: LOC2
     *GENETICS: CD
     *COMMENTS: Inferred phenotypes excluded.

     *DATA:
     *1326 0/0 0/0 0/0 0/0 1/3 1/2 1/2 1/2 1/3 1/2 2/3
      2/3 1/1                                          genotype
     *1327 2/5 1/3 3/5 0/0 1/5 3/4 1/4 3/5 1/4 3/5 3/5
      4/5
     *1328 0/0 0/0 0/0 0/0 7/9 5/5 5/9 5/9 5/7 5/7 5/9
      5/9 5/7 5/7 5/9
     *13281 7/9 5/5 1/5 4/8 5/9 4/5 5/9 4/5 5/9
     *1329 0/0 0/0 0/0 0/0 6/8 1/1 1/8 1/8 1/8 1/6
     *13291 2/10 1/5 6/8 1/1 5/10 1/8 1/5 1/5 1/10 5/8 8/10
      5/8 1/5
     *END       order same as in
                family definition
```

FIGURE 3.11 A part of a MAPMAKER input file.

The way in which MAPMAKER might be used to construct a dense map around a putative disease locus is illustrated in the following dialogue. You would normally need to press **[return]** at the end of each MAPMAKER command. This has been omitted for clarity. A commentary has been provided to the right of the dialogue. Ignore the precise values of the numbers which constitute the prompt. They are there as an approximate count and will vary between sessions.

mapmaker [return]

```
******************************************************************
Welcome to:
MAPMAKER
(version 1.9)

Copyright 1987-1990, Whitehead Institute for Biomedical Research
******************************************************************
```

Converts the data into a form which can be used by the program more easily

```
Type 'help' for help.
1> prepare data
Input file to be prepared: chr5.raw
(60 families, 8 loci)
data successfully prepared
```

```
1> load data chr5.data
loaded data file 'chr5.data'
CEPH data (60 families,8 loci)
```

Loads the prepared data into the internal memory space of the program

```
2> use all
```

```
2> sequence *all
The current sequence is now 1-8
```

Sets the current sequence to be that of the pre-defined sequence *all, meaning all markers in the data set

```
3> two point
```

Compute two-point lod scores using currently set values of sex-specificity, etc. This sets up the two-point sequence

```
Two point data is loaded
```

```
3> big lods
```

Displays lods greater than a certain minimum value. If no value is given, 3.0 is assumed

Locus 1	Locus 2	Theta	LOD	cM
1	2	0.11	4.78	12.57
1	4	0.16	6.17	19.49
1	5	0.15	3.17	17.50
2	3	0.09	24.30	9.74
2	4	0.04	29.58	3.91
2	5	0.22	3.29	29.75
3	4	0.14	7.78	16.43
4	5	0.29	3.20	44.21
5	7	0.12	3.23	13.66

Mapping function is set to Haldane by default

```
3> sequence { 2 3 4 }
The current sequence is now '{2 3 4}'
```

2 3 4 selected because of tight linkage between all three pairs. Curly braces represent any order of the loci between them

```
4> compare
```

```
Best 3 orders. Sequence = {2 3 4}
order 1: 3 2 4 log-likelihood: -234.70
order 2: 3 4 2 log-likelihood: -239.67
order 3: 2 3 4 log-likelihood: -241.96
```

Computes log likelihood of all maps for the current sequence ordered by decreasing likelihood

```
4> sequence { 1 5 7 }
The current sequence is now '{1 5 7}'.
```

Another tightly linked triplet

```
5> compare
do you wish to test the trial markers
Best 3 orders. Sequence = {1 5 7}
order 1: 1 5 7 log-likelihood: -95.34
order 2: 1 7 5 log-likelihood: -97.51
order 3: 7 1 5 log-likelihood: -97.89
```

Best order is ~100:1 more likely than next best

```
5> sequence <4 2 3><1 5 7>
The current sequence is now '<4 2 3> <1 5 7>'.
```

Angled brackets mean that the order within is defined, but the orientation is unknown

```
6> compare

Best 4 orders. Sequence = <4 2 3> <1 5 7>
order 1: 4 2 3 1 5 7 log-likelihood: -408.07
order 2: 3 2 4 1 5 7 log-likelihood: -412.91
order 3: 4 2 3 7 5 1 log-likelihood: -414.37
order 4: 3 2 4 7 5 1 log-likelihood: -418.63
```

There are four possible ways to orient the above sequence

```
6> sequence 4 2 3 1 5 7
The current sequence is now '4 2 3 1 5 7'.
```

This is our best order so far. Two markers left to fit

```
7> try 6 8

markers: 4 2 3 1 5 7
intervals: (0) (1) (2) (3) (4) (5) (6)
Which intervals would you like to place them in: [all]
>

Computing 14 maps...
```

Try them both in all possible intervals

```
  RELATIVE LIKELIHOODS:
         6        8
    ----------------
     | -3.11    -0.13
  4  |
     | -26.21  -31.63
  2  |
     | -25.14  -34.87
  3  |
     | -13.52  -14.85
  1  |
     | -6.64    -9.37
  5  |
```

Likelihoods are given relative to the best position (interval), which is set to 0.0. Here the best place for 6 is at the end of the sequence. As long as the adjacent likelihood differences are large enough, we can reject the alternative placements

```
      |   -4.10    -5.72
  7   |
      |    0.00     0.00
inf   |
      |   -3.19    -0.13
      -------------------
BEST  -419.91   -467.86
```

Best order ~100000:1 relative odds over next best. This is fine.

~~Place 3 on the end~~

```
7> sequence 4 2 3 1 5 7 6
The current sequence is now '4 2 3 1 5 7 6'.
```

Computes the maximum likelihood map for the current order

```
8> map
========================================================
MAP:
  4 -- 2          4.7 cM               4.5 %
  2 -- 3          9.5 cM               8.7 %
  3 -- 1          7.2 cM               6.7 %
  1 -- 5         16.4 cM              14.0 %
  5 -- 7         10.2 cM               9.2 %
  7 -- 6         21.8 cM              17.6 %
  ---------
  69.8 cM


log-likelihood = -419.913752

========================================================
```

Change orders of all triplets in the current sequence, computing the likelihood of the resulting order, adjusting the distances as appropriate. The likelihood is expressed relative to the current order

```
8> ripple

The map for the current sequence is:
      4     2     3     1     5     7     6   log-likelihood: -419.91
map:  4.7   9.5   7.2  16.4  10.2  21.8

--4 3 2-- --2 4 3-- --2 3 4-- --3 4 2-- --3 2 4--
  -9.02     -5.29    -11.24     -7.91     -4.94
```

As long as all values are < -2.0, we are okay.

```
--2 1 3-- --3 2 1-- --3 1 2-- --1 2 3-- --1 3 2--
  -0.89     -9.02    -10.72     -3.96    -11.07
```

Orientation of 1 and 3 is uncertain

```
--3 5 1-- --1 3 5-- --1 5 3-- --5 3 1-- --5 1 3--
  -7.82     -0.89    -11.66    -15.73    -16.94

--1 7 5-- --5 1 7-- --5 7 1-- --7 1 5-- --7 5 1--
  -4.78     -7.82     -7.73    -11.19     -8.45

--5 6 7-- --7 5 6-- --7 6 5-- --6 5 7-- --6 7 5--
  -4.10     -4.78     -6.44     -6.64     -6.28
```

Up till now, sexes have been considered together. They can be separated with the sex-specific on command

```
8> sex specific on
```

'sex specific' is on.

8> **map**

Here both male and female maps have been computed. Note that the female map is somewhat longer than the male

```
============================================================
MALE-MAP:        FEMALE-MAP:
4 -- 2          8.1 cM        7.5 %    0.0 cM        0.0 %
2 -- 3          11.3 cM       10.1 %   8.4 cM        7.7 %
3 -- 1          8.2 cM        7.6 %    8.4 cM        7.7 %
1 -- 5          14.5 cM       12.6 %   19.1 cM       15.9 %
5 -- 7          4.8 cM        4.6 %    14.3 cM       12.5 %
7 -- 6          6.2 cM        5.9 %    49.3 cM       31.3 %

                53.1 cM                99.5 cM

log-likelihood = -417.469710

============================================================
```

8> **sex specific off**   **Turn it off again**
'sex specific' is off.

8> **link 6**

```
unlinked: 4 2 3 1 5 7 * 6 log-likelihood: -423.10
linked: 4 2 3 1 5 7 6 log-likelihood:-419.91
Difference in log-likelihood: 3.19
```

8> **try 8**

Try and place the last marker

```
loci: 4 2 3 1 5 7 6
intervals: (0) (1) (2) (3) (4) (5) (6) (7)
Which intervals would you like to place it in :[all]
```

```
    8
    --------
    | -0.49
4   |
    | -30.51
2   |
    | -35.43
3   |
    | -15.63
1   |
    | -9.89
5   |
    | -7.41
7   |
    | -2.35
6   |
    | 0.00
```

```
inf  |
     | -0.49                              Best position is on the end
     -----------
BEST -477.51
```

```
8> sequence 4 2 3 1 5 7 6 8
The current sequence is now '4 2 3 1 5 7 6 8'.       Add it to the sequence
```

```
                          Is 8 really linked
8> link 7                 to the group?
```

```
unlinked: 4 2 3 1 5 7 6 * 8 log-likelihood: -478.00
linked: 4 2 3 1 5 7 6 8 log-likelihood: -477.51
difference in log-likelihood: 0.49
                                            No, not good enough
```

```
9> map
============================================================
MAP:
  4 -- 2         4.8 cM            4.6 %
  2 -- 3         9.0 cM            8.2 %
  3 -- 1         7.2 cM            6.7 %          Check marker is linked.  The 6
  1 -- 5        16.8 cM           14.3 %          refers to the interval  number
  5 -- 7        10.9 cM            9.8 %          between markers  7 and 6
  7 -- 6        24.8 cM           19.5 %
  6 -- 8        51.3 cM           32.1 %

 124.7 cM

log-likelihood = -477.505710

============================================================
```

```
                                        So, take it off again
9> sequence 4 2 3 1 5 7 6
The current sequence is now '4 2 3 1 5 7 6'.
```

```
10> cent func 2                         Change mapping function from
map function 2 (kosambi) selected.      Haldane to Kosambi
```

```
10> map
                                        Generate a maximum likelihood
==============================================         map for the current order
MAP:
  4 -- 2         4.4 cM            4.4 %
  2 -- 3         8.6 cM            8.5 %
  3 -- 1         5.6 cM            5.6 %
  1 -- 5        13.1 cM           12.8 %
  5 -- 7         8.7 cM            8.6 %
  7 -- 6        17.9 cM           17.1 %

                58.2 cM
```

```
log-likelihood = -419.870930
```

```
===========================================================
```

Print a lod table

`10> lod table`

	4	2	3	1	5	7	7
2	3.8						
	29.58						

Recombination fraction on top . Pairwise lod score below

	4	2	3	1	5	7	7
3	14.4	8.9					
	7.78	24.30					
1	16.7	11.3	14.7				
	6.17	4.78	0.86				
5	33.6	24.1	10.8	15.2			
	3.20	3.29	2.87	3.17			
7	51.5	31.2	27.9	55.0	12.2		
	0.50	1.63	1.32	0.17	3.23		
6	52.2	59.1	27.9	43.6	21.8	19.4	
	0.17	1.63	1.32	0.50	3.23	1.65	

```
The bottom number is the pairwise LOD score. The top
number is the recombination fraction.
```

```
10> translate
  4 LOC4
  2 LOC2
  3 LOC3        Show real names of loci
  1 LOC1
  5 LOC5
  7 LOC7
  6 LOC6
```

```
11> quit
```

```
Do you really want to quit? [no] yes
Now saving chr5.2pt...
Now saving chr5.data...
```

```
Goodbye...
```

MAPMAKER has now given us a template on which to hang the disease gene. We will return to how this may be achieved in Section 7.2.

7.1.2 CRI-Map

CRI-Map is a system for multipoint analysis of codominant and fully penetrant dominant traits in extended pedigrees. The current version is 2.4 and it is available from Dr Phil Green. It is distributed as C source code and is particularly easy to port to any C compiler supporting 32 bit (or greater) addressing. It will compile using the new 64-bit DEC alpha compiler, with a small change to one of the source files. It is the software most often used to construct whole chromosome maps for the CEPH consortia (Dracopoli et al., 1991; Spurr et al., 1992). A utility exists (link2cri, from John Attwood) which can convert a pair of LINKAGE files into CRI-Map representation.

A portion of a CRI-Map data file for the APC chromosome 5 data set used in earlier sections is reproduced in Figure 3.12. Data are held in a single file, named `chrx-y.gen`, where x is replaced by digit(s) representing the chromosome for which it contains data, and y is any string of 0 or more characters.

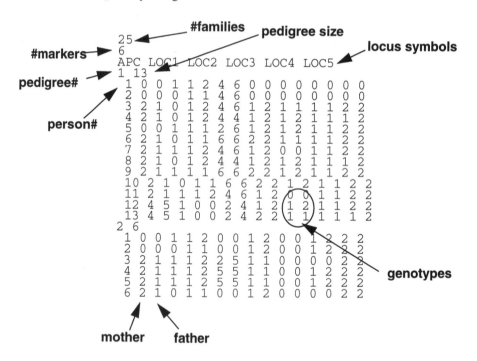

FIGURE 3.12 Part of a CRI-Map input file.

CRI-Map uses a very efficient algorithm for optimizing the likelihood function but does lose some information from potentially uninformative meioses. Population allele frequencies are not used to determine relative phase probabilities in families with untyped founders. In disease families (where often not all members are typed), this could result in almost all the data being lost. Therefore, likelihoods, lod scores and measures of support will all reflect the incomplete nature of the analysis and will probably differ from those computed by LINKAGE.

CRI-Map is a development of the MAPMAKER program but has ceased to be interactive and has instead gained the ability to perform analyses in a semi-automatic batch mode. Although still limited to codominant loci (or those where the phenotype unambiguously infers the genotype) it has the major advantage of being able to handle complex general pedigrees. The program is always invoked with two command-line parameters: a number representing the chromosome to be mapped and the program option to be used, as

`crimap <n> <option>`

where `<n>` refers to a file of the form `chr<n>.par` and `<option>` can be one of **all, build, chrompic, fixed, flips, instant, quick, prepare** or **twopoint**. Full descriptions of the options are given in the user guide. The option **prepare** must be run prior to any of the others, which preprocesses the data file, as with MAPMAKER. This is the only interactive part of using the program, and is also an opportunity to set various parameters, such as tolerance and sex-equal analysis, and to group together loci to be treated as haplotypes during future runs. Output from the command

`crimap 10 prepare`

will be `chr10.dat` (the processed data file), `chr10.par` (the parameter file), `chr10.loc` (the mapping between locus numbers and names, and the numbers of informative meioses for each locus) and `chr10.ord` (which will become a database of ordering information as the map is built up).

CRI-Map can perform several useful functions. It can estimate the recombination fraction and associated lod scores between pairs of markers. It can perform multipoint likelihood calculations and show where recombinations occur in families. It is also a useful tool for building multilocus maps in a reasonably automated way.

Unlike MAPMAKER and LINKAGE, CRI-Map has no automatic way of saving its output; everything is outputted to the screen. The best way to use CRI-Map is to run it as a background job and redirect its output to a file. Thus, a more typical invocation would be (under UNIX)

`crimap 10 build > mybuild.txt &`

The file `mybuild.txt` will grow as the program runs and can be examined at will with **cat, more, tail** or **lpr**.

One of the most powerful options that CRI-Map provides is to construct a map following a set of well-defined heuristics. This is the **build** option. CRI-Map can be given a pair of loci, defined in the .par file, and build up as large a map as possible by stepwise addition of the remaining loci. The .ord file is used to keep track of possible "backtracking" points. For example, if the current map is 1 2 3 and locus 4 cannot be fitted uniquely at the selected level of support but could be either side of, say, locus 2 then the orders database will store two alternative maps, 1 4 2 3 and 1 2 4 3, and the next candidate locus will be tried in both maps. Initially, only phase-known data are used to increase speed, but all the data are used before the locus is finally placed or rejected. The parameter PK_LIKE_TOL states, on a log 10 scale, by how much the best position must exceed the next best in order for a locus to be provisionally placed. During the subsequent, definitive test, placement is controlled by the value of PUK_LIKE_-TOL. Normally, both of these would be set to 3 (equivalent to odds of 1000:1).

If there is *any possibility* of the machine crashing during a build run then keep a copy of the .ord file first as the crash will almost always make the current one unreadable.

Convergence during iterative MLE calculations is controlled by the tolerance parameter in the .par file, which defaults to 0.01 but is better set to 0.001. This can be set once at the beginning of the analysis and will be propagated throughout subsequent runs. If care is exercised, parameter files can be altered with a text editor after the **prepare** option has been used. However, if a completely new order is to be used, the parameter file should be recreated in order to re-initialize the orders database too. After a successful build, the new order should if possible be cut and pasted from the output file into the parameter file to avoid transcription errors.

Weaver et al. (1992) describe some very useful utilities that can be used with CRI-Map, including translating to and from LINKAGE, and generating statistics on informative meioses and possible data problems.

7.1.3 MAP

MAP (Morton and Andrews, 1989) uses two-point lod scores as the basic material from which to construct a genetic map. Its main advantage is that lod scores can be combined irrespective of the raw data from which they derived. Its input consists of pairs of recombination fractions and lod scores (θ and Z) for each pair of markers to be considered. Because of this, it is very much faster than equivalent multipoint methods, requires less computer resources for a given problem size, and can properly allow for interference.

It has the ability to improve automatically a given order and the advantage that the input data can come from anywhere (published lod score tables as well as locally generated data). MAP is a powerful tool for map-making, especially in the smaller laboratory where it is impossible to generate enough data locally. MAP should be considered where computing resources are limited or where large numbers of loci must be mapped, since all problems associated with reduced penetrance, missing data, multiple alleles or consanguinity loops have effectively already been dealt with when calculating the pairwise lod scores.

The present version of the program can perform the following functions:

- Evaluate and improve a trial map.
- Insert loci into a map at a specified level of support.
- Insert loci, as above but within a restricted range of possible locations.
- Remove a locus already in the map, and test its fit elsewhere in all (or a restricted range) of possible alternative positions.
- Permute up to 5 markers along the length of the map in order to test for improvements in order.
- Optionally allow for an error rate in the data (e.g. 1.0%).

MAP requires two input files, one containing the data and another which specifies the problem. The data must be laid out in columns (as in input to LIPED) but the problem file is line-based. Upper-case characters must be used throughout. A example is given below,

```
ABL        ABO            0.1     4.4
ABL        AK1            0.08    2.1
ABL        ASS            0.15    4.2
ABL        D9S10          0.0    12.3
ABL        D9S11          0.3     1.8
ABL        D9S14          0.21    2.4
ABL        D9S16          0.11    3.8
ABL        D9S17          0.15    3.2
ABL        D9S21   0.2    1.29    0.0     2.43
ABL        D9S23   0.17   1.52
ABL        D9S26   0.06   2.89    0.0     2.11
ABL        D9S31                                  0.21    2.4
ABL        D9S7                                   0.31    1.5
ABL        ORM1                                   0.27    2.5
```

and consists of 3 alphanumeric fields (avoid punctuation characters here), followed by up to 3 pairs of numeric fields (a θ value and corresponding lod score). The θ/lod score pairs are, from left to right, male, female, and sex-averaged, for the pair of markers specified in the first two fields (the third field contains a reference code, and is unused in this version, but must still be present even if it is left blank).

MAP can cope with a reasonable amount of missing data. It can handle multiple entries for the same pair of markers, which allows local lod scores to be combined with published ones. If none of the data is sexes-separate then all of the entries should be in the first pair of columns (for male θ/lod score pair) and the sex ratio should be set to 1.00.

When a pair of markers are unlinked (and, by definition, the maximum lod score is 0.0 at 50% recombination) use, if available, the negative lod score where θ = 0.3, as this gives information on the significance of the assumption that they are truly unlinked.

A minimal jobfile is shown below:

```
MA (ABL, AK1, ORM1, ABO)
FM (3A7, 6F10.4)
PA (0.1) (P = 0.35)
IT (S) (D = 0.1, E = 3.0, X = 1
CC C9.DAT
```

The first (MA) line describes the locus order to be investigated, with the loci named exactly as in the data file. Locus names are separated by commas (and optional spaces) and the entire list is enclosed in parentheses. Note that no line in this file may exceed 80 characters in length; if necessary, a line may be continued on to the next by ending it with an asterisk character:

```
MA (ABL, AK1, ORM1, ABO, *
                D9S10, D9S11, D9S16)
```

Job files are always prepared, and modified, with a suitable text editor. Data files may be either prepared by hand with a text editor, generated automatically, or be a mixture of the two as published data is added by hand to an automatically generated file of local data.

MAP is usually invoked as **map** followed by four obligatory parameters: (1) the job file, (2) the data file, (3) the terse output file and (4) the prolix output file. The first two must already exist, or an error will occur, whilst the last two will be created (it is an error if they already exist) to hold the results of the run. It is convenient to use a consistent filename with an extension indicating the file type. Thus MAP might be called as:

map c9.job c9.lods c9.ter c9.pro &

but even this is a lot of typing. An alternative is to construct a shell script which contains the names of all the files and types them for you when invoked by its name (which might be **c9**). The above line (without the **&**) could be typed into a file called c9, and then that file made executable by typing

chmod +x c9

and then simply typing

c9 &

will cause MAP to be invoked, using c9.job and c9.lods as input and producing c9.ter and c9.pro as output.

If all goes well, MAP will produce a pair of output files, in which the terse one contains the answer and the prolix one contains a log of the processes used to arrive at it.

An important concept to understand, in interpreting the results, is that of ChiZ, the use of which is fundamental to the operation of MAP as it is the value minimized by the bootstrap procedure. ChiZ is the binomial chi square and is calculated as

$$(2\log_e 10) \, (ZO - ZE) \qquad \text{(EQ 3.7)}$$

where ZO and ZE are the observed and expected lod scores for the whole map, a pair of markers within it, or a single marker. This is a statistic which measures the goodness of fit between the current map and the starting data. The smaller the difference, the better the fit.

ChiZ values can be compared as with likelihoods. A map of the same set of markers with a lower ChiZ is a better map. Unlike likelihoods, the absolute value of a ChiZ is meaningful in its own right and, in particular, pairs of loci with ChiZ > 10.0 are badly placed. MAP lists these in the prolix file.

Map distance estimations are iterative processes which terminate when two successive iterations produce likelihoods that are close enough together to be indistinguishable within a specified tolerance. This is called convergence. However if, after 50 iterations, convergence is not reached, then the process is halted as it will probably not converge within a reasonable amount of time. For each ChiZ that it calculates, MAP shows (in the prolix file) the number of iterations required (ITER) and the difference between successive estimations (CONV). Where ITER = 50, and CONV is large (greater than about 0.01), the results are imprecise and should be treated with caution. Bad orders often do not converge and must be improved by hand (from physical or other data) before MAP can be used effectively.

The best map found is presented as a list of locus names (with its ChiZ, ITER and CONV). For a good map, ZO and ZE will be in reasonable agreement. If the ChiZ for the map is interpreted as a chisquare statistic (a fair approximation), N would be the degrees of freedom.

7.1.4 Typing Errors and Their Detection

Much interest has been generated around the issue of genotyping errors in reference databases such as the CEPH (Dausset et al., 1990). Consortium mapping efforts using data from this database have estimated the residual error rate at somewhat less than 1% (Dracopoli et al., 1991; Spurr et al., 1992). This is the estimated error rate after some attempt has been made to identify intralocus recombinants, double recombinants over short distances, and families which contain an atypical number of recombinants (equivalent to an analysis of heterogeneity, see Section 6). The residual error rate puts an upper limit on the resolution of the maps obtainable using this kind of approach. There is some evidence that the data used to construct the maps of Weissenbach et al. (1992) have a lower error rate than the mixture of RFLP, VNTR and PCR marker systems in the main CEPH database. Some attempt has been made to build the possibility of error within the framework of the likelihood model (Lincoln and Lander, 1992) and Haines (1992) has described a method for detecting errors based on the differential inflation in map length by marker systems containing errors. Multiple two-point approaches such as MAP are more robust in the presence of typing errors (N. E. Morton, personal communication).

In the absence of a generally available statistical screening tool for reference data, researchers are advised to be wary of data sets which have not been subject to scrutiny by one of the CEPH consortia. Screening of haplotypes is as important here as anywhere else in linkage analysis.

It has been stressed that the maps produced using any of the methods described in this chapter should be reconciled with the primary data. Of particular importance are the way in which haplotypes segregate within families. The *chrompic* option in CRI-Map provides one way of examining haplotypes without having to work them out by hand. The only other automatic system of which I am aware is PATCH (Wijsman, 1987), which suffers from the restriction that haplotypes could only be constructed from completely phase-known meioses.

7.1.5 Other Developments

Thompson (1987) considered that likelihood methods would be unfeasible for large numbers of loci and described the implementation of a minimum recombinant approach using a branch-and-bound algorithm.

Matise et al. (1993) have developed an expert system (MULTIMAP) based around CRI-Map as the engine for computing likelihoods. It builds on the CRI-Map ability to use heuristics in order to construct a map, and promises to deliver a largely automated system, including error analysis. Within the Imperial Cancer Research Fund, we have considered an alternative approach, based on a number of cooperating processes, which communicate *via* a shared data area.

7.2 Placing an Unknown Marker on a Reference Map

One strategy for map construction is to successively place unmapped markers into an order having high support. The log likelihood difference to the base e at each position relative to the log likelihood of free recombination with the group is termed the location score. The position with the highest location score is the MLE of the marker location. The traditional way this is done is to use the LINKMAP component of LINK-AGE (Section 7.2.1). LINKMAP is very demanding on computational resources and attention has recently focused on the development of more efficient algorithms which perform the same function. This has most notably resulted in the FASTMAP program (Curtis and Gurling, 1993) which is described in Section 7.2.2.

7.2.1 LINKMAP

A multipoint marker map obtained in the earlier module using MAPMAKER or CRI-Map could now be used as a template on which to place the APC locus. The statistical ideas are very similar to estimating the recombination fraction. The competing hypotheses are now the position of the unknown locus relative to a fixed map of marker loci. The most likely position of the unknown locus is that which maximizes the likelihood of the resulting map. Here is demonstrated how to use the LINKMAP component of LINKAGE to try to place the APC locus. This is almost equivalent to the *try* option in MAPMAKER, except that distances are not recomputed for each placement of the unknown locus.

Start LCP with

lcp [return]

and edit the first screen to use the files **apc.ppd** as the *PEDIGREE File Name* and **apc.par** as the *PARAMETER File Name*. Set the *COMMAND File Name* to **mymap**. [ctrl-n] to the *Pedigree Options* screen and select *General Pedigrees*.

Type [ctrl-n] to move to the *General Pedigree Analysis Options* screen and select the *LINKMAP* option. [ctrl-n] again to the *LINKMAP - Test Interval Options* screen and select *All Intervals*. [ctrl-n] and select the *No Sex Difference* option, then [ctrl-n] to the *LINKMAP - Map Specification Command Screen*. Set the test locus to *p1* and the fixed loci to *p2 p4 and p3*. Set the recombination fractions to 0.04 and 0.20. [ctrl-n] then [ctrl-z] to finish.

Execute the script file by typing **mymap [return]**. This may take some time.

When the job has completed, run LRP with

lrp [return]

Hit [ctrl-n] at the *Input File and Report Title* menu and [ctrl-n] to select *General Pedigree Reports* from the *Report Options* menu.

Use the cursor keys to select *Location Score Report* (LINKMAP) from the *General Pedigree Report Options* menu. [ctrl-n] to the *Location Score Report (LINKMAP) Formats* menu and select *Table Format*. [ctrl-n] to the *Report Output Options* screen and select *Output Report to the Screen*. Hit [ctrl-n]. LRP takes a few seconds to lay out the report. If the report is more than one page long, [ctrl-n] allows you to move a page at a time. [ctrl-z] finishes.

LRP will highlight the interval within which the maximum likelihood location lies. Subsequent screens show alternative intervals with the odds ratio given against the most likely interval (Figure 3.13).

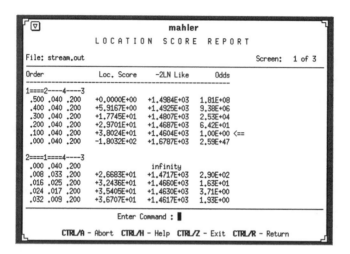

FIGURE 3.13 A screen from LRP showing part of a LINKMAP analysis.

A ratio of greater than 1000:1 is deemed to be significant. The results may be represented graphically by a figure which will have to be drawn by hand (Figure 3.14).

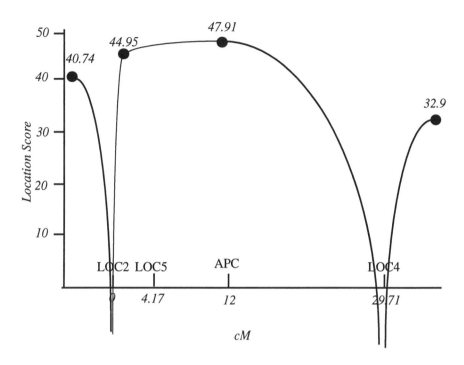

FIGURE 3.14 Graphical representation of the LINKMAP output from Figure 3.13.

7.2.2 FASTMAP

FASTMAP (Curtis and Gurling, 1993) uses multiple two-point methods to construct a location score curve similar to the output from LINKMAP. Preliminary studies show that the results are almost identical to those from LINKMAP, but that the program requires a small fraction of the computing resources. FASTMAP is available from Dr Dave Curtis.

8   General Trait Mapping

The preceding dialogue on trait mapping has emphasized the computation of likelihoods where the mode of inheritance, while perhaps not known with a great deal of certainty, is fully specified in the analysis. For traits which follow a clearly defined pattern of segregation, where incomplete penetrance is not a problem and where heterogeneity is absent, the methods described so far have high power to detect linkage and are robust. For many traits, to which may be attached the term *general*, encompassing *com-*

plex and *multivariate*, very little may be known about the parameters determining inheritance, and an alternative strategy may be needed (Risch, 1990a). Neumann and Rice (1990) pointed out the precautions that need to be taken when the mode of transmission is unknown. In some cases, the reduction in power due to model misspecification may be slight (Elston, 1989). Greenberg (1990) showed that assuming a single-locus mode of inheritance, given a two-locus case, did not significantly affect the ability to detect linkage. This will not apply universally, and in many cases it is appropriate to use "model-free" methods. This is a very new and exciting area of analysis and in consequence few of the implemented algorithms have reached a wide circle of practitioners. It is as well to also bear in mind other factors which may affect the accuracy of a linkage analysis. The change in diagnostic status of a single individual may influence the lod score in a family by as much as 1.2 units (Hodge and Greenberg, 1992). A sensitivity analysis, whereby the status of individuals is altered and the effects on the expected lod score distribution noted, should be performed wherever possible. At the moment, this would be done by systematically exploring the data set with software such as SIMLINK (Boehnke, 1986) in conjunction with LIPED or LINKAGE. This approach can also be used to determine the sensitivity of the analysis to the effect of model misspecification. The approaches described below tend to draw on research in Monte Carlo simulation, statistical power and derivatives of the affected-pedigree-member methods.

8.1   Simulation and Power Analyses

The first use of simulation on pedigrees was described by Edwards (1988). MacCluer et al. (1986) described a very general '"gene-dropping" technique and Ott (1989) presented a range of linkage problems which could be tractable using Monte Carlo methods. They have since found utility in the random generation of genotypes (Lange and Matthysse, 1989) and the computation of approximate location scores (Lange and Sobel, 1991). They can be used routinely with programs such as SIMLINK (Boehnke, 1986) to perform power and sensitivity analyses (Ploughman and Boehnke, 1989; Narod and Amos, 1990), and the determination of required sample sizes to detect linkage (Boehnke, 1990). Chen et al. (1992) used simulation methods with a model for schizophrenia to examine the reduction of power in the presence of heterogeneity, an approach also used by Martinez and Goldin (1990) in the study of a general heterogeneous disorder with low penetrance. They have been used to show that standard methods may lack sufficient power to detect linkage at all given a particular trait model (Matthysse and Parnas, 1992).

8.2   Affected Pedigree Member Methods

The technique of Penrose (1935) led to the development of the general sib-pair method (Suarez, 1978), of immense value in analysis of the HLA region (Blackwelder and Elston, 1982; Louis et al., 1983; Hodge, 1984; Payami et al., 1984; Ethier and Hodge, 1985; Motro and Thomson, 1985; Dawson et al., 1990) and in the study of quantitative traits (Haseman and Elston, 1972). The method uses identity by descent distributions to make inferences about linkage. The method was later generalized to sib-sets (Lange, 1986a) and identity by state (Lange, 1986b). Weeks and Lange (1988) applied the method to extended pedigrees and encouraged the development of general affected pedigree member methods. They used the algorithm of Karigl (1981) to compute multiple person kinship coefficients (Karigl, 1982) and implemented the result in the program KIN (Weeks and Lange, 1988). Bishop and Williamson (1990) and Risch (1990b) examined how the power of affected pairs was affected by degree of relationship. Recent developments have included the ability to include marker information from unaffecteds as well as affecteds in computing the expected distribution of IBS scores (Ward, 1993) and in using the information from all relative pairs simultaneously (Olson and Wijsman, 1993).

Alternatives to KIN include PEDSCORE (Weitkamp and Lewis, 1989), which use Monte Carlo methods in conjunction with an identity by descent statistic to test for deviation from Mendelian expectation.

8.3   Combining Segregation and Linkage Analysis

Segregation analysis is usually conducted prior to, and separately from, a linkage analysis. Systematically combining linkage with segregation analysis offers an attractive way of exploring a data set. A recent development incorporating Monte Carlo methods has been reported by Guo and Thompson (1992) and shows great promise in shedding light on this area.

9   Data Presentation

9.1   Pedigree/Draw

This is a highly polished piece of software for the Apple Macintosh (Mamelka et al., 1987) which is available without charge from Dr Jean MacCluer. Pedigree/Draw can produce output similar to Figure 3.1 with minimal user intervention, but can also create PICT files which can be imported into software similar to MacDraw for sophisticated annotation. Highly inbred pedigrees, which are often problematic to reproduce graphically, can be preprocessed by an associated utility (ARBOR) before display. Data entry is carried out in typical Apple Macintosh fashion. Pedigree/Draw files are just text files formatted in a particular way and can be created by GENBASE and XShell or even a text editor.

9.2 PEDRAW

PEDRAW is a package written by Dave Curtis at St Mary's Hospital Medical School in London, and available free of charge to academic users. It can read data from LINKSYS export files, LINKAGE input files and its own text file format. Output is in the form of Microsoft Paint files which can be printed from within Microsoft Windows (the program itself cannot run inside Windows) or, failing this, sent to a 9- or 24-pin Epson type dot-matrix printer with an included utility program.

PEDRAW is very fussy about input file formats and assumes that a .SDF contains data in LINKSYS format, a .PED file in LINKAGE format, and a .DAT file in its own custom format. Loading a file with one of these extensions when, in fact, the data are laid out differently will have unpredictable and possibly unpleasant consequences.

9.3 XShell

XShell has an associated utility for presenting lod score curves directly with minimal user intervention. LINKAGE files are produced, run and the results interpreted before being displayed on the screen or sent to a Postscript printer using the ACE/gr public domain software (see Figure 3.6 for an example).

9.4 PedPack

PedPack (Thomas (1987a,b) is really a complete pedigree analysis environment. It has not had a very large take-up in the community so far but does offer some very attractive features. It can perform likelihood calculations and interface to the PAP package (Hasstedt and Cartwright, 1981), as well as displaying complex pedigrees using marriage node graphs (Thomas, 1988). There is a version set up at the UK HGMP RC but interested users are advised to contact Dr Alun Thomas in the first instance.

9.5 Cyrillic

Cyrillic (Chapman, 1990) is a system for managing pedigree data on a PC and interfacing to the MLINK component of LINKAGE. The current version runs under Microsoft Windows and is distributed by Cherwell Scientific in Oxford, England.

10 Integration of Maps

An area which is receiving a great deal of attention currently is the integration of genetic and physical maps. Up until now, this has mostly been done in a very informal way, by taking into account evidence on order from other methods when constructing maps. The location database (ldb) of Morton et al. (1992) is an attempt to place the integration of maps on a more quantitative, formal basis. ldb is defined in terms of data and algorithms with which diverse mapping evidence can be used to produce a summary map projected on to a megabase scale, based on current estimates of chromosomal length (Morton, 1991). It has already been used to produce integrated maps of chromosome 1 (Collins et al., 1992) and 2 (Cox et al., in preparation).

Alternative approaches include the System for Integrated Genome Map Assembly (SIGMA) from the LANL in the USA (see Chapter 5) and CPROP (Letovsky and Berlyn, 1992).

All these projects are at a very early stage. SIGMA is available by anonymous ftp from `atlas.lanl.gov`. Researchers interested in ldb should contact Professor Newton Morton in the first instance.

11 Other Topics

11.1 Bulletin Boards

The Genetic-Linkage bulletin board, part of the BioSci system, is a valuable way of rapidly discussing a topic without the expense of an actual meeting. The disadvantages of the medium mean that most of the discussion is informal, but the board has generated substantial interest and some very valuable and timely dialogues have been conducted. It is fair to say that the board has established itself within the community and that many of the people mentioned in this review are regular contributors.

For general information on bulletin boards, the reader is referred to Chapter 1. The correct address for messages is different depending on which part of the world you are based. For example, in the UK, mail messages should be sent to

> `gen-link@daresbury.ac.uk`

Researchers outside the UK should consult the details in Appendix 2.

11.2 Newsletters

The LINKAGE Newsletter is distributed by Jurg Ott of Columbia University, about every six months, and is also placed on the Genetic-Linkage bulletin board.

11.3 Training Courses

Courses on genetic linkage analysis are periodically run by the UK HGMP-RC. These courses are from one to five days duration and are open to all registrants of the centre, including those from overseas. For more information, contact

```
Mrs Christine Bates
HGMP Resource Centre
Clinical Research Centre
Watford Road
Harrow HA1 3UJ, UK
```

Courses are also organized by Professor Jurg Ott in New York and Zurich and are advertised in the Linkage newsletter. Courses are also held at the Porto Conte Research and Training Laboratories in Alghero, Italy. These are convened by Professor Marcello Siniscalco and are advertised on the Genetic Linkage bulletin board, as well as in journals such as "Nature". Travelling fellowships are often available.

12   Acknowledgements

Some of the material included here was derived from courses sponsored by the UK Human Genome Mapping Project under the auspices of the UK Medical Research Council. John Attwood, Sue Povey and John Yates were jointly responsible for some of the original material from which this chapter was derived, but the ultimate responsibility for accuracy rests with myself. The Imperial Cancer Research Fund provided support during the preparation of this manuscript.

13   References

Attwood J and Bryant S (1988). A computer program to make analysis with LIPED and LINKAGE easier to perform and less prone to input errors. Ann. Hum. Genet. 52, 259.

Ball SP, Dorkins HR, Ellis FR, Hall JL, Halsall PJ, Hopkins PM, Mueller RF and Stewart AD (1993). Genetic linkage analysis of chromosome 19 markers in malignant hyperthermia. Br. J. Anaesth. 70, 70-75.

Bishop DT and Williamson JA (1990). The power of identity-by-state methods for linkage analysis. Am. J. Hum. Genet. 46, 254-265.

Blackwelder WC and Elston RC (1982). Power and robustness of sib-pair linkage tests and extension to larger sibships. Commun. Statist.-Theor. Methods 11 (5), 449-484.

Bodmer WF, Bailey CJ, Bodmer J, Bussey HJR, Ellis A, Gorman P, Lucibello FC, Murday VA, Rider SH, Scambler P, Sheer D, Solomon E and Spurr NK (1987). Localization of the gene for familial adenomatous polyposis on chromosome 5. Nature 328, 614-616.

Boehnke M (1986). Estimating the power of a proposed linkage study: a practical computer simulation approach. Am. J. Hum. Genet. 39, 513-527.

Boehnke M (1990). Sample-size guidelines for linkage analysis of a dominant locus for a quantitative trait by the method of lod scores. Am. J. Hum. Genet. 47, 218-227.

Botstein D, White RL, Skolnick M and Davis RW (1980) Construction of a genetic linkage map in man using restriction fragment length polymorphisms. Am. J. Hum. Genet. 32, 314-331.

Bowcock AM, Crandall J, Daneshwar L, Lee GM, Young B, Zunzunegui V, Craik C, Cavalli-Sforza LL and King M-C (1986). Genetic analysis of cystic fibrosis: linkage of DNA and classical markers in multiplex families. Am. J. Hum. Genet. 39, 699-706.

Bryant S (1991) Software for genetic linkage analysis. In "Protocols in Human Molecular Genetics. Methods in Molecular Biology" (ed, C Mathew), Vol. 9, pp. 403-418. Humana, Clifton.

Cannings C, Thompson EA and Skolnick MH (1978). Probability functions on complex pedigrees. Adv. Appl. Prob. 10, 26-61.

Cavalli-Sforza LL and King M-C (1986). Detecting linkage for genetically heterogeneous diseases and detecting heterogeneity with linkage data. Am. J. Hum. Genet. 38, 599-616.

Chapman CJ (1990). A visual interface to computer programs for linkage analysis. Am. J. Med. Genet. 36, 155-160.

Chen WJ, Faraone SV and Tsuang T (1992). Linkage studies of schizophrenia: a simulation study of statistical power. Genet. Epidemiol. 9, 123-139.

Collins A, Keats BJ, Dracopoli N, Shields DC and Morton NE (1992). Integration of gene maps: chromosome 1. Proc. Natl Acad. Sci. USA 89, 4598-4602.

Curtis D and Gurling H (1993). A procedure for combining 2-point lod scores into a summary multipoint map. Hum. Hered. 43, 173-185.

Dawson DV, Kaplan EB and Elston RC (1990). Extensions to sib-pair linkage test applicable to diseases characterized by delayed onset. Genet. Epidemiol. 7, 453-466.

Dausset J, Cann H, Cohen D, Lathrop M, Lalouel J-M and White R (1990). Centre d'etude du Polymorphisme Humain (CEPH): collaborative genetic mapping of the human genome. Genomics 6, 575-577.

Donis-Keller H, Green P, Helms C, Cartinhour S, Weiffenbach B, Stephens K, Keith TP, Bowden DW, Smith DR, Lander ES, Botstein D, Akots G, Rediker KS, Gravius T, Brown VA, Rising MB, Parker C, Powers JA, Watt DE, Kauffman ER, Bricker A, Phipps P, Muller-Kahle H, Fulton TR, Ng S, Schumm JW, Braman JC, Knowlton RG, Barker DF, Crooks SM, Lincoln SE, Daly MJ and Abrahamson J (1987). A genetic linkage map of the human genome. Cell 51, 319-337.

Dracopoli NC, O'Connell P, Elsner TI, Lalouel JM, White RL, Buetow KH, Nishimura DY, Murray JC, Helms C, Mishra SK, Donis-Keller H, Hall JM, Lee MK, King M-C, Attwood J, Morton NE, Robson EB, Mahtani M, Willard HF, Royle NJ, Patel I, Jeffreys

AJ, Verga V, Jenkins T, Weber JL, Mitchell AL and Bale AE (1991). The CEPH consortium linkage map of human chromosome 1. Genomics 9 (4), 686-700.

Edwards AWF (1972). "Likelihood". Cambridge University Press, Cambridge.

Edwards AWF (1988). Computers and Genealogies. Biol. Society 5, 73-81.

Elston RC (1989). Man bites dog? The validity of maximizing lod scores to determine mode of inheritance. Am. J. Med. Genet. 34, 487-488.

Elston RC and Stewart J (1971). A general model for the genetic analysis of pedigree data. Hum. Hered. 21, 523-542.

Ethier SN and Hodge SE (1985). Identity-by-descent analysis of sibship configurations. Am. J. Med. Genet. 22, 263-272.

Greenberg DA (1990). Linkage analysis assuming a single-locus mode of inheritance for traits determined by two loci: inferring mode of inheritance and estimating penetrance. Genet. Epidemiol. 7, 467-479.

Guo SW and Thompson EA (1992). A Monte Carlo method for combined segregation and linkage analysis. Am. J. Hum. Genet. 51, 1111-1126.

Haines JL (1992). Chromlook: an interactive program for error detection and mapping in reference families. Genomics 14, 517-519.

Haseman JK and Elston RC (1972). The investigation of linkage between a quantitative trait and a marker locus. Behav. Genet. 2 (1), 3-19.

Hasstedt SJ and Cartwright PE (1981). "PAP - Ppedigree Analysis Package. University of Utah, Department of Medical Biophysics and Computing, Technical Report No. 13". University of Utah, Salt Lake City.

Hodge SE (1984). The information content contained in multiple sibling pairs. Genet. Epidemiol. 1, 109-122.

Hodge SE and Greenberg DA (1992). Sensitivity of lod scores to changes in diagnostic status. Am. J. Hum. Genet. 50, 1053-1066.

Karigl G (1981). A recursive algorithm for the calculation of identity coefficients. Ann. Hum. Genet. 45, 299-305.

Karigl G (1982). A mathematical approach to multiple genetic relationships. Theor. Popul. Biol. 21, 379-393.

Keats BJB, Sherman SL, Morton NE, Robson EB, Buetow K, Cartwright PE, Chakravarti A, Francke U, Green PP and Ott J (1990). Guidelines for human linkage maps: an international system for human linkage maps (ISLM, 1990). Genomics 9, 557-560.

Lander ES (1987). Mapping complex genetic traits in humans. In "Genome Analysis - a Practical Approach" (ed, K Davies), pp. 171-189. IRL Press, Oxford.

Lander ES and Green P (1987). Construction of multilocus genetic linkage maps in humans. Proc. Natl Acad. Sci. USA 84, 2363-2367.

Lander ES, Green P, Abrahamson J, Barlow A, Daly MJ, Lincoln SE and Newburg, L (1987). MAPMAKER: an interactive computer package for constructing genetic linkage maps of experimental and natural populations. Genomics 1, 174-181.

Lange K (1986a). A test statistic for the affected-sib-set method. Ann. Hum. Genet. 50, 283-290.

Lange K (1986b). The affected sib-pair method using identity by state relations. Am. J. Hum. Genet. 39 (1), 148-150.

Lange K and Elston RC (1975). Extensions to pedigree analysis I. Likelihood calculation for simple and complex pedigrees. Hum. Hered. 25, 95-105.

Lange K and Matthysse S (1989). Simulation of pedigree genotypes by random walks. Am. J. Hum. Genet. 45, 959-970.

Lange K and Sobel E (1991). A random walk method for computing genetic location scores. Am. J. Hum. Genet. 49, 1320-1334.

Lange K, Weeks D and Boehnke M (1988). Programs for pedigree analysis - Mendel, Fisher and Dgene. Genet. Epidem. 5 (6), 471-472.

Larsson C, Skogseid B, Oberg K, Nakamura Y, Nordenskjold M (1988). Multiple endocrine neoplasia type I gene maps to chromosome 11 and is lost in insulinoma. Nature 332, 85-87.

Lathrop GM and Lalouel JM (1984). Easy calculations of lod scores and genetic risks on small computers. Am. J. Hum. Genet. 36, 460-465.

Lathrop GM, Lalouel JM, Julier C and Ott J (1985). Multilocus linkage analysis in humans: detection of linkage and estimation of recombination. Am. J. Hum. Genet. 37, 482-498.

Letovsky S and Berlyn MB (1992). CPROP: a rule-based program for constructing genetic maps. Genomics 12, 435-446.

Lincoln SE and Lander ES (1992). Systematic detection of errors in genetic linkage data. Genomics 14, 604-610.

Louis EJ, Thomson G and Payami H (1983). The affected sib method. II. The intermediate model. Ann. Hum. Genet. 47, 225-243.

Lu S, Day SE, Degos L, Lepage V, wang P-C, Chan SH, Simons M, McKnight B, Easton D, Zeng Y and de-The G (1990). Linkage of a nasopharyngeal carcinoma susceptibility locus to the HLA region. Nature 346, 470-471.

Maclean CJ, Ploughman LM, Diehl SR and Kendler KS (1992). A new test for linkage in the presence of locus heterogeneity. Am. J. Hum. Genet. 50, 1259-1266.

MacCluer JW, VandeBerg JL, Read B and Ryder OA (1986). Pedigree analysis by computer simulation. Zoo Biol. 5, 147-160.

McConville CM, Formobone CJ, Hernandez D, Thick J and Taylor AMR (1990). Fine mapping of the chromosome 11q22-23 region using PFGE, linkage and haplotype analysis; localization of the gene for ataxia telangectasia to a 5cM region flanked by NCAM/DRD2 and STMY/CJ52.75,f2.22. Nucl. Acids Res. 18 (15), 4335-4343.

Mamelka PM, Dyke B and MacCluer JW (1987). "Pedigree/Draw for the Apple Macintosh". Department of Genetics, Southwest Foundation for Biomedical Research, San Antonio.

Martinez M and Goldin LR (1990). Power of the linkage test for a heterogeneous disorder due to two independent inherited causes: a simulation study. Genet. Epidemiol. 7, 219-230.

Matise TC, Perlin M and Chakravarti A (1993). Automated genetic linkage mapping. Cytogenet. Cell Genet. 62, 103.

Matthysse S and Parnas J (1992). Extending the phenotype of schizophrenia: implications for linkage analysis. J. Psychiat. Res. 26, 329-344.

Morton NE (1955). Sequential tests for the detection of linkage. Am. J. Hum. Genet. 7, 277-318.

Morton NE (1991). Parameters of the human genome. Proc. Natl Acad. Sci. USA 88, 7474-7476.

Morton NE and Andrews V (1989). MAP, An expert system for multiple pairwise linkage analysis. Ann. Hum. Genet. 53, 263-269.

Morton NE, Collins A, Lawrence S and Shields DC (1992). Algorithms for a location database. Ann. Hum. Genet. 56, 223-232.

Motro U and Thomson G (1985). The affected sib method. I. Statistical features of the affected sib-pair method. Genetics 110, 525-538.

Narod SA and Amos C (1990). Estimating the power of linkage analysis in hereditary breast cancer. Am. J. Hum. Genet. 46, 266-272.

Neumann RJ and Rice JP (1990). Note on linkage analysis when the mode of transmission is unknown. Genet. Epidemiol. 7, 349-358.

Olson JM and Wijsman EM (1993). Linkage between quantitative trait and marker loci: methods using all relative pairs. Genet. Epidemiol. 10, 87-102.

Ott J (1974). Estimation of the recombination in human pedigrees: efficient computation of the likelihood for human linkage studies. Am. J. Hum. Genet. 26, 588-597.

Ott J (1987). A short guide to linkage analysis. In "Genome Analysis - A Practical Approach" (ed, K Davies), pp. 19-32. IRL Press, Oxford.

Ott J (1989). Computer simulation methods in linkage analysis. Proc. Natl Acad. Sci. USA. 86, 4175-4178.

Ott J. (1991). "Analysis of Human Genetic Linkage". revised edition. Johns Hopkins University Press, Baltimore.

Pascoe L and Morton N (1987). The use of map functions in multipoint mapping. Am. J. Hum. Genet. 40, 174-183.

Payami H, Thomson G and Louis EJ (1984). The affected sib method. III. Selection and recombination. Am. J. Hum. Genet. 36, 352-362.

Penrose LS (1935). The detection of autosomal linkage in data which consist of brothers and sisters of unspecified parentage. Ann. Eugen. 6, 133-138.

Ploughman LM and Boehnke M (1989). Estimating the power of a proposed linkage study for a complex genetic trait. Am. J. Hum. Genet. 44 (4), 543-551.

Porter DE, Cohen BB, Wallace MR, Carothers A and Steel CM (1993). Linkage mapping in familial breast cancer: improved localization of a susceptibility locus on chromosome 17q12-21. Int. J. Cancer 53, 188-198.

Povey S, Attwood J, Janssen LAJ, Burley M, Smith M, Flodman P, Morton NE, Edwards JH, Sampson JR, Yates JRW, Haines JL, Amos J, Short MP, Sandkuyl LA, Halley DJJ, Fryer AE, Bech-Hansen T, Mueller R, Al-Ghazali L, Super M, Osborne J (1991). An attempt to map two genes for tuberous sclerosis using novel two-point methods. Ann. N. Y. Acad. Sci. 615, 298-305.

Risch N (1990a). Linkage strategies for genetically complex traits: I. multilocus models. Am. J. Hum. Genet. 46, 222-228.

Risch N (1990b). Linkage strategies for genetically complex traits: II. The power of affected relative pairs. Am. J. Hum. Genet. 46, 229-241.

Spurr N, Cox S, Bryant SP, Attwood J, Robson EB, Shields DC, Steinbrueck T, Jenkins T, Murray JC, Kidd KK, Summar MJ, Tsipouras P, Retief AE, Kruse TA, Bale AE, Vergnaud G, Weber JL, McBride OW, Donis-Keller H, White RL (1992). The CEPH consortium linkage map of human chromosome 2. Genomics 14, 1055-1063.

Suarez BK (1978). The affected sib pair IBD distribution for HLA-linked disease susceptibility genes. Tissue Antigens 12, 87-93.

Thomas A (1987a). "Pedpack: User's Manual. Technical Report No. 99. Department of Statistics, GN-22a", University of Washington, Seattle.

Thomas A (1987b). "Pedpack: Manager's Manual. Technical Report No. 100. Department of Statistics, GN-22b", University of Washington.

Thomas A (1988). Drawing pedigrees. IMA J. Math. Appl. Med. Biol. 5, 210-213.

Thompson EA (1986). "Pedigree Analysis in Human Genetics". The Johns Hopkins University Press, Baltimore.

Thompson EA (1987). Crossover counts and likelihood in multipoint linkage analysis. IMA J. Math. Appl. Med. Biol. 4, 93-108.

Ward PJ (1993). Some developments on the affected-pedigree-member method of linkage analysis. Am. J. Hum. Genet. 52, 1200-1215.

Weaver R, Helms C, Mishra SK and Donis-Keller H (1992). Software for analysis and manipulation of genetic linkage data. Am. J. Hum. Genet. 50, 1267-1274.

Weeks DE and Lange K (1988). The affected-pedigree-member method of linkage analysis. Am. J. Hum. Genet. 42, 315-326.

Weissenbach J, Gyapay G, Dib C, Vignol A, Morissette J, Millasseay P, Vaysseix G and Lathrop M (1992). A second-generation linkage map of the human genome. Nature 359, 794-801.

Weitkamp LR and Lewis RA (1989). PEDSCORE analysis of identical by descent (IBD) marker allele distributions in affected family members. Cytogenet. Cell. Genet. 51, 1105-1106.

Wijsman EM (1987). A deductive method of haplotype analysis in pedigrees. Am. J. Hum. Genet. 41, 356-373.

CHAPTER 4

Physical Mapping Projects and ACEDB

Ian Dunham[1], Richard Durbin[2], Jean Thierry-Mieg[3] and David R. Bentley[1]

[1] Paediatric Research Unit, Division of Medical and Molecular Genetics, UMDS, 8th floor Guy's Tower, London Bridge, London SE1 9RT, UK
Internet: idunham@crc.ac.uk
[2] MRC Laboratory for Molecular Biology, Hills Road, Cambridge CB2 2QH, UK
Internet: rd@mrc-lmb.cam.ac.uk
[3] CNRS-CRBM, Route de Mende, BP 5051, 34033 Montpellier, France
Internet: mieg@kaa.cnrs-mop.fr

1   Introduction

Rapid advances in recombinant DNA technology during the middle and late 1980s have changed our perspectives on physical mapping of complex genomes. Over this period, methodologies were introduced that enabled rapid analysis of stretches of DNA ranging in size from the single nucleotide level to whole human chromosomes (Table 4.1).

TABLE 4.1 A summary of the major technical advances in physical mapping during the past decade

Technique	Resolution	Reference	Comments
Polymerase chain reaction (PCR)	50 bp - >2 kb	Saiki et al., 1988	Increased speed of detection and isolation of DNA species within complex samples
Pulsed field gel electrophoresis (PFGE)	20 kb - 10 Mb	Schwartz and Cantor, 1984	Long-range restriction site mapping
Yeast artificial chromosome (YACs)	50 kb - 1.5 Mb	Burke et al., 1987	>10-fold increase in size of DNA that could be cloned
Fluorescent in situ hybridization (FISH) with prereassociation (metaphase or prometaphase)	1 Mb - whole chromosome	Lichter et al., 1988, 1990 Pinkel et al., 1988	More rapid ordering than PFGE and provided a link to cytogenetics
Radiation hybrid mapping	500 kb - 20 Mb	Cox et al., 1990	Provided an alternative to genetic mapping
Interphase FISH	50 kb - 1 Mb	Lawrence et al., 1988 Trask, 1991	
Micro-satellite polymorphisms for genetic mapping	*	Weber and May, 1989	

* The level of resolution of genetic maps is dependent on the number and separation of the markers and on the distribution of recombinants

The consequences of these technical developments were broadly twofold. Firstly, the time required for pertinent data to be produced and to enter the literature was reduced, thereby increasing the rate of accumulation of these data. Secondly, there was a realization that the time was ripe for a shift of emphasis away from physical mapping around genes or genomic regions of defined interest towards a genome-wide approach which would be general in its application. The epitome of this change was the call for a "Human Genome Project" (Watson, 1990), a global effort to be undertaken first to clone and then sequence the DNA of all the human chromosomes, thereby providing a universal resource that some have termed the "dictionary of life". The result has been a dramatic increase in the scale of physical mapping projects and the amount of associated data. These changes present challenges both to those constructing their own physical maps and to those who wish to use the data generated by the Human Genome Mapping Project. In order to deal with the challenges of data-handling and accessibility, workers in the field have begun to make use of computer programs to act as both databases and display tools for their maps.

In this chapter we shall deal with the way in which physical map data can be organized and presented in a database program. We shall present lessons learnt from our experiences of data-handling during an ongoing project to construct a physical map of human chromosome 22. We shall also draw examples from the physical map of the nematode (*Caenorhabditis elegans*) genome. In particular we will focus on the graphical database program ACEDB (Durbin and Thierry-Mieg, 1991) as a paradigm and describe first how to look at data held in the program and then how to enter and maintain data from one's own mapping project. Before doing so it is useful to describe what is meant by physical mapping.

The term "physical mapping" has come to mean the determination of the order and distance between landmarks in stretches of DNA by physicochemical and biochemical methods. Physical maps can be produced by use of a wide range of techniques in which resolution varies from the cytogenetically visible fractions of chromosomes to the single nucleotide level. Thus, cytogenetic maps produced from in situ hybridization and restriction maps derived from DNA sequence are both physical maps. One important type of physical map is a map based on overlapping cloned DNA segments, e.g. YACs or cosmids. Clone maps are built by establishing overlaps between clones, often by testing landmarks against them (see below). Physical clone maps have a significant advantage for the experimentalist in that the DNA between landmarks is easily recoverable. However, maps which depend purely on clones may not be entirely representative of the chromosomal DNA because of the possible introduction of rearrangements or other artefacts during the cloning procedure. Thus, it is important to compare clone maps with physical maps of uncloned DNA.

Physical maps of the same DNA segment which are drawn from different techniques and different data sets may be different in their resolution, relative positionings and their units of measurement. Thus the use of different physical mapping techniques necessitates integration of different types of data to form a combined consensus map. This is achieved when reagents define landmarks common to two or more sets of data. For instance the use of the same locus-specific probe for in situ hybridization and to identify a PFGE restriction fragment relates the restriction map and the cytogenetic map at that point. Likewise a clone that forms part of a contig containing a sequence tagge site (STS) which assays a genetic marker may be used for in situ analysis to integrate the STS map, the clone map, the genetic and cytogenetic maps at that point. These links between maps may be termed anchors.

Physical maps are distinct from genetic maps, in which the frequency of meiotic recombination between landmarks is used to infer their order and distance. Physical and genetic mapping both aim to determine the positions of the loci on a DNA molecule, however the orders and distances may be different. Genetic mapping allows positioning of phenotypes of potential biological or medical importance on the physical map by linkage to specific markers. In addition, while making physical maps, genetic information is called upon to place local maps within the broader scale or to resolve contradictions in the physical maps. Therefore a complete physical map will also incorporate all the useful genetic landmarks. A database must therefore be able to display both types of maps and the relationships between them.

2   The Construction of Physical Maps

Although a number of technically complex methods are used to generate the data from which physical maps are made, the broad principles of map construction are the same. We wish to determine the relative order of a number of DNA sequences and, if possible, to estimate the distance between them. In addition, we want to place our local map onto the long-range genomic map. We might accomplish this by the following idealized steps.

1. We define a number of assayable landmarks (markers) within the DNA region of interest.

2. We test these markers for their presence or absence in a set of reagents which breaks the region into intervals. The order of landmarks is deduced from the placement of the markers into these intervals.

3. If we have measurements of the lengths of our test reagents this should enable us to deduce maximum and minimum separations for the markers.

4. We can place the local map onto the chromosome map or genetic map either by inclusion in the mapping experiment of a marker whose position is known or by placing one of our newly defined markers by in situ hybridization or in a genetic cross. This marker becomes an anchor marker tying the local map to the rest of the genome.

The way these idealized steps relate to actual experiments is described below.

2.1   Landmarks

The landmarks that are used in physical maps are of several types and have specific properties.

1. Restriction sites are defined by the sites of cleavage of restriction endonucleases and are associated with a specific nucleotide sequence determined by the properties of the endonuclease. The products of restriction endonuclease digestion of a DNA sample are assayed by some form of gel electrophoresis. Thus a restriction site landmark is defined by its presence at one of the ends of a DNA restriction fragment of a specific length. The minimum information we have about any restriction site is its sequence and its distance from another site. A restriction site may also be identified by its association with a neighbouring sequence, e.g. the NotI site adjacent to hybridization probe A.

2. Hybridization probes are DNA fragments that are labelled and used to detect their complementary sequence by DNA-DNA annealing. The DNA sequence of a hybridization probe need not be known. Generally the length of the probe, its history and information relevant to its use will be known. We may know the region of origin of the probe or we may use a mapping experiment to determine this. Hybridization probes may detect polymorphic loci of utility in genetic mapping usually in the form of a restriction fragment length polymorphism (RFLP) (Botstein et al., 1980).

3. Sequence tagged sites (STSs) are short (60 - 1000 bp) DNA segments of defined length which are detected by in vitro amplification using the polymerase chain reaction (PCR) via a specific pair of oligonucleotide primers (Olson et al., 1989). Usually at least part of the DNA sequence of the region which is amplified will be known and a set of experimental parameters will be associated with the STS. Again, the location of a STS in the genome may be known. STSs may detect polymorphic loci if they amplify a region including a suitable restriction site or a region of variable length such as a microsatellite repeat (Weber and May, 1989).

4. Cytogenetic landmarks are the physical properties of chromosomes that may be viewed under the microscope. For mammalian chromosomes, these include the centromere, the telomeres, banding patterns caused by differential staining of the chromosome using reagents such as Giemsa, and deletions and breakpoints in rearranged chromosomes such as the Philadelphia chromosome. The positions of these landmarks may be expressed in terms of the fractional length along the chromosome or relative to other cytogenetic landmarks. For instance, the Philadelphia chromosome break-

point may be localized to within the q11 Giemsa stained band of human chromosome 22. The limits of the 22q11 band are then expressed according to position on the chromosome.

Hybridization probes and STSs are very similar in the information that they provide. Indeed STS DNAs may be used as hybridization probes and hybridization probes may be converted to STSs. Usually both types of landmarks are unique to a single genomic locus. However this is not always the case and, in fact, repetitive loci can give valuable information (Zucchi and Schlessinger, 1992).

2.2   Making the Map

In order to construct a map given certain landmarks we proceed as follows. If we have three landmarks A, B and C, we test each against an appropriate reagent. For instance, we might assay for the presence of restriction sites, probes or STSs A, B and C in a set of YAC clones, in a set of radiation or somatic cell hybrids, or in a set of PFGE restriction fragments. The information we obtain will be that the landmarks are either present in or absent from a particular clone, hybrid or restriction fragment. If the two landmarks, A and B, are present on the same reagent 1, we deduce that they probably lie close to each other, within the distance that is spanned by the DNA within reagent 1. If C is not present on this reagent, we deduce that the extent of the DNA fragment contained in reagent 1 does not include C. We continue the analysis to make the map (Figure 4.1, Table 4.2).

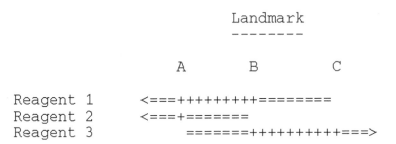

```
                      Landmark
                      --------


                A        B          C

Reagent 1    <===+++++++++++=========
Reagent 2    <===+=======
Reagent 3        =======+++++++++++===>
```

FIGURE   4.1 Putative physical map derived from data presented in Table 4.2. + represents the continuity of a reagent based on the presence of landmarks, = indicates regions of uncertainty. < and > indicate that the bounds of the reagent are unknown. Since there is no information on distance between landmarks, they are placed at an arbitrary distance of 1 unit from each other.

TABLE 4.2 Hypothetical experimental data for a physical mapping experiment. The presence of the landmark within the reagent is indicated by +, the absence of the landmark from the reagent by -

Landmark	Reagent 1	Reagent 2	Reagent 3
A	+	+	-
B	+	-	+
C	-	-	+

Not only do we establish possible orders of the landmarks but the extent of the reagents relative to each other are indicated.

If we now were to have information about the size of the reagents used in the example above we would be able to place estimates on the distance separating the landmarks. If A and B are probes that both hybridize to a 500 kb NotI PFGE restriction fragment or YAC clone, we know that A and B must be no more than 500 kb apart. If B and C are contained in reagent 3 which is 100 kb, we can redraw the map as in Figure 4.2.

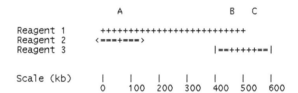

FIGURE 4.2 Refined physical map from Figure 4.1. I indicates the extent of the region in which the reagent must lie. < and > indicate that the bounds of the reagent are unknown. The positions of the landmarks within the intervals are unknown. Reagent 3 may overlap with reagent 1 by 100 kb less the size of landmark C, and therefore the distance of the left hand end of reagent 3 from the right end of reagent 1 is limited to that 100 kb.

The more observations we have that concur with our interpretation, the more certain we can be about the map. However, given knowledge of the pitfalls of the technique used to generate the data and of the possibilities of absent, incomplete or conflicting data, we may wish to use appropriate statistical tests to determine the map. For instance, in radiation hybrid mapping, statistical analysis of the retention of markers in a panel of hybrids (see below) is necessary to construct the map (Frazer et al., 1992). The map of human chromosome 21 was constructed using STS analysis of YACs using a simulated annealing energy minimization algorithm to order landmarks and contigs (Chumakov et al., 1992).

2.3 Mapping Methods and Types of Maps

The choice of mapping method depends on the reagents, techniques and expertise that are available. However even if a mapping approach cannot be performed in-house it is very likely that information will be available from outside sources and it is as well to bear in mind how methods relate. Where possible, it is necessary to tie together the maps by anchor landmarks that the maps share in common. Examination of the different types of map illustrates how they differ in terms of units and resolution (see also Table 4.1).

2.3.1 In situ/Cytogenetic Map

A cytogenetic map is constructed by hybridization of fluorescently labelled DNA probes (often cosmids or YACs) to metaphase chromosome spreads. The position of the hybridization signal is recorded relative to the banding pattern of the chromosome or as a fractional length of the chromosome from one telomere. Determination of the order of different hybridization probes which are not obviously distinct requires a dual hybridization experiment where the two probes are labelled and detected by two different systems. Advances in the methods of labelling and detection have allowed multiple probes to be used at one time. The lower limit of resolution of metaphase or prometaphase FISH is probably no less than 1 Mb. If two markers are close it may not be possible to order them. Metaphase FISH is ideal to place local maps on to the chromosome skeleton.

A related technique is FISH on interphase nuclei. Here the chromosomes are not condensed and their morphology cannot be seen but the window of resolution is in the size range 50 kb - 1 Mb. In fact in a dual hybridization experiment, the difference between two signals is measured in microns and a series of calibration experiments with markers known distances apart is required to relate the separation to kb. Because of the way that the chromosome is packed in the interphase nucleus, high resolution microscopy and statistical analysis of many nuclei are required to deduce the order of markers (Trask, 1991).

2.3.2 STS- or Probe-Content Maps

STS- or probe-content mapping involves determination of the STSs/probes which are present in a particular reagent, i.e. its STS/probe content (Green and Olson, 1990). This method has been effectively applied to physical mapping of chromosomal regions using YACs. Green and Olson (1990) used 16 STSs from the human CFTR region to isolate a contig of YACs covering 1.5 Mb. More recently Chumakov et al. (1992) used 198 STSs to construct an overlapping YAC contig of human chromosome 21q which may cover 50 Mb. Foote et al. (1992) used 160 Y chromosome STSs to produce a YAC contig covering 98% of the euchromatic region of the Y chromosome. The units of an

STS map are the STSs themselves. The STSs will not be evenly distributed and this means that the map units will not have a simple relationship to distance in kb.

2.3.3 Somatic Cell Hybrid and Deletion/Duplication Iinterval Maps

These methods involve testing for the presence of landmarks in various hybrid cell lines by STS/probe-content mapping. The maps are then constructed as described above. The map that is derived from specific hybrids or deletions describes the relationships of the landmarks and specific hybrids relative to each other. For instance, Vollrath et al. (1992) placed 132 Y chromosome STSs into 43 ordered intervals by analysis of DNA from 96 individuals with partial Y chromosomes. Delattre et al. (1991) placed 38 chromosome 22 DNA probes into 14 different subregions based on their presence in a panel of 17 somatic cell hybrids. However, distance can only be inferred from this type of mapping experiment if there is some outside information. For somatic cell hybrids and deletions it is frequently the case that the extent of the DNA contained in the hybrid or missing from the deletion is estimated from cytogenetics. It is important to be aware that the DNA in somatic cell hybrids may be rearranged and that multiple non-contiguous segments of DNA may be present. If a map of the landmarks is already known, the same experiments have the effect of placing the hybrids or deletions onto the map. This may be important if, for instance, a gene of interest is known to lie in a deletion.

2.3.4 Radiation Hybrid Maps

In radiation hybrid mapping, the landmarks are tested against a panel of hybrids that have been generated by X-irradiation of a parent hybrid cell line containing a chromosome or chromosomal region of interest followed by fusion of the irradiation products with a rodent cell line (Cox et al., 1990). The resulting radiation-reduced hybrids contain pieces of the DNA originating from the parent cell line, and the frequency of X-ray breakage between linked landmarks is analysed statistically to determine the order and distance along the chromosome (see Frazer et al., 1992, for summary of methods of analysis). The frequency of X-ray breakage depends on the dose, and this may be tuned to alter the resolution of the map. The maps produced are measured in centirays (cR) for a particular dose of X-rays. For instance, a distance of 1 cR8000 corresponds to a frequency of 1% breakage between two markers after exposure to 8000 rad of X-rays, and corresponds to approximately 50 kb (Cox et al., 1990; Burmeister et al., 1991).

2.3.5 Restriction Maps

Restriction mapping involves placement of the restriction sites within a DNA molecule by a series of digests of the DNA in single, double and even triple combinations. When the DNA sample being analysed is complex such as in a genomic digest used for PFGE mapping, the DNA fragments of interest are detected by Southern blot hybridization. Since the size of the restriction fragments is known, a map can be deduced which shows both the order of restriction sites and the distances between sites in kb.

2.3.6 Fingerprint Maps

Another approach to assembling physical maps is to assess the content of the reagent being mapped by means of a fingerprint. While the STS content might be considered to be a fingerprint, the name is conventionally applied only to approaches where the fingerprint consists of information that is less specific. For instance a HinfI digest of a cosmid clone will give a set of fragments with specific sizes (Knott et al., 1988). While many non-overlapping cosmid clones might contain say a 200 bp Hinf I fragment, two clones that have several fragments in common are more likely to overlap. Thus, fingerprinting approaches utilize a statistical assessment of the likelihood of overlap between two clones. Fingerprinting has been used successfully to build physical maps of genomes of a number of organisms including *Escherichia coli* (Kohara et al., 1987), *Saccharomyces cerevisiae* (Olson et al., 1986) and the nematode *C. elegans* (Coulson et al., 1986). While some fingerprints will produce maps that are in kb, others such as the HindIII/Sau3A fingerprint used in the nematode mapping project give maps that are in fingerprint units which may not be linearly related to the kb scale.

2.3.7 DNA Sequence Maps

If the nucleotide sequence of a region of DNA is known, features of the DNA which are defined by sequence such as potential DNA-binding protein sites, restriction sites, open reading frames, etc., may be detected, usually using appropriate programs. In addition, features such as transcription start sites or splice sites that have been mapped to the sequence by experiment can be represented by their sequence coordinates. This creates a feature map of the DNA sequence which is essential to the understanding of its function (Chapter 8).

Each of these types of map must be accommodated in a physical mapping database, since each may contribute to a consensus map. It is also essential to represent the primary data used for each type of map in the database since previous interpretations must be continually reassessed in the light of new experiments. As new data come to light the consensus map is refined and the map becomes more robust. In addition, the weight given to each type of data may differ from investigator to investigator, leading to differing interpretations and further tests of the robustness of the map.

3 Requirements for Physical Mapping Database Programs

It is clear from the many types of information and maps involved in physical mapping that the requirements for a physical mapping database are complex. We want to have a database that will hold physical mapping and related information and analysis and display tools to allow us to view and manipulate the maps that are held. We can summarize some of these requirements as follows.

1. The database must be able to store a variety of types of data in a coordinated way reflecting the diverse sources of information utilized by physical mappers, i.e. it should be flexible.

2. The database must have "evolvability" so that changes in methods or types of data can be accommodated.

3. It must be possible to import data from and export data to other databases such as the global standard repositories.

4. The display tools should be customizable to allow the user to see what he or she wants.

5. While text-based tables are an essential component to viewing physical data, the display tools should also be able to present maps in a graphical form. It should be possible to scroll and zoom the maps so that the position and resolution of the view can be readily altered.

6. It must be possible to display the interrelationships of the maps. This means that we should be able to move rapidly and flexibly between the map displays, and also be able to compare the maps to each other.

7. It is important that the ability to interpret raw data is not lost. The database should be able either to hold or to provide access to the primary data that are used to make the maps. If possible the program should be able to reconstruct the maps from these data.

8. The program should be user-friendly, mouse-driven and have fast response times.

A number of programs exist in the physical mapping arena which meet these requirements to varying degrees. These displays may be classified into two types, text-based or graphical. One example of a text-based display is the Genome Data Base (GDB), which also is the global database repository for human genome mapping information (Pearson et al., 1992). GDB uses a commercially available relational database program (Sybase) to hold and make available data from around the world, thus coordinating the worldwide human genome mapping effort. The data are presented to the user as a series of tables and listings about the objects in the database and a user may move between objects via the tables. However, text-based displays are limited in their presentation of maps and, increasingly, graphical displays are being introduced. A good example of a graphical display system is ACEDB, which has been used for a number of different genome projects and is freely and widely available. ACEDB is being used as the graphical front end of the Integrated Genomic Database (IGD) being developed by Otto Ritter and coworkers. We will restrict the rest of this chapter to a description of ACEDB, since this is the program with which we have most experience and since it illustrates how the needs of the physical mapper may be satisfied.

4 ACEDB

ACEDB (A *C. elegans* Database) is the database system written by R. Durbin and J. Thierry-Mieg (1991) to meet the needs of the nematode genome project. Versions of the system have also been used for *Arabidopsis* data (AATDB), human genome data, *Drosophila* (FLYBASE) and a number of other animal and plant genome projects. The program is written in C and is graphic, flexible and portable. Since February 1992 it has been tested on various Unix workstations (SUN, DEC, NEXT, SGI and PC-486), on all sorts of X terminals and as a stand alone Apple Macintosh program. The system contains its own portable graphic library, an original object oriented database manager, a series of applications and a set of files corresponding to the nematode data but which are configurable to the user's needs. The system is freely available and instructions for obtaining the system, documentation and subscribing to the ACEDB e-mail list are given in Appendix 2.

There are two main modes of use for ACEDB: read-only and update. Firstly, there are people who want to look at data held in a publicly maintained database such as that for *C. elegans*. To do this they need to be familiar with the methods of browsing ACEDB. The second type of use is by those who want to hold their own data in a local copy of ACEDB. This might be a local copy of an implementation developed by someone else to which their own data can be added or they might develop their own implementation. In this second case it is necessary to know how to manage the program, how data are entered and saved in ACEDB, and how to best use the data structures available. We will deal with viewing a copy of the database before we move on to maintaining and adding data to your own copy of ACEDB, but first we will briefly discuss how the data are organized in ACEDB.

4.1 Basic Concepts of ACEDB

All the information in ACEDB is stored in objects, which fall into a number of classes. Each object belongs to just one class, and has a unique name in that class. The classes are standard units such as genes, alleles, strains, clones, papers, authors, journals, etc. (see Figure 4.5), and the names are in most cases the standard names. What can be stored in an object and how it is displayed and used is governed by the class. The idea is to make all the information about an object reachable from that object. Much of it is in other objects, so objects often contain pointers to other objects. They can also contain basic data, such as numbers (e.g. map distances) and text (e.g. titles of papers).

The information in each object is stored hierarchically, in a tree structure. The branches of the tree contain labels, or tags, describing the information, which is at the leaves of the tree. The advantage of a tree is that it is very flexible: it can be extended arbitrarily far in any direction as more information is gathered about some particular aspect of the object. In general when you look at an object, such as a gene, a window pops up showing you the tree of data, with the tags. An example of an object tree for a clone from human chromosome 22 is shown in Figure 4.3.

```
prKl424.1

Gene        D22S161
Position    Chromosome      Chromosome 22
            Filter_number   M22.213         1.10.92
            Hybridizes_to   22poly1         A141B3
                                            B48F2
                                            B58C2
Origin      Vector          lambda charon 21A flow sort library
            Cutter_used     HindIII         1.9 kb repet
Location    Karolinska
In_pool     pool1
FingerPrint     Probe_id    395
Reference   Isolation of anonymous, polymorphic DNA
                fragments from human chromosome
                22q12-qter
```

FIGURE 4.3 Object tree for a probe prKl424.1. The object, prKl424.1, is a member of the class Clone. Its name is given in the top left hand corner of the tree and below this are a set of tags (e.g. Gene, Position, Chromosome, etc.) which indicate the information held at the leaves of the tree. At the right of the figure are pointers to other objects in the database which are linked to this clone such as Chromosome 22. Also present in this tree are numbers associated with the object, such as its Probe_id, which is the integer 395, and text information, such as Filter_number M22.213.

Attached to each class is a list of possible information that can be added, together with the relevant tags and where to put the information in the hierarchy. This information is called the model. The model itself is structured as a tree and stored as an object with the name "?Classname" (e.g. ?Gene is the model for the Gene class), so it can be displayed like any other object. An important feature of ACEDB is that the model for an object can be expanded throughout the lifetime of the system, to allow for information about new features to be added to the database without losing any of your earlier work. It is also possible to add a comment anywhere in a tree.

In general all objects may be displayed as these text trees. However, in a number of cases it is possible to display an object through a graphical display which is appropriate for that object. For instance, objects that lie on the chromosome map, such as genes and chromosome bands, are displayed by default in a genetic map display called the gMap window. Figure 4.4 shows an example of the gMap for human chromosome 22. We shall discuss the content of this map in Section 4.3.

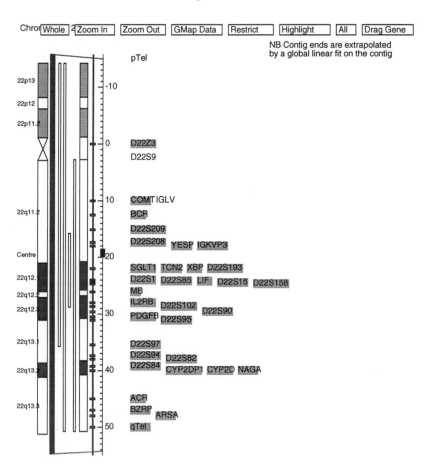

FIGURE 4.4 The gMap display of human chromosome 22. See text for description. The open boxes running vertically next to the chromosome ideogram represent somatic cell hybrids.

4.2 Browsing ACEDB

On starting ACEDB you will see a pair of windows entitled "Main Window" and "Selection List" appearing in the top left corner of the screen (Figure 4.5). This is the starting point for any journey around an ACEDB dataset.

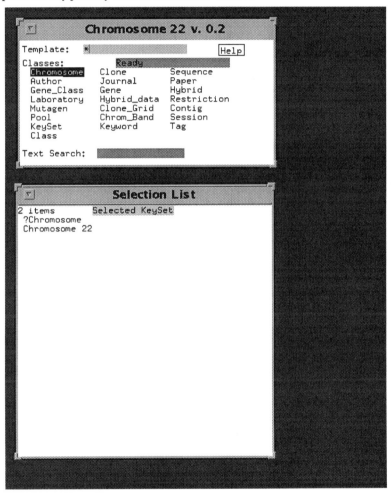

FIGURE 4.5 The main window and selection list for the chromosome 22 version of ACEDB. The main window is entitled "Chromosome 22 v. 0.2" and contains a list of the visible classes with the class Chromosome highlighted. The selection list contains two items, the model for a chromosome, ?Chromosome, and the object, Chromosome 22.

The mouse is used to control the ACEDB Graphical User Interface; the functions of the mouse buttons are summarized in Table 4.3.

TABLE 4.3 Mouse functions in ACEDB under X11. There is no time out between the first click to highlight a box and the second click to initiate an action. - indicates that the action has no function. The left button is used to pick windows or objects. Usually, if the pointer is placed over a box, a single click with the left mouse button highlights the box and a second click initiates an action, such as opening a window that displays the object in the box. The middle button is used in some graphic windows to recentre a map (single click) or to zoom and recentre (by holding down the middle button and dragging in horizontal and vertical directions). Pressing down the right button is used to access menus contained within a window. To select a menu option the right button is held down and the mouse dragged down to highlight the desired option.

Action	Left button	Middle button	Right button
	PICK	**ADJUST**	**MENU**
Single click	Select box	Recentre map at cursor position	-
Single click and drag	-	On cursor: recentre map and zoom in or out	Access pull-down menu in window and drag to select menu option
Second click	Initiates action for selected box		-

By using the left mouse button to pick objects and open their corresponding windows one can browse through ACEDB in a natural way. Figure 4.6 illustrates how a series of windows have been opened by a succession of selection and opening operations.

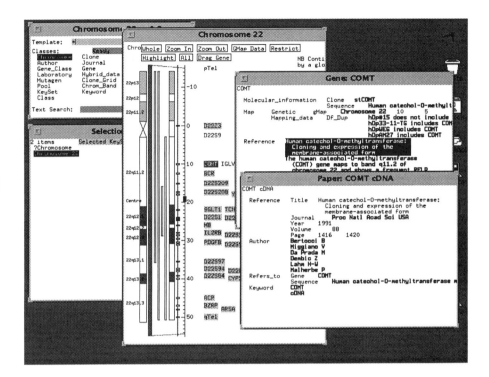

FIGURE 4.6 Browsing ACEDB by picking with the left mouse button. First, Chromosome 22 was selected (highlighted) and opened by double clicking, producing the window showing the gMap of the chromosome. Next the gene COMT (catechol-O-methyltransferase) was selected (it is shaded dark) and its window opened to see data related to it. Finally the reference highlighted has been selected by double clicking to open a window containing the details of that reference. Note that many windows are generated by a succession of selections and the new windows are sequentially layered on top of the previous windows. Hence, the path of this series of events can be followed with the objects picked remaining highlighted in their windows. If the screen becomes too cluttered, all the windows except the main window can be removed by selecting "clean up" from the main window menu.

Although selecting and opening objects provides the main means to move around ACEDB, many more facilities are available from the menus accessed in each window (see Figure 4.7).

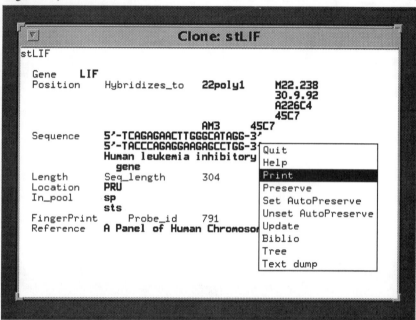

FIGURE 4.7 Accessing the menu in an ACEDB window. The menu options are selected by pressing the right mouse button to bring up a menu, keeping the button pressed and moving the mouse until the desired option is highlighted, then releasing the button. The tree for a clone called stLIF is shown and the menu from the tree window has been pulled down and dragged to the print option.

The menu in each window is specific to the type of window and provides functions that are deemed appropriate for that window. In some windows the menu options are also placed in a series of buttons across the top of the window so that they may be accessed by clicking with the left mouse button as well. All the ACEDB menus have a "Quit" option at the top of them. This kills the window, except in the case of the main window, where it kills the program. A description of the menu functions is available in the on-line help for the program which is available in every window by selecting the help option through the menu. We shall deal later with more of the database functions in ACEDB, but first we shall illustrate how maps and other biological data are displayed through the application functions.

4.3 Biological Application Displays in ACEDB

A number of application functions are included in ACEDB to display and manipulate biological data and maps in graphical forms. We shall describe the principles of these applications and how they have been used for various physical mapping data.

4.3.1 The Physical Map Display (pMap)

The pMap display is the application used to display all the clones in the database which have a physical map position, i.e are mapped into contigs. The clones are displayed in their physical relationships with the other clones to which they are neighbours. In addition, pMap provides links to the other map display applications, gMap and fMap. You may get to the pMap by picking a clone, for instance from a clone grid, or by picking the yellow bar in the genetic map (see later).

pMap is a horizontal display which is split into two regions. The top region shows the clones that are present in contigs, together with comments and attached genes, while the bottom region contains an expanded view of the loci in the neighbourhood of the currently displayed segment of the map. Figure 4.8 shows the pMap display for the region around the gene lin-9 on *C. elegans* chromosome III. In the nematode, cosmids overlapped by fingerprinting are the basis for the physical map (Coulson et al., 1986). The cosmids are shown in the overlapping register which was assembled by the FORTRAN program CONTIG 9 from the primary fingerprinting data. The units of the map are HindIII sites since these are the basic element of the fingerprint. The YACs at the upper part of the display were placed onto the maps by hybridization to grids of the cosmids (Coulson et al., 1988).

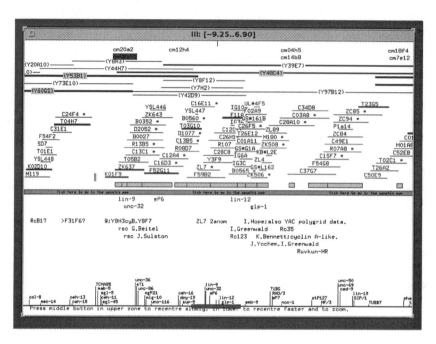

FIGURE 4.8 The pMap display of ACEDB with *C. elegans* data. The region around the gene lin-9 on chromosome III is shown. At the top of the display are a series of names which indicate cloned DNA probes. One of these, cm08g11, has been picked and is highlighted in red (dark grey). Below this are shown lines indicating the extent of first YACs and then below this cosmids. The three YACs to which the probe hybridizes are highlighted in pink (light grey). There are a number of extra features of the cosmid map. For instance, clones that are canonical for others that have been "buried" have an asterisk after their names. Clones that are present on filter hybridization grids are written with a thicker line. The gap between two cosmid contigs (clones C24F4 and K01F9 define the end of each contig) is denoted by a double vertical line. The yellow bar (light shading) indicates that DNA sequence is available for this region.

Thus the extent of the YACs is determined by the cosmids which they cover and is not directly related to the fingerprint scale. By convention, YAC endpoints have been placed in the centre of the last clone to which they hybridize. An interesting point arises where the YACs have bridged a gap in the fingerprinted clones to join two contigs. In these cases the size of the gap is unknown, although it must be less than the size of the YAC and a double line "break" symbol is used to display this.

The clone names at the top of the nematode pMap display are cDNA clones that have been positioned by hybridization to the gridded array filters of the YACs. This information is made available by picking the clone which is then highlighted in red, while the gridded YACs to which it hybridizes are highlighted in pink. For instance in Figure 4.8, the clone cm08g11 hybridizes to gridded YAC clones Y60G2, Y53B1 and Y48C4. The hybridization information can also be displayed through the Clone_Grid function (see below). In fact, this is a general feature of the pMap display so that objects which are related to an object that has been picked (red) are highlighted in pink. Below the clones is a line of yellow boxes which indicate the availability of sequence for particular clones. These boxes can be picked to get to the sequence display (see below). The green bar in the middle of pMap allows one to pick to get to the genetic map display. Below this, there are two lines which list the genes contained in the contigs, and below this a number of comments that are associated with objects in the display. Finally, at the very bottom of the pMap is a line which indicates position relative to the genetic markers of the chromosome.

Although the pMap display was based on the fingerprinting approach to contig assembly, it is possible to display physical maps generated by other means. Figure 4.9 shows part of a contig of YACs from human chromosome 22.

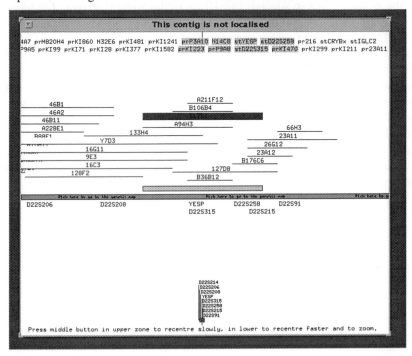

FIGURE 4.9 The pMap display of ACEDB with human chromosome 22 data. The probes and STSs used to assemble the contig are displayed in the top two lines. In this case the YACs are placed in the same position as the cosmids were in the nematode display. The YAC highlighted in red (dark grey), 117C1, has been picked and the probes and STSs that are in pink (light grey) are those contained in this YAC.

This contig was generated by probe- and STS-content analysis of the YACs with a large number of probes and STSs. The contig was then assembled using the contasp program of CONTIG 9 (Sulston et al., 1988, 1989), having previously assigned each probe an arbitrary number called the probe_id. This places the YACs according to the probes (probe_id integers) that they have in common in an identical way to the assembly by cosmid fingerprints. The contig was then entered into ACEDB for display. In this instance the units of the map are the probes/STSs themselves such that each YAC has a length corresponding to the number of probes/STSs that it contains.

4.3.2 The Genetic Map Display (gMap)

The gMap display is used to display the positions of genes and markers along a chromosome. The display acts as an entry point by which to access specific regions of a chromosome or to display the position of cloned DNA in its chromosomal context. It provides a link to the pMap display via a yellow bar representing each contig, or to genetic markers by picking them. In addition it can be used to display data at a whole chromosome level such as somatic cell hybrid analysis.

The nematode chromosome III gMap is shown in Figure 4.10.

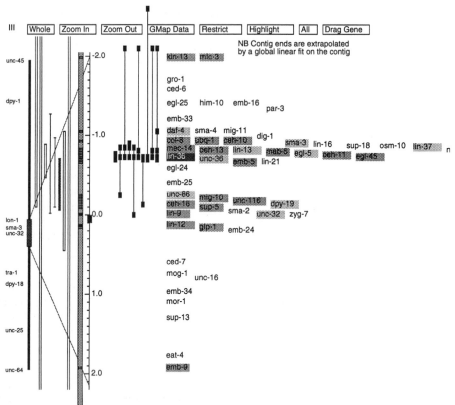

FIGURE 4.10 gMap display for the nematode, *C. elegans* chromosome III. The chromosome is shown running vertically on the left hand side of the window. The extent of the chromosome which is visible to the right is indicated by the slider bar which may be recentred and zoomed using the mouse. To the left of the scale bar, the yellow (light grey) bars represent contigs, and provide a link between the genetic and physical maps. If you click on one of them you get to a physical map centred at the appropriate point. The function of the "GMap Data" button has been illustrated for the gene lin-36. Just to the left of the gene names are lines corresponding to individual pieces of three-point recombination data concerning lin-36.

The chromosome is shown on the left hand side of the display with a second representation to its right showing the extent of the chromosome currently being viewed. At the right are shown the genes on the genetic map. There is extensive genetic mapping information in *C. elegans*. Hence the gMap display uses genetic map units to place the genes. Genetic map distance is scaled vertically, with each gene placed at its map position. The horizontal axis of the display is used to indicate the degree of uncertainty in the map positions, so that genes with more certain map positions are placed to the left while less certain placements are progressively further right. Genes that are also located on the physical map are highlighted by a yellow background. In addition a large number of genetically mapped deletions, duplications and rearrangements are known and the positions of these are represented by the open boxes and lines. The lines represent deletions while the boxes are duplications. The gMap display allows the results of mapping experiments relative to the rearrangements to be displayed through the "GMap Data" button. We shall illustrate this function used for somatic cell hybrid data on human chromosome 22 below.

The gMap for human chromosome 22 (Figure 4.4) shows the chromosome band ideogram on the left with the medium resolution Giemsa light and dark bands and a constriction at the centromere. Although there are a number of genetic maps for human chromosome 22, the Giemsa banded ideogram is a widely recognized view of the chromosome. The scales of the genetic maps and the Giemsa banding are different and, in addition, the genetic maps do not cover the whole of the chromosome. To accommodate these differences in a single representation, and to allow other map type such as radiation hybrid map data to be displayed, we have drawn the chromosome 22 gMap according to a scale which approximates to the physical length of the chromosome. The genetic map of Dumanski et al. (1991) has been placed onto the map by scaling the genetic map units to reflect the physical length of the chromosome. The genetic markers are placed close to the left. Other markers which have been mapped by somatic cell hybrids or in situ data have then been placed onto the map with the degree of uncertainty reflected in general by their rightwards position. However, in the case of NAGA, CYP2D and CYP2DP1 the loci have the same map position.

Mapping information for the currently selected object can be obtained using the "GMap Dand ata" button. Selecting a rearrangement and pressing this button will show all the genes mapping inside the rearrangement boundaries in green, all those outside in blue. Similarly, when applied to a gene it shows all the rearrangements that the gene maps to in green, and all those that it is outside in blue. In addition, the existence of two- and three-point genetic mapping data is displayed by lines. This is illustrated in

Figure 4.11 where we have used this function to represent somatic cell hybrid data, from chromosome 22.

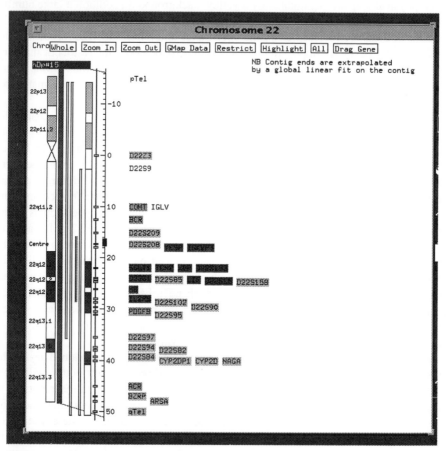

FIGURE 4.11 An example of somatic cell hybrid data for human chromosome 22. The irradiation hybrid hDp#14 has been selected and is highlighted in red (filled vertical box). Pressing the "GMap Data" button reveals 11 markers that have been shown to be present in this hybrid highlighted in green (dark grey) while 4 markers were not present and are coloured in blue (lighter grey). The remaining markers were not tested and their highlighting has not changed (Collins et al., 1992).

4.3.3 The Clone_Grid Display

In recent years many physical mapping projects have made use of clone libraries ordered in microtitre arrays. These clones are often gridded out on to filter membranes, grown and then lysed to give hybridization filters (Bentley et al., 1992; Evans and

Lewis, 1989; Coulson et al., 1988; Nizetic et al., 1991). ACEDB provides a tool to represent hybridization data from these gridded filters, and we have made extensive use of this for management of clone libraries. The Clone_Grid display consists of a set of squares laid out in the same pattern as the clones on the filter (Figure 4.12).

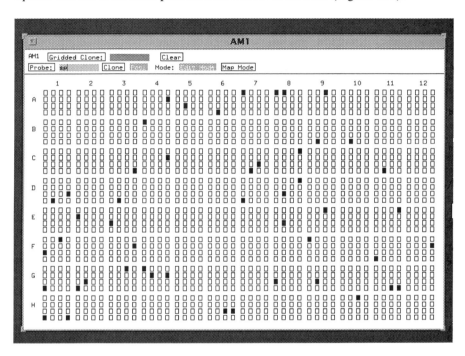

FIGURE 4.12 The Clone_Grid display. We have displayed the hybridization pattern for a pool, sp, that is the pool of all clones and pools that have ever been hybridized to these YACs, so that all YACs that have ever been scored positive with any probe (and also STS) specific for chromosome 22 are coloured blue.

In this case it is a representation of a high density 4×4 array of YACs. It is possible to display hybridization patterns on this grid as is shown. By entering the name of a clone in the probe text entry box and pressing return, the hybridization pattern for that clone on a particular grid is displayed, positively hybridizing clones being represented by the blue boxes. It is also possible to view the hybridization of a pool of clones. Pools can contain collections of clone probes and subpools, and may be real or virtual clone pools. The hybridization pattern for a pool is the union of the patterns for all its clones and subpools, together with any data attached specifically to itself. An example of the display for a pooled hybridization is shown in Figure 4.12. A further option available through the menu enables one to view two hybridization patterns on the same grid at the same time. The "Center<->Surround" option places the current pattern in a surround to each highlighted box. You can then load a new pattern and compare it to the one stored in the surround. These tools have proved extremely useful for YAC library management.

4.3.4 The Sequence Feature Map (fMap)

The sequence feature map display represents DNA sequence in a graphical form. It uses a series of coloured boxes to present the biologically important features of the sequence on a scaled map. The sequence display window is brought up by picking a DNA sequence from the selection list or from a physical map (Figure 4.13).

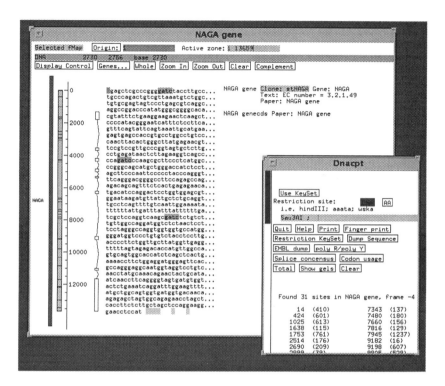

FIGURE 4.13 A sequence fMap for the human N-acetylgalactosaminidase (NAGA) gene. At this level of resolution the whole sequence is not displayed. Instead each line shows an incomplete segment of sequence ending with ... , indicating that more sequence is available if you zoom in further. The first base of each line is indicated by the scale. The "box and spring" graphic depicts the intron/exon structure of the gene, the rectangular boxes being the exons connected by springs, the introns. We have used the DNA analysis tool to search for Sau3AI restriction sites within the sequence and the positions of these have been marked as blue (black) lines on the yellow bar. Sau3AI sites in the displayed sequence are highlighted in blue.

The map shows the DNA sequence, graphics for features in the sequence and picka-ble boxes showing objects attached to the sequence objects such as papers. The content of the map is user-definable by selecting the "Display Control" button. Analyses can be performed on the sequence using the analyse option from the menu. Selecting "Ana-lyse" will bring up the DNA analysis window (Figure 4.13).

4.4   Selecting and Searching for Objects

The ACEDB main window lets you select objects by name or text content. You can also issue global directives such as quitting the whole program, performing a general dump or activating an application. The main window contains a list of available classes. If a class is selected by double clicking, all the objects in that class are displayed in the selection list. Any object in the selection list can then be picked. If the number of objects is large, you will need to scroll down through the list to find the object you desire. In addition, there are two special input fields in the main window: Template and Text Search. If the selection list is too long, you can restrict it to a shorter list by typing into the template input field and finishing with return or clicking the template box. This is illustrated in Figure 4.14.

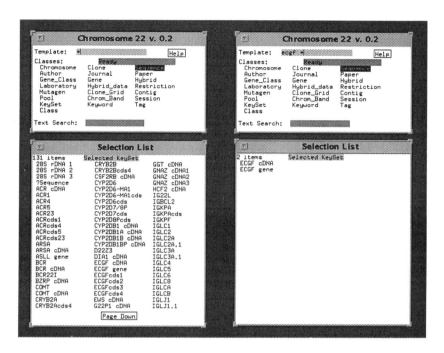

FIGURE 4.14 Restricting the selection list by using the template input field. In the left hand example we have selected the Sequence class by double clicking on Sequence in the main window, and the selection list shows the 131 items in the Sequence class. It is often useful to type the first character or two of a name, then "*", then return to bring the desired name near the head of the list. This is illustrated in the example to the right where we have slected the Sequence class by clicking once with the left mouse button and have then restricted the objects selected by typing "ecgf *" with the cursor in the window. By now hitting return we have obtained only the two entries that contain this text string in their names. There are two allowed wild cards in the template string: "*", for anything of any length, and "?" for a single character.

If you pick the Text Search box and type in at least 3 characters followed by the enter/return key, you will obtain all the objects in the database that contain text matching what you type.

4.5 More Complex Searching and Manipulation Facilities

In addition to the basic database operations provided via the main window and Selection List window, a number of more advanced features are available for searching the database and for dumping data sets out of the database. We shall describe these here because they are useful for constructing customized sets of objects of special interest. More detailed descriptions are available in the on-line help and documentation.

The Selection List window (Figure 4.14) is in fact a special example of a general "keyset display" window, which lets you look at and manipulate a list of objects. A keyset is a set of objects or keys. Keysets can be constructed through the main window using the special input fields, through the Query function (see below), or by various manipulations of other keysets such as copying, union, or intersection. Several actions that are initiated from elsewhere in the program act on a keyset. Since there may be several keyset windows open, the one the action will apply to is the last one the mouse has picked, indicated by "Selected Keyset" highlighted in pink.

The keyset window menu provides a number of functions to act on the keyset, e.g. ones to dump data out of the database. The names of all the items in the keyset may be written to a file by choosing the "Name Dump" option. Alternatively, all the information for each of the objects in the keyset can be dumped to a file by choosing "Ace Dump". Figure 4.15 illustrates some of the features of manipulation of keysets.

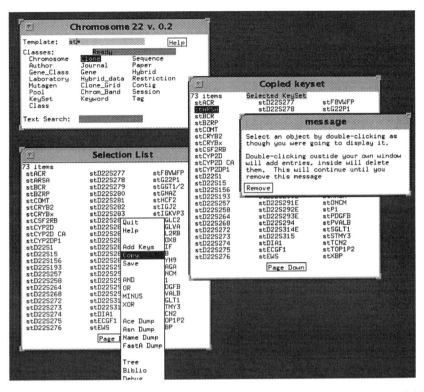

FIGURE 4.15 Example of keyset manipulations. We have used the template input field to generate a selection list of 73 items containing all clones whose names begin with st*. In practice this corresponds to all the STSs in the database. We have then copied the keyset by choosing the copy option from the keyset menu as shown. Finally we have selected the "Add Keys" option to remove certain items from the keyset. The message indicates that by clicking on an object in the selected (copied) keyset we will delete it from the keyset. The object stARSA (in fact the STS for arylsulphatase A) is shown highlighted. One further click on this object will delete it from the keyset.

Complex queries of the database may be made through the Query and Table Maker options in the main window. The basic operation is to apply a search command to each item in the current selected keyset. The search commands are specified on lines in the "Commands:" region at the bottom of the Query window (see Figure 4.16).

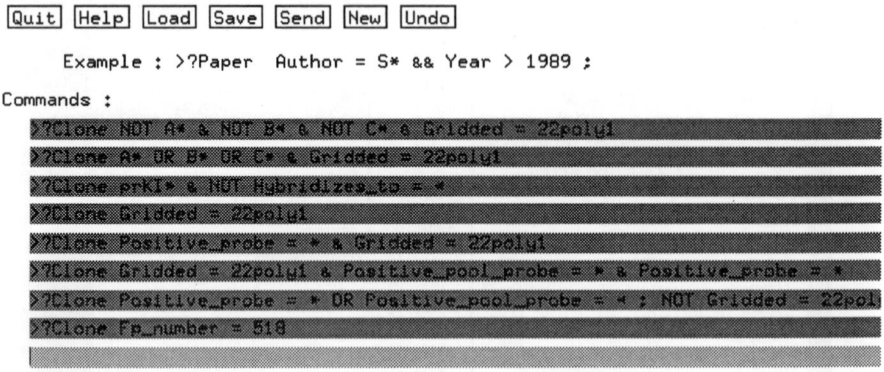

| Quit | Help | Load | Save | Send | New | Undo |

      Example : >?Paper Author = S* && Year > 1989 ;

Commands :

>?Clone NOT A* & NOT B* & NOT C* & Gridded = 22poly1

>?Clone A* OR B* OR C* & Gridded = 22poly1

>?Clone prKI* & NOT Hybridizes_to = *

>?Clone Gridded = 22poly1

>?Clone Positive_probe = * & Gridded = 22poly1

>?Clone Gridded = 22poly1 & Positive_pool_probe = * & Positive_probe = *

>?Clone Positive_probe = * OR Positive_pool_probe = * ; NOT Gridded = 22pol

>?Clone Fp_number = 518

FIGURE 4.16 The Query window. A series of example commands are shown loaded from a local .qry file.

The command lines are text entry boxes, so you can type into the active box using a simple line editor and click on the box again or return to issue the query. The syntax of the commands is very general and is described in its own help page. A few brief examples will give an idea of the possibilities.

    1. Find all authors whose name begins with s or a:

        >?Author s* OR a*

    2. Find all papers published in journals beginning with N published after 1987:

        >?Paper Journal = N* AND Year > 1987

    3. Find all clones that are on Clone_Grid "22poly1" and have at least three probes hybridizing to them:

        >?Clone Gridded = 22poly1
        AND COUNT Positive_probe = >= 3

It is also possible to read a set of commands into the Query window from a file by choosing "Load". A simple way to proceed is to load and edit examples which are provided in the directory /wquery. As you gain more experience and find queries that are of routine utility you can save useful commands in their own files for later use.

5 Entering and Maintaining Your Own Data in ACEDB

If you are looking at an implementation of ACEDB that is maintained by someone else such as the standard nematode database or AATDB, then it is unlikely that you will want to make significant changes to the database. You will most likely be satisfied with adding the official updates as they are released (see help on "Add Update"). In fact, if you start making significant changes, the database may no longer accept the official updates. However, you may wish to develop a private copy of a database from the official release or you may wish to use ACEDB for a new genome project. In this section we shall briefly illustrate how this may be done. However, we shall not touch on any changes to the program itself. In particular, changes to the database kernel should not be attempted without consultation with Richard Durbin and Jean Thierry-Mieg.

Before contemplating changes to a copy of ACEDB, you must be thoroughly familiar with the program and with both the users' guide and the installation guide. You do not need to be a Unix expert, but you must know how to move between directories and how to create and edit text files, i.e. be familiar with a text editor and you should read the configuration guide.

5.1 Write Access

In order to add or remove anything from the database you will need to have write access. A general principal of the program is that write access to the database is organized in macro transactions that are called "sessions". A session is initiated by selecting the menu option "Write Access" and is terminated by saving from the main window. The changes you make during a session are valid for that session but will not be permanently saved until you explicitly make a global save. This means that if you get write access, make changes, and then quit the program without saving, the data will be unchanged and you will not have corrupted your data. This can be useful if you wish to test out a change without making it permanent. Alternatively, if you are entering a lot of data you may wish to do this in several sessions, saving each time from the main menu.

Once you have write access you may modify and add comments to objects in the database. However, to get the most out of ACEDB you need to make use of an extra set of facilities that become available if you set the environment variable ACEDB_SU (Figure 4.17).

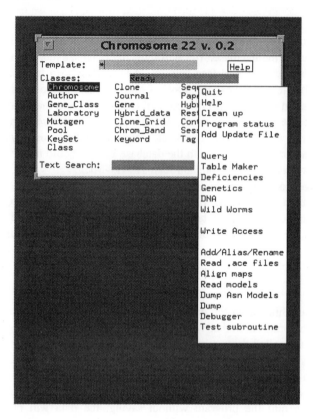

FIGURE 4.17 Once you have set ACEDB_SU, and started ACEDB, a number of extra options become available in the main window menu.

Details of these options are given in the configuration guide, but we shall deal mainly with the first two, "Add/Alias/Rename" and "Read .ace files".

5.2   Two Methods to Add Data to the Database

There are two ways to add data to your database. The first is "interactive" in the sense that you see where you are making changes and the data are added one piece at a time within the database. This method is useful for making relatively small changes. The second method involves parsing data into the database from an external text file, known as a .ace file, which must be formatted according to a simple syntax. This method is particularly suitable for entry of large amounts of data such as one's own data from another source or a selected dataset downloaded from another database such as GDB or GenBank. We shall discuss these two methods in turn.

5.2.1 Interactive Data Entry: The Update Mode of the Tree Display

If you wish to add a new object to the database, a simple way is to select the "Add/Alias/Rename" option from the main window. A small window will appear which allows you to select the class to which your new object belongs and then to enter the name of the object (Figure 4.18). The "Add/Alias/Rename" option can also be used to delete objects and to rename them in a very similar way. In order to add data to objects in the database we need to use the "Update" mode of the tree display.

The update mode is reached by choosing Update from the tree menu (Figure 4.18). In update mode, the tree itself is extended with entries from the corresponding model, which are indicated by a light blue background as shown in Figure 4.18. These allow you to add new data to the object. There also menu options to delete and change existing entries. When you have made all the entries you want, you can save the changes. If you want to cancel operations that have been accepted you have to Quit from the window, choosing the option not to save your changes when prompted.

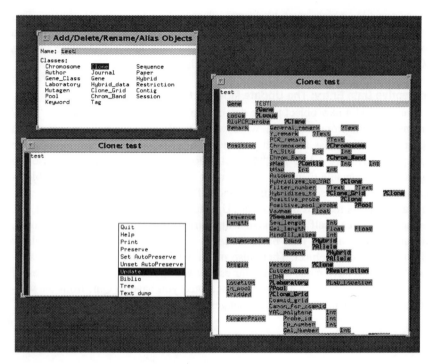

FIGURE 4.18 Adding a new object to the database using the "Add/Delete/Rename/Alias" tool. Moving anti-clockwise from the top left, the steps in creating and editing a new object are shown. If we wish to add a clone called "test" we select the class Clone and type "test" into the text entry box. Then we select the option "create" from the "Add/Alias/Rename" window and the program creates the object. When this is done the object appears as a new window which is empty. In order to add data to the tree for the clone "test", we then use the update mode of the tree display. We have opened the update mode of the tree for test by selecting update from the menu within the window for the clone "test". We have decided to add a pointer to a gene whose name is "TEST gene" into the tree for the clone "test". This might mean that the clone contains part or all of the gene. This is done by double clicking on the blue box "?Gene" next to the tag "Gene" and then typing "TEST gene" into the text entry box. Hitting return will create the pointer to the gene "Test gene". Remember that changes made are available during the session but will not become permanent until a global save from the main window is made.

5.2.2 Parsing Data into the ACEDB Using .ace Files

In general if you have a lot of data to enter into your database or if you have text files of data, for instance DNA sequence data, the Add objects and Update method of entry is too laborious and you will need to use .ace files. The option "Read .ace files" in the main window allows you to parse new data into the system. The format for .ace files is relatively simple but it is necessary to be familiar with it to add data successfully. In addition the .ace format is the means by which you can transfer data between various implementations of ACEDB. You can dump .ace files for any set of objects from a database by creating a selection list containing the appropriate objects and selecting the "Ace dump" option.

A .ace file is organized in paragraphs, which are separated by one or more blank lines. Each paragraph corresponds to an object, and starts with its class name, followed by an optional colon and the object name. On succeeding lines come data items for that object, each specified by a tag, then the data separated by white space (spaces or tabs) or commas. If an item contains white space or a comma (such as a title, and many object names), then it must be surrounded in double quotes. If you want to continue onto the next line then put a backslash at the end of the line. Figure 4.19 illustrates some features of a .ace file. When constructing .ace files it is always a good idea to follow examples generated by dumping .ace files containing objects similar to the ones you wish to create. These serve as good templates to copy until you are thoroughly familiar with the format.

```
// file:adora1.ace
// .ace file adding sequence for the human adenosine A1 receptor plus the
// reference for the sequence. Only the first 60 nucleotides of the true
// sequence are shown here - 2/2/93.


Sequence : "ADORA1 cDNA"
Title              "A1 adenosine receptor [human, brain hippocampus, mRNA]"
DNA                "ADORA1 cDNA" // NB must be the same name as the sequence object
Length             60
Library            Genbank S45235
Date               02-DEC-1992
Gene               ADORA1
Clone              stADORA1
cDNA
Reference          "ADORA1 cDNA"

Paper : "ADORA1 cDNA" // NB quotes needed since the name contains a space
Title              "Cloning and functional characterization of a human A1 adenosine
receptor."
Journal            "Biochem Biophys Res Commun"
Year               1992
Volume             187
Page               919 926
Author             "Libert F"
Author             "Van Sande J"
Author             "Lefort A"
Author             "Czernilofsky A"
Author             "Dumont J E"
Author             "Vassart G"
Author             "Ensinger H A"
Author             "Mendla K D"
Keyword            cDNA
Keyword            ADORA1
Keyword            RECEPTOR

DNA : "ADORA1 cDNA"
gagctctgccagctttggtgaccttgggtgcttgcctcgtgccccttggtgcccgtctgc
```

FIGURE 4.19 The features of a .ace file. This .ace file will add three objects to the database; a sequence entry called "ADORA1 cDNA", a reference for the sequence which has the same name, and the DNA sequence itself. The need to split the details of the sequence and the DNA sequence itself comes from the way ACEDB handles DNA sequences, the DNA being held separately. Note that the three entries are separated by blank lines and that within each object the data items follow on separate lines specified by their own tags. The sequence shown is an example only and consists of the first few nucleotides of this cDNA.

5.3 Dealing with Mapping Data

Having learnt how to enter data into ACEDB, one needs to decide how to go about converting one's own map data into a form that will be displayed meaningfully by the program. Several examples have already been seen.

1. The .ace file in Figure 4.19 will produce a sequence entry that gives an fMap displaying the sequence. If one wants to add more sequences, the same kind of format is used but other tags to display the exons and other sequence features must also be used. A good way to discover these is to look at the nematode database to see how the tree entries for sequences correspond to the fMap displays.

2. We also showed in Section 4.3.1 on the pMap display how the output from the CONTIG 9 contig assembly programs can be used to produce physical map displays in ACEDB. In fact, the data in these cases were dumped from CONTIG 9 and converted into .ace file format using a pair of simple routines written by Richard Durbin. In future this will not be necessary as the CONTIG 9 functionalities are being ported into ACEDB. In addition, future developments of the pMap display could allow other sorts of mapping data to be entered more readily.

3. In Section 4.3.3 on the Clone_Grid display, we described how we have used ACEDB to handle hybridization and STS data for a large YAC library screening project. Hybridization data can rapidly be entered into the database via the Clone_Grid. There are two modes of operation of the Clone_Grid display, map and edit. In map mode, when you double click on a box you transfer to the pMap display for that YAC. In edit mode, clicking a box defines a hybridization pattern. One click in a box gives a dark blue fill, a second makes it pale blue, signifying a weak signal, and a third will clear it. If you have write access, you may then save the pattern with a probe by choosing the "save data with probe" entry from the menu. In this way a large amount of data on hybridization of probes to filters can be entered into the database.

4. Finally in Section 4.3.2 on the gMap display we discussed how we have dealt with somatic cell hybrid data. Again this approach could be extended to radiation hybrid mapping or in situ hybridization. To illustrate this further, in Figure 4.20 we show a .ace file that could be used to reproduce part of the gMap display of human chromsome 22 shown in Figure 4.4 including the banding and some of the somatic cell hybrid data, together with comments that indicate the purpose of the parts of the .ace file.

```
// .ace file to illustrate construction of a chromosome gMap

// Two consecutive forward slashes (///) signify the start of a comment. Any
// text following them is ignored. It is useful to put a comment at the start
// of a .ace file to say what it contains, and where it comes from.

// The first object to define is the chromsome which has attached to it a
// series of chromosome bands (Chrom_Band), genes and somatic cell hybrids
```

```
// (Rearrangement). pTel and qTel are markers which have been arbitrarily
// defined to mark the ends of the chromosome. The "hDp" part of the
// hybrid name is a necessary relic of the early program development.

Chromosome : "Chromosome 22"
Centre             18.5 67
Chrom_Band         "22q11.1-22p11.1"
Chrom_Band         "22p11.2"
Chrom_Band         "22p12"
Chrom_Band         "22p13"
Chrom_Band         "22q11.2"
Chrom_Band         "22q12.1"
Chrom_Band         "22q12.2"
Chrom_Band         "22q12.3"
Chrom_Band         "22q13.1"
Chrom_Band         "22q13.2"
Chrom_Band         "22q13.3"
Gene               "ACR"
Gene               "MB"
Gene               "pTel"
Gene               "qTel"
Rearrangement      "hDpWEGROTH"
Rearrangement      "hDpAM27"
Rearrangement      "hDp33-11-TG"
Rearrangement      "hDp#15"


// Next we define a series of Chrom_Bands with their positions along the
// chromosome. The bands are normally white corresponding to Giemsa light
// unless we call them to be Dark (dark grey) for Giemsa dark bands or NOR
// (light grey) for the nucleolar organizing region. The band at the
// centromere is "waisted" if we define it as Centromere.


Chrom_Band : "22p11.2"
gMap               "Chromosome 22" -2 -7
NOR

Chrom_Band : "22p12"
gMap               "Chromosome 22" -7 -9

Chrom_Band : "22p13"
gMap               "Chromosome 22" -9 -15
NOR

Chrom_Band : "22q11.1-22p11.1"
gMap               "Chromosome 22" 2 -2
Centromere

Chrom_Band : "22q11.2"
gMap               "Chromosome 22" 2 20

Chrom_Band : "22q12.1"
```

```
gMap                 "Chromosome 22" 20 25
Dark

Chrom_Band : "22q12.2"
gMap                 "Chromosome 22" 25 26

Chrom_Band : "22q12.3"
gMap                 "Chromosome 22" 26 30
Dark

Chrom_Band : "22q13.1"
gMap                 "Chromosome 22" 30 375

Chrom_Band : "22q13.2"
gMap                 "Chromosome 22" 375 40
Dark

Chrom_Band : "22q13.3"
gMap                 "Chromosome 22" 40 50


// Next we create an entry which describes each piece of hybrid mapping
// data. In each case the result refers to the hybrid, the gene concerned,
// a result that describes whether the hybrid includes the gene which must
// be written to this form and a line of the type A_includes_B which is
// necessary for the functionality. Note that this form is only valid if
// the classes Df_Dup_data and Rearrangement have been renamed to
// Hybrid_data and Hybrid in the file wspec/options.wrm.

Hybrid_data : "#15.1"
Rearrangement        "hDp#15"
Gene                 "MB"
Results              "hDp#15 includes MB"
A_includes_B

Hybrid_data : "#15.2"
Rearrangement        "hDp#15"
Gene                 "ACR"
Results              "hDp#15 does not include ACR"
A_does_not_include_B

Hybrid_data : "33-11-TG.1"
Rearrangement        "hDp33-11-TG"
Gene                 "MB"
Results              "hDp33-11-TG includes MB"
A_includes_B

Hybrid_data : "33-11-TG.2"
Rearrangement        "hDp33-11-TG"
Gene                 "ACR"
Results              "hDp33-11-TG includes ACR"
A_includes_B
```

```
Hybrid_data : "AM27.1"
Rearrangement      "hDpAM27"
Gene               "MB"
Results            "hDpAM27 includes MB"
A_includes_B

Hybrid_data : "AM27.2"
Rearrangement      "hDpAM27"
Gene               "ACR"
Results            "hDpAM27 does not include ACR"
A_does_not_include_B

Hybrid_data : "WEG.1"
Rearrangement      "hDpWEGROTH"
Gene               "MB"
Results            "hDpWEG includes MB"
A_includes_B

Hybrid_data : "WEG.2"
Rearrangement      "hDpWEGROTH"
Gene               "ACR"
Results            "hDpWEG includes ACR"
A_includes_B

// We now define the positions of the Hybrids (renamed from Rearrangement) on
// the chromosome, and their attached Hybrid_data.

Hybrid : "hDp#15"
gMap               "Chromosome 22" 15 28
Df_Dup             "#15.1"
Df_Dup             "#15.2"

Hybrid : "hDp33-11-TG"
gMap               "Chromosome 22" 50 2
Df_Dup             "33-11-TG.1"
Df_Dup             "33-11-TG.2"

Hybrid : "hDpAM27"
gMap               "Chromosome 22" -15 35
Df_Dup             "AM27.1"
Df_Dup             "AM27.2"

Hybrid : "hDpWEGROTH"
gMap               "Chromosome 22" -15 50
Df_Dup             "WEG.1"
Df_Dup             "WEG.2"

// Finally we define the positions of the genes on the chromosome map. In
// this case we have positioned the genes arbitrarily. Note also that we
// have used a comment on the tag Correct_name to avoid creating a second
// entry for ACR under Acrosin but to allow us to display the name.
// A number of special modifiers are available that allow you to add comments
// (-C), delete objects or fields (-D), or to rename or alias (-R or -A).
```

```
Gene : "ACR"
Correct_name        -C "Acrosin"
gMap                "Chromosome 22" 45 5
Df_Dup              "#1515"
Df_Dup              "33-11-TG15"
Df_Dup              "WEG15"
Df_Dup              "AM2715"

Gene : "MB"
gMap                "Chromosome 22" 261 0
Df_Dup              "#151"
Df_Dup              "33-11-TG1"
Df_Dup              "WEG1"
Df_Dup              "AM271"

Gene : "pTel"
Map                 -C "Virtual gene to add and end to the p arm of gMap"
gMap                "Chromosome 22" -15

Gene : "qTel"
Map                 -C "Created to provide an end to the map"
gMap                "Chromosome 22" 50 0
```

FIGURE 4.20 A .ace file to reproduce part of the chromosome 22 gMap.

6 Acknowledgements

Many thanks to Peter Botcherby for his help in setting up the network at Guy's and with printing the figures. Thanks to Drs Charlotte Cole and Roli Roberts for commenting on early drafts of the manuscript. Part of this work was supported by the Spastics Society. I.D. holds a Wellcome Trust Postdoctoral Fellowship.

7 References

Bentley DR, Todd C, Collins JE, Holland J, Dunham I, Hassock S, Bankier A, and Giannelli F (1992). The development and application of automated gridding for efficient screening of yeast and bacterial ordered libraries. Genomics 12, 334-341.

Botstein D, White R L, Skolnick M and Davis R W (1980). Construction of a genetic linkage map in man using restriction fragment length polymorphisms. Am. J. Hum. Genet. 32, 314-331.

Burke D T, Carle G F and Olson M V (1987). Cloning of large segments of exogenous DNA into yeast by means of artificial chromosome vectors. Science 236, 806-812.

Burmeister M, Suwon K, Price E R, De Lange T, Tantravahi U, Myers R M and Cox D R (1991). A map of the distal region of the long arm of human chromosome 21 constructed by radiation hybrid mapping and pulsed-field gel electrophoresis. Genomics 9, 19-30.

Chumakov I M, Rigault P, Guillou S, Ougen P, Billault A, Guasconi G, Gervy P, Le Gall I, Soularue P, Grinas L, Bougueleret L, Bellanne-Chantelot C, Lacroix B, Barillot E, Gesnouin P, Pook S, Vaysseix G, Frelat G, Schmitz A, Sambucy J-L, Bosch A, Estivill X, Weissenbach J, Vignall A, Riethman H C, Cox D R, Patterson D, Gardiner K, Hattori M, Sakaki Y, Ichikawa H, Ohki M, Le Paslier D, Heilig R, Antonarakis S E and Cohen D (1992). Continuum of ovelapping clones spanning the entire human chromosome 21q. Nature 359, 380-387.

Collins J E, Everett L A, Bentley D R and Dunham I (1992). A panel of human chromosome 22-specific sequence tagged sites. Genomics 14, 1098-1103.

Coulson A, Sulston J, Brenner S and Karn J (1986). Toward a physical map of the genome of the nematode *Caenorhabditis elegans*. Proc. Natl Acad. Sci. USA 83, 7821-7825.

Coulson A, Waterston R, Kiff J, Sulston J and Kohara Y (1988). Genome linking with yeast artificial chromosomes. Nature 335, 184-186.

Cox D R, Burmeister M, Price E R, Kim S and Myers R M (1990). Radiation hybrid mapping: a somatic cell genetic method for constructing high resolution maps of mammalian chromosomes. Science 250, 245-250.

Delattre O, Azambuja C J, Aurias A, Zucman J, Peter M, Zhang F, Hors-Cayla M C, Rouleau G A and Thomas G (1991). Mapping of human chromosome 22 with a panel of somatic cell hybrids. Genomics 9, 721-727.

Dumanski J P, Carlbom E, Collins V P, Nordenskjold M, Emanuel B S, Budarf M L, McDermid H E, Wolff R K, O'Connell P, White R, Lalouel J-M and Leppert M (1991). A map of 22 loci on human chromosome 22. Genomics 11, 709-719.

Durbin R and Thierry-Mieg J (1991). A *C. elegans* Database documentation code and data. Available from anonymous FTP servers at lirmm.lirmm.fr, cele.mrc-lmb.cam.ac.uk and ncbi.nlm.nih.gov.

Evans G A and Lewis K A (1989). Physical mapping of complex genomes by cosmid multiplex analysis. Proc. Natl Acad. Sci. USA 86, 5030-5034.

Foote S, Vollrath D, Hilton A and Page D C (1992). The human Y chromosome: overlapping DNA clones spanning the euchromatic regions. Science 258, 60-66.

Frazer K A, Boehnke M, Budarf M L, Wolff R K, Emanuel B S, Myers R M and Cox D R (1992). A radiation hybrid map of the region on human chromosome 22 containing the neurofibomatosis type 2 locus. Genomics 14, 574-584.

Green E D and Olson M V (1990). Chromosomal region of the cystic fibrosis gene in yeast artificial chromosomes: a model for human genome mapping. Science 250, 94-98.

Knott V, Rees D J G, Cheng Z and Brownlee G G (1988). Randomly picked cosmid clones overlap the pyrB and oriC gap in the physical map of the *E. coli* chromosome. Nucleic Acids Res. 16, 2601-2613.

Kohara Y, Akiyaina K and Isono K (1987). The physical map of the whole *E. coli* chromosome: application of a new strategy for rapid analysis and sorting of a large genomic library. Cell 50, 495-508.

Lawrence J B, Villnave C A and Singer R H (1988). Sensitive high-resolution chromatin and chromosome mapping in situ: presence and orientation of two closely integrated copies of EBV in a lymphoma line. Cell 52, 51-61.

Lichter P, Cremer T, Tang C C, Watkins P C, Manuelidis L and Ward D C (1988). Rapid detection of human chromosome 21 aberrations by in situ hybridization. Proc. Natl Acad. Sci. USA 85, 9664-9668.

Lichter P, Tang C C, Call K, Hermanson G, Evans G A, Housman D and Ward D C (1990). High-resolution mapping of human chromosome 11 by in situ hybridization with cosmid clones. Science 247, 64-69.

Nizetic D N, Zehetner G, Monaco A P, Gellen L, Young B D and Lehrach H (1991). Construction arraying and high density screening of large insert libraries of the human chromosomes X and 21: their potential use as reference libraries. Proc. Natl Acad. Sci. USA 88, 3233-3237.

Olson M, Dutchik J E, Graham M Y, Brodeur G M, Helms C, Frank M, MacCollin M, Scheinman R and Frank T (1986). Random-clone strategy for genomic restriction mapping in yeast. Proc. Natl Acad. Sci. USA 83, 7826-7830.

Olson M, Hood L, Cantor C and Botstein D (1989). A common language for physical mapping of the human genome. Science 245, 1434-1435.

Pearson P L, Matheson N W, Flescher D C and Robbins R J (1992). The GDB(TM) human genome data base anno 1992. Nucleic Acids Res. 20 (Supplement), 2201-2206

Pinkel D, Landegent J, Collins C, Fuscoe J, Segraves R, Lucas J and Gray J (1988). Fluorescence in situ hybridisation with human specific libraries: detection of trisomy 21 and translocations of chromosome 4. Proc. Natl Acad. Sci. USA 85, 9138-9142.

Saiki R K, Gelfand D H, Stoffel S, Scharf S J, Higuchi R, Horn G T, Mullis K B and Erlich H A (1988). Primer-directed enzymatic amplification of DNA with a thermostable DNA polymerase. Science 239, 487-491.

Schwartz D C and Cantor C R (1984). Separation of yeast chromosome-sized DNAs by pulsed field gel electrophoresis. Cell 37, 67-75.

Sulston J, Mallett F, Staden R, Durbin R, Horsnell T and Coulson A (1988). Software for genome mapping by fingerprinting techniques. Comput. Applic. Biosci. 4, 125-132.

Sulston J, Mallett F, Durbin R and Horsnell T (1989). Image analysis of restriction enzyme fingerprint autoradiograms. CABIOS 5, 101-106.

Trask B J (1991). Fluorescence in situ hybridization. TIG 7, 149-153.

Vollrath D, Foote S, Hilton A, Brown L G, Beer-Romero P, Bogan J S and Page D C (1992). The human Y chromosome: A 43-interval map based on naturally occurring deletions Science 258, 52-59.

Watson J D (1990). The human genome project: Past present and future. Science 248, 44-49.

Weber J L and May P E (1989). Abundant class of human DNA polymorphisms which can be typed using the polymerase chain reaction. Am. J. Hum. Genet. 44, 388-396.

Zucchi I and Schlessinger D (1992). Distribution of moderately repetitive sequences pTR5 and LF1 in Xq24-q28 human DNA and their use in assembling YAC contigs. Genomics 12, 264-275.

CHAPTER 5

Comparative Mapping and Sequencing

Martin Bishop

Human Genome Mapping Project Resource Centre, Watford
Road, Harrow, Middlesex HA1 3UJ, UK
Internet: mbishop@crc.ac.uk

1   Genetic and Physical Mapping in Humans

1.1   Goals of the Human Genome Project

Genome projects may be distinguished from other endeavours in molecular biology by their large scale systematic approach to the acquisition of genetic linkage, physical mapping and DNA sequence data for the entire genome of an organism. A catalogue of the gene sequences is a step in the collection of knowledge about gene function and control of gene expression during development and in the differentiated cell types of the organism. A catalogue of the sequences of the encoded proteins forms the basis for work on protein function and on the protein-protein and protein-nucleic acid interactions which are crucial to cellular mechanisms.

In the human genome project, high priority is given to the discovery of the molecular basis of variants of medical importance. Disease phenotypes can be located on the genetic map by linkage to molecular markers studied in human families (Chapter 3). This narrows down the physical region of the DNA to perhaps 5-10 Mb. It remains remarkably difficult to locate the gene whose variant is responsible for the disease. For example, a restriction fragment length polymorphism (RFLP) linked to Huntington's disease was obtained in 1983 but the DNA encoding the gene was not sequenced until 1993.

Genetic variation is an important parameter of any species. The haploid human genome is thought to comprise 3×10^9 nucleotides and any two individuals may differ by 3×10^6 nucleotides. Study of the present human population of 5×10^9 individuals (were this feasible) might produce a catalogue of sequence differences with 15×10^{15} entries. It will be possible in the future to collect some of this sort of information.

Data of importance resulting from the human genome project will therefore include:

- Genetic linkage maps for males and females.
- A catalogue of gene sequences.
- Sequences of variants of medical importance.
- Population variation.

The present speed and cost of DNA sequencing is such that these goals will take considerable time to realize in the absence of a technology breakthrough. This chapter will consider further computing tools for examining genome information (additional to ACEDB and IGD described in Chapter 4) and will emphasize the value of comparative studies with other genomes.

1.2   Resolution of Human Genetic Maps

In model organisms such as the nematode, fruit fly (Sturtevant, 1913) or mouse it is possible to obtain very accurate genetic linkage maps because of the short generation time and lack of ethical constraints on breeding programmes. Human genetic maps are relatively poorly determined and estimation of map length is subject to appreciable error (Morton, 1991). Small sample size and undetected errors in typing markers can lead to errors in assigning locus order along the chromosome and the problem of insuffi-cient meioses becomes acute for closely spaced loci (Morton, 1988). Nevertheless, the genetic map is the indispensible link between an observable phenotype and the underly-ing molecular basis for it.

The current state of the human genetic linkage map is reported by the NIH/CEPH Collaborative Mapping Group (1992) and the chromosome maps are available by ftp from ftp.chlc.org and are also included in GDB. An aim of the US Human Genome Project is to produce a genetic map at an average resolution of 2-5 cM requiring at least

3,000 polymorphic markers. Maps in GDB are represented in text form and each map has a symbol (Figure 5.1). Details of one of the maps, C21M3, is shown in Figure 5.2.

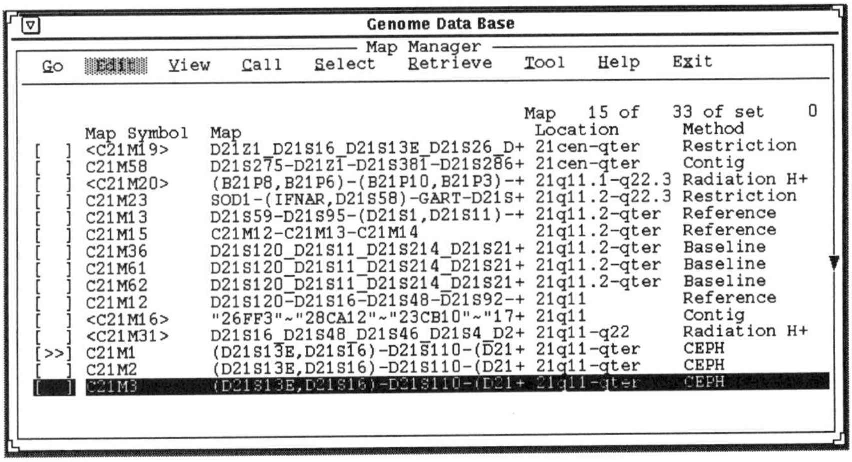

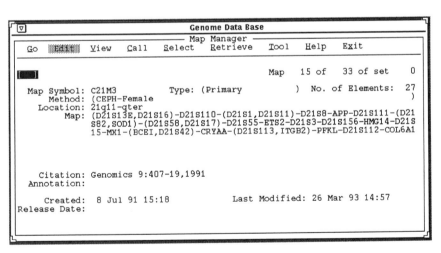

FIGURE 5.1 A GDB screen showing some of the maps available for chromosome 21.

FIGURE 5.2 A GDB screen showing table detail for map C21M3.

After finding linkage of flanking markers to a disease locus the region of interest may be more closely defined by haplotype analysis (Chapter 3). Assuming a relatively small number of founder mutations for the disease, chromosomes in affected individuals will be descended from a common ancestor and will tend to share the same variants (linkage disequilibrium). Linkage disequilibrium is lost by recombination, and the closer a marker is to the disease, the less likely it is that recombination has occurred. This approach led to the localization of the Huntington's disease gene to a 500 kb segment and hence to the cloning of the gene by exon amplification (Huntington's Disease Collaborative Research Group, 1993).

1.3   Resolution of Human Physical Maps

Traditional access to the physical DNA has been by cytogenetic techniques including in situ hybridization of DNA probes to banded chromosomes, the use of rodent-human hybrid cell lines with single human chromosomes and the production of radiation hybrids in which DNA is partially deleted. Natural transpositions of human chromosomes can also be used very effectively in mapping. Resources relating to these materials are described in Chapter 2 and methodology in Chapter 4.

The nucleotide length of a visible human chromosome band is about 10 Mb, which is little different to the current resolution of 10 cM provided by genetic mapping. Knowledge of gene order in humans has traditionally been arranged by chromosome band and GDB gives access to data in this organization (Figure 5.3).

	Location	Symbol	P	Name	Locus 1 of 500 of set 1 Mode	D
	21pter-p12	D21S131		probe C65	S	
[ ]	21pter-p12	D21S142		probe E79	S	
[ ]	21pter-q11	D21F19S4		probe pUNC724	A,S	
[ ]	21pter-q21.1	D21S6	Y	probe pPW237D	S	
[ ]	21pter-q21.2	D21F66S1		probes fVC1.34,pVC1.34a	S	
[ ]	21pter-q21	AD1		Alzheimer disease 1	L	
[ ]	21pter-q21	ASNSL2		asparagine synthetase-like 2	A,S	
[ ]	21pter-q22.2	D21S61		probe pPW227	S	
[ ]	21p13	D21F20S4		probe pACR1		
[ ]	21p13 and 21+	D21S187		probe pVC10a	S	
[ ]	21p13	D21S188		probe fVC1.12	S	
[ ]	21p13	D21S191		probe pVC1.23c	S	
[ ]	21p13	D21F39S7		probes p21B7,pB4	A,S	
[ ]	21p12	RNR4	Y	RNA, ribosomal 4	A	
[ ]	21p13 and 21+	D21S187		probe pVC10a	S	

FIGURE 5.3 A GDB screen showing the cytogenetic location of markers around the Alzheimer disease 1 locus.

Restriction maps using rare-cutting restriction enzymes have been prepared for regions of human DNA. Pulsed-field gel electrophoresis (PFGE) allows electrophoretic separation of DNA fragments as large as 10 Mb. Pulsed-field gel maps are included in GDB.

10 Mb of DNA may contain several hundred genes and mapping at higher resolution is now becoming possible for total human DNA. This is achieved using libraries of cloned human DNA (Chapter 4). Overlapping yeast artificial chromosome (YAC) clone maps of chromosomes 21 and Y have been prepared using sequence tagged site (STS) markers and are included in GDB.

It is a goal of the US Human Genome Project to place STS markers at an average spacing of 100 kb requiring at least 30,000 markers. Using the polymorphic markers from the genetic linkage studies to screen YACs will result in correlation of the genetic map to the YAC contig map. Building a human overlapping YAC clone map for the entire genome will the finest physical resolution yet achieved. The problem of determining all the gene sequences will still remain. The use of clones from cDNA libraries, CpG Island libraries and exon trapped DNA will be the major methods of accessing human genes in the search for disease gene candidates. Databases will need to be developed to store this information as it is accumulated.

1.4   Map Building and Display Software

1.4.1 SIGMA

SIGMA (System for Integrated Genome Map Assembly) is an object-oriented, X-windows based, graphical map assembly tool available from the Center for Human Genome Studies at Los Alamos National Laboratory.

Some of the key features of SIGMA include:

- Graphical map editing.
  With SIGMA, most map editing is done through mouse based point and click operations. SIGMA is based on the OpenLook interface standard.

- Integrated genome maps.
  SIGMA allows data to be entered on any type of map object (e.g. clones, probes, YACs, genes, markers, contigs, etc.) with measurements being specified in any units (e.g. bp, kb, cM, cM(F), cM(M), FLpter, etc.). This allows data from many different types of maps (e.g. linkage, breakpoint, contig, etc.) to be combined into a single, integrated map.

- User-configurable views.
  Because of the difficulties of presenting large quantities of data in a usable style, SIGMA provides a mechanism that allows the user easily to specify

alternative views on a single map, each of which might emphasize a different aspect of the data.

- Automatic map evaluation.
  Maps in SIGMA are made up of two major components: the graphical representation and the underlying data. This allows SIGMA to provide feedback to the user on how well the current drawing agrees with the data. Further, when SIGMA indicates that there is a problem in the map, it informs the user about exactly which data (and from which source) are not being satisfied. This makes it very unlikely that any data will be accidentally ignored either during the original assembly process or during subsequent revisions.

- Support for collaborative map building.
  Because SIGMA is available in a version that uses the ObjectStore client-server database management system, researchers from geographically disparate locations may work on the same map. This feature can be used to allow closely collaborating groups to keep their data in a single location, or to permit, for example, chromosome editors to work on a consensus map easily between meetings.

- GDB Interface.
  SIGMA is able to import maps from GDB for viewing and protocols that will enable SIGMA maps to be submitted directly to GDB in electronic form are being developed.

SIGMA was designed by Michael Cinkosky and Jim Fickett. The software was developed by Michael Bridgers, William Barber, Mohamad Ijadi and Charles Troup. SIGMA is available from Los Alamos without charge (although a small licensing fee is required for the ObjectStore version). To retrieve the software and documentation, connect to atlas.lanl.gov with ftp (log in as "anonymous" and supply your e-mail address as the password). The files can be found in pub/sigma. An example SIGMA screen is shown in Figure 5.4.

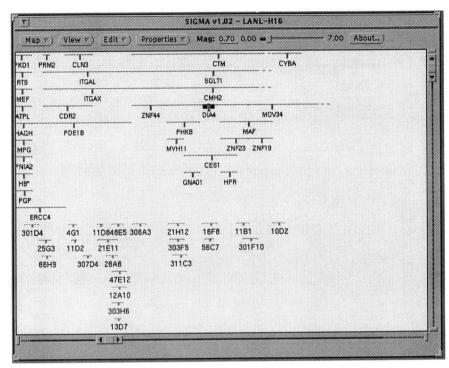

FIGURE 5.4 SIGMA display of a portion of the map of chromosome 16, including data from the Los Alamos National Laboratory and Adelaide Childrens Hospital.

1.4.2 GnomeView

GnomeView is a graphical user interface that displays colour representations of genomic maps for review and manipulation. The latest release of GnomeView integrates information from both GenBank and the GDB.

Cross-references supplied by each database are used to navigate smoothly back and forth between these databases. This utilization of the cross-references from each database allows the user to identify and display GenBank sequence loci associated with a particular GDB locus, and vice versa.

Information retrieval is controlled by user queries. The query process involves the use of a graphical user interface and minimal keyboard entry. The user may submit queries at either the chromosome level (Figure 5.5) or the DNA sequence level. In response to user queries, GnomeView locates and presents maps and other information in an organized fashion. This information can then be viewed in the form of high level lists or genomic maps (Figure 5.6).

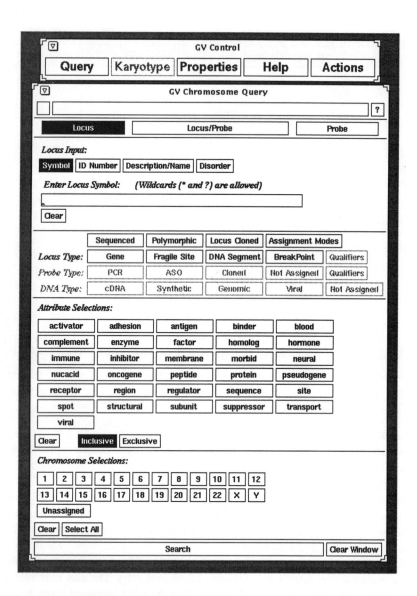

FIGURE 5.5 GnomeView query form.

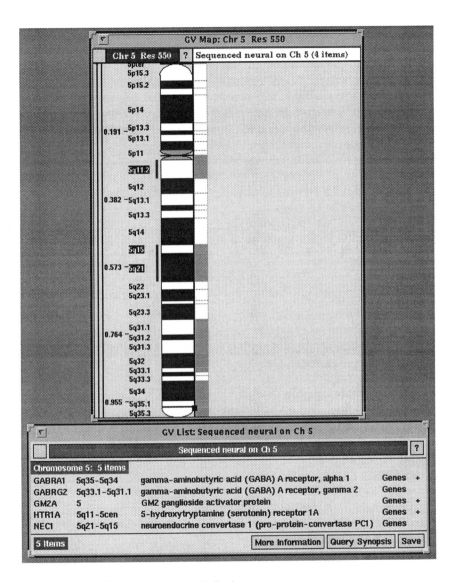

FIGURE 5.6 GnomeView chromosome 5 display.

GnomeView uses a progressive disclosure approach when presenting information that includes one-to-one, one-to-many and many-to-many data relationships. Progressive disclosure is accomplished by always returning lists of information. Any desired object can then be chosen from a list and more information requested on that object. As long as there is an information trail and data associated with the current object, progressive disclosure can continue in this fashion.

GnomeView employs several genomic map representations. Any combination of chromosomes can be displayed with objects (loci, probes, sequences) mapped to them using colour coded density representations. GenBank features can be displayed as colour coded objects mapped to sequence representations. All maps are displayed in windows offering complete zoom and pan capabilities.

2 Genetic and Physical Mapping in Mammals

2.1 The Mouse

2.1.1 GBASE

This is the genetic database of the mouse at the Jackson Laboratory. The database contains genetic maps, literature references on locus mapping and a list of locus names and symbols, information about alleles at polymorphic loci for over 1,000 inbred strains. The locus list is published in Mouse Genome (Hillyard et al., 1992) The database is implemented in Ingres and the software shell is being used for mapping projects in other vertebrates (see Section 2.2).

2.1.2 MRC Radiobiology Unit Databases

The Genetics Division of the MRC Radiobiology Unit maintains databases of information on mouse genetics which complement the information available from the Jackson Laboratory. Information is published in Mouse Genome (Lyon and Kirby, 1992), and some of the data are available on-line at the Human Genome Mapping Project Resource Centre.

2.1.3 Encyclopedia of the Mouse Genome

The Encyclopedia of the Mouse Genome provides a comprehensive collection of the mouse genetic information contributed by independent groups and presented in archives such as Genetic Strains and Variants of the Laboratory Mouse, The Biology of the Laboratory Mouse and The Mouse in Biomedical Research, GBASE, The Chromosome Atlas, and The Mouse Locus Catalog.

The Encyclopedia provides three tools to examine the above data: two display genetic maps, and through the maps give users access to literature references and other text based genetic information, such as notes concerning gene nomenclature or mapping history. LinkMap displays linkage maps, CytoMap displays cytogenetic maps. The user interface in the tools is straightforward: a mouse click on a gene label causes any relevant text to appear in a window. The tools have a mechanism for resolving the maximum detail provided by the data, so that densely mapped areas can be easily examined through scrolling and magnification. An example of a linkage map for mouse chromosome 1 is shown in Figure 5.7. The tools also feature a list based search facility for selecting loci by symbol or name. The third tool is Cats (catalogue searcher), a text retrieval system featuring the use of inverted files, a Boolean search syntax, and a point and click user interface. It is fully integrated with the maps: when a locus is selected on a map, Cats will display any catalogue articles corresponding to the locus.

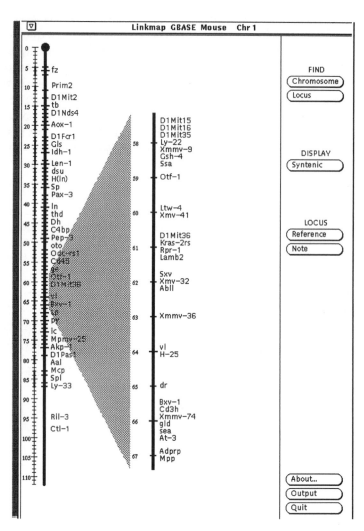

FIGURE 5.7 Linkage map for mouse chromosome 1 from the Encyclopedia of the Mouse Genome.

2.1.4 Mouse Backcross Database (MBX)

Mouse backcross breeding programmes involving the sibling species *Mus domesticus* and *M. spretus* give DNA which can be unambiguously typed as domesticus or spretus either by RFLPs in Southern blot analysis or by polymerase chain reaction (PCR) analysis of microsatellite polymorphisms. This procedure can be used to detect crossovers in backcross animals and is very informative about marker order.

The European Collaborative Interspecific Backcross (EUCIB) is a facility for high resolution genetic mapping of the mouse genome. It is a 1,000 animal interspecific backcross between *M. domesticus* C57BL/6 and *M. spretus* and DNA has been prepared from each animal. It provides a genetic resolution of 0.3 cM with 95% confidence. DNA from each animal has been scored for 3-4 markers per chromosome to give an anchor map of 70 loci. This permits a rapid two step mapping of new probes by first studying a panel of 40-50 individual DNAs in order to establish linkage to a chromosome region. A panel of mice with recombinants in that region then permits fine mapping by haplotype analysis.

The backcross has an associated database called MBX developed in Sybase. MBX contains mouse, locus and probe data and stores allele type (domesticus or spretus) at each locus for an individual animal. Recombinant mice can be selected from this table for the fine mapping. MBX will calculate the available lod scores for linked markers (Figure 5.8) and also determines genetic order of closely linked markers by minimizing the number of recombinants (Figure 5.9).

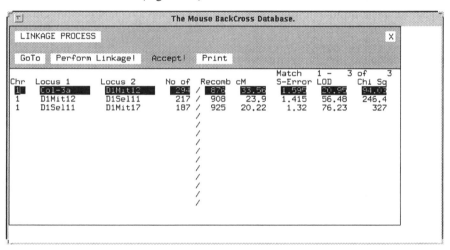

FIGURE 5.8 Recombination fractions from the MBX database.

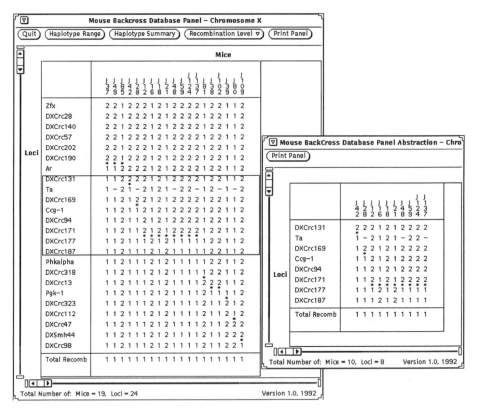

FIGURE 5.9 Construction of detailed mapping panels in the MBX database.

2.2 Farm Animals

A major motivation for genetic mapping in farm animals is to attempt to discover quantitative trait loci affecting the quality of meat or other products. However, there is also value in the study of inherited disorders which affect humans and other mammals. The identification of a mutation in the ryanodine receptor gene (RYR1) as the probable cause of malignant hyperthermia was described first in pigs (Fujii et al., 1991) and secondly in humans (Gillard et al., 1991).

The mapping of animal genomes will allow the further development of animal models of human disease. The animal models can be experimentally manipulated for the study of molecular and physiological processes. Animal models will be important for the evaluation of the appropriate therapies. Pigs and sheep are the most similar in size to humans and will be the most appropriate for such investigations.

2.2.1 PiGBASE

The PiGMaP project involves 17 European laboratories and plans to place 200 polymorphic genetic markers on the pig genome to give a resolution of 20 cM. Informative reference populations have been established using a Chinese Meishan and European Large White cross and diverse crosses between Wild Boar and various European commercial breeds. The F2 individuals are highly informative. The database of the PiGMaP project is PiGBASE which uses the GBASE database software. To date, about 200 markers have been mapped.

2.2.2 BoVMaP

This is the bovine mapping project based at the Institut National de la Recherche Agronomique (INRA) at Jouy-en-Josas, France. A database for the project is being developed in Oracle. James Womack of Texas is also active in cattle mapping.

2.2.3 SheepMap

SheepMap is the national New Zealand research programme in sheep genetic mapping with the immediate goal of producing a 20 cM resolution map of the sheep genome. It is at the Invermay Agricultural Centre and uses the GBASE software shell.

2.2.4 Mendelian Inheritance in Animals (MIA)

MIA is a database created and maintained by Dr Frank Nicholas, Sydney, Australia, which contains details of genetic disorders for a wide range of animals including cattle and pigs. It resembles McKusick's OMIM.

3 Comparative Biology

3.1 Introduction to the Comparative Method

Populations of biological organisms change with time and we can study how their genetic material is reassorted at meiosis and transmitted from one generation to the next (Cannings and Thompson, 1981). Over longer time spans we cannot usually observe the changes in the genetic material directly but we can study the genetic properties of extant populations which we assume to have diverged from each other (Thompson, 1975). DNA sequencing is a direct way of characterizing the genetic constitution of an individual and DNA can be recovered from bones dated by stratification in archaeological sites. Studies of fossil DNA, for example from Miocene leaves, have been reported. For the majority of extant species we are unlikely to be able to study the DNA of their antecedents.

The comparative method in biology has been pursued for several hundred years on morphological criteria and for several decades on molecular criteria. The ideas of Darwinian evolution came out of a consideration of a combination of animal and plant breeding, adaptation of organism to environment, and comparative studies both morphological and biogeographical. The aim of phylogenetic inference in narrower but is an essential theoretical framework. It attempts to elucidate the order of descent of organisms from common ancestors, most commonly on a tree. A popular example is of the three primates man, chimp and gorilla. There are three possible ways these animals could be related on a tree: (man (chimp, gorilla)); ((man, chimp) gorilla) and ((man, gorilla) chimp). Different datasets and different methods of analysis indicate different answers to the problem (a present consensus of these suggests the relationship is the second listed). If phylogenetic analysis is to be more than idle speculation then a statistical foundation to the subject is needed with explicit assumptions and testable hypotheses. Most progress has been made in this with regard to DNA sequences but other sorts of information such as chromosomes and the orders of genes along them are amenable to similar treatment. Conflicts between results from different datasets indicate that one should look for reasons in terms of functional constraints and selection.

3.2   Data for Comparative Biology

In any field of comparative biology (with or without an evolutionary flavour) one needs to enumerate similarities and differences between individuals, populations and species. It is easy to be tricked by convergent evolution, that is, characteristics coming to resemble one another from unrelated lines of descent and this is as much a problem for molecular as for morphological data. The scale of measurement has to be explicit and it must be possible to cover all outcomes. For DNA sequences there can be nucleotide substitution and shrinking or growing by deletion or insertion. It is easy to score the differences between similar sequences in these terms and to enumerate the steps by which one might have changed into another. Size and shape of skulls can be measured and the transformation of one into another described in spatial coordinates. Morphological characters are hard to place in a single scale and, traditionally, character weighting has been invoked as an artificial means of doing so in the construction of taxonomies. Such artifices are meaningless for phylogenetic inference.

Molecular data tend not to suffer from this disadvantage of not knowing how to measure like things and much can be related to the underlying DNA sequence. Unfortunately, the functional aspects of genes and proteins are not easy to relate to sequence so interpretation may be very difficult. The karyotype, the genetic linkage map, DNA sequences, protein sequences and protein three dimensional structures can all be expected to contain historical information. Biological macromolecules serve to specify the development and function of the organism not to record historical information. We cannot expect to obtain the answers to all our phylogenetic questions but hopefully many problems will be tractable.

To illustrate the range of possibilities here are a few examples of molecular evidence which has been used to elucidate the relationships of primates.

Cell surface polymorphisms have long been available as the ABO system in man. Chimps have A and O (O is rare in other primates) and the gorilla has B only.

The major histocompatibility antigen (MHC) system has perhaps 100 linked loci, many of which have multiple (as many as 20) alleles. There is a considerable similarity in the MHC system between man and chimp, less between man and gorilla.

Chromosome staining techniques give banding patterns, man/chimp retaining 13 identical chromosome pairs, man/gorilla 9 and man/orang 8. It is apparent that blocks have been shuffled.

Enzyme polymorphisms can be readily studied by gel electrophoresis. Of 23 enzymes studied in man, chimp and gorilla there are so few differences that historical information is not forthcoming.

Immunological cross-reactions were the first line of evidence that man, chimp and gorilla formed a group with orang utang being more distant. Previously it had been assumed that man was more distant from the other animals.

DNA hybridization data (reannealing rates in mixed populations of molecules) support the relationship ((man, chimp) gorilla).

3.3 Models for Phylogenetic Iinference

A tree model for the relationships of organisms is the first prerequisite in any attempt to infer species phylogenies. The tree has the leaf nodes representing the extant organisms with the internal nodes representing the splitting on the lineages leading to the present species. A vertical axis represents time in the units of the process of change being studied and can be scaled to siderial time if a splitting point can be estimated from the fossil record. There is a computational problem which results from the fact that there is no way of finding the best tree shape and times to match the data under consideration except by evaluating all trees (this is called an NP-complete problem by computer scientists). Phylogenetic inference is therefore very difficult for more than a few species because of the exponential growth in possibilities (for 10 species there are more than 10 million trees to evaluate). There are ways of avoiding evaluating trees which are sure to be losers (branch and bound algorithms) and opportunities for parallel processing (10 million processors each working on an instance could evaluate the trees in one unit of time). The tree model is a good model for sexually reproducing organisms without inbreeding (as in mammals) and can be derived by a large scale collapsing of the genealogy. With inbreeding and separation and subsequent joining of populations, closed loops are introduced into the genealogical graph and the estimation problem becomes more complex. Migration confounds the study of the evolution of human populations. When a "molecular clock" stochastically constant process of evolutionary change is not imposed as part of the model an unrooted tree is the appropriate graph.

The other component required is the model of change of the property being studied. The model has to be appropriate to the data and includes the assumptions being made about the evolutionary behaviour of the property. In the case of human population gene frequencies for blood groups, Thompson (1975) used a Brownian motion approximation for random genetic drift as the statistical model. Felsenstein (1981) used a Poisson process model of mutation for the evolution of DNA sequences (in the absence of insertion and deletion). These models are a simplification of reality but can be refined as we obtain more understanding of the processes involved. Without a model, no statistical inferences are possible. Inferences are necessarily made within the framework of the model (Bishop et al., 1987) and it is the model which should be the subject of criticism rather than the inferences themselves (conflicting inferences of phylogeny for the same species with different data give a warning signal).

Likelihood inference has been the method of choice for phylogenetic studies (Edwards, 1972). Likelihood theory advocates that the merits of hypotheses are ranked according to their associated likelihood on the same data. The likelihood of an hypothesis H given data D is

$$L(H) = P(D|H) \qquad \text{(EQ 5.1)}$$

All the information in the data on the relative merits of two hypotheses is contained in the likelihood ratio

$$\frac{L(H1)}{L(H2)} \qquad \text{(EQ 5.2)}$$

In the phylogenetic inference problem one is looking for the tree shape and times of the internal nodes which give the highest likelihood. This is a problem in maximum likelihood estimation. It is possible that there may be no single clear winner.

It is important to investigate the fit of the data to the model and not to assume that one has chosen a good model the first time round. Goldman (1993) has devised useful tests of the fit of data to model for the case of DNA sequences.

The popular parsimony estimates of phylogeny (which seek to find the tree topology which minimizes the amount of evolutionary change) are inferior because the model is rather incomplete and has no time structure (Goldman, 1990). However, it should be pointed out that all the methods described in Chapter 7 rely on parsimony.

4 Comparative Genetic and Physical Maps

Chromosomal evolution has added dimensions over the the problem of DNA sequence evolution. Some groups of genes are controlled together and need to be physically adjacent. Others can be located anywhere and we see shuffling of blocks of DNA both within and between chromosomes. Telomeres are important structures to prevent loss of DNA from chromosome ends. Centromeres seem less important and can come and go.

Eventually we hope to know the complete gene orders of the large chromosomes of many higher organisms. At present we know the complete gene orders of the much smaller organelles (mitochondria and chloroplasts). DNA coding for structural RNA or for protein is usually the only part of the genome which is adequately preserved across distant taxa to permit phylogenetic inference. However, these molecules are under considerable selective pressure and must be able to perform their cellular function. Even a single point mutation in double dose can be lethal (sickle cell anaemia is the classic example).

There are doubtless some constraints on gene order but these are less than the constraints on the sequences of functional macromolecules (Farr and Goodfellow, 1991). Gene order is another line of evidence which can be used for phylogenetic inference (Sankoff et al., 1990). By "moving up" a level to gene order rather than gene sequence there may be some advantages in that selective effects are reduced and computation is simpler. Gene order is most directly obtained by the tedious task of complete sequencing, as in the case of the mitochondrial genomes, but a variety of other techniques enable gene order to be established to varying degrees of confidence.

Genetic mapping by linkage and haplotype analysis enables the order of loci to be established along the chromosome. Comparative studies of maps from different species have shown that there are linkage groups conserved across vertebrates (O'Brien, 1987). A review of the conservation of linkage in mammals is given by O'Brien et al. (1988). The most extensively studied pair of species are man and mouse (Searle et al., 1989). Interest in mapping genes in a variety of other mammals (pig, sheep, ox, horse, dog) now gives the opportunity for further studies.

Visible changes in chromosomes arise frequently and are called chromosome aberrations (Suzuki et al., 1981). The changes can involve chromosome parts, whole chromosomes or whole chromosome sets. Changes in chromosome structure are classified as

- Deletions
- Duplications
- Inversions
- Translocations

Any aberration is a group of chromosome segments joined together according to certain basic rules. When aberrations become fixed in a populations they lead to the evolution of a new stable karyotype. The evolutionary model describes the transformation of one karyotype into another by the same basic rules applied over time. The position of centromeres is also subject to change.

Cytological properties of chromosomes have long been studied in relation to animal evolution (White, 1973). The number and morphology of chromosomes varies considerably from species to species. Bands on the giant chromosomes from dipteran salivary glands were noted by Balbiani in 1881 (though he did not realize the structures are chromosomes). Rearrangements of these banding patterns in sibling species of *Drosophila* have enabled the phylogenetic relationships to be inferred (Carson and Kaneshiro, 1976). Banding patterns in the chromosomes of mammals are revealed by the use of dyes (Bickmore and Sumner, 1989). This method makes possible the identification of each of the 23 human chromosomes and the detection of chromosomal abnormalities. The phylogenetic relationships of the primates have been inferred from banding patterns of the chromosomes (Yunis and Prakash, 1982).

It is possible to develop statistical models for the processes of chromosome evolution and tests to check whether a particular combination of tree and chromosomal evolution model is an acceptable explanation of the observed chromosome segment data. The data are the arrangements of the segments in the extant species. Segments may be characterized by their banding patterns (drosophila, primates) and parsimony has been used to analyse the phylogenetic relationships. The recently available data on the order of molecular markers are a much more powerful method of characterizing segments.

There is an interesting complication in the use of molecular markers, which to be adequately conserved over the species of interest will normally be genes coding for proteins. The sequences themselves are evolving and will not be identical in the different species. Genes are also duplicating and deleting to form multigene families of considerable complexity. Visible chromosomal duplications are not the only cause of the proliferation of multigene families. Other processes may be involved such as tandem duplication of individual genes, gene conversion (alteration of part of one copy of a gene by another member of the family), and reverse transcription (incorporation of RNA messages back into genomic DNA).

For single copy genes there is no problem. However, in the case of multigene families a careful study of the members in the species of interest is a pre-requisite for accurate labelling of similar segments from different karyotypes. Intraspecific studies of the distribution of members of multigene families are meaningful. [The two concepts may be described as "species phylogeny" of "orthologous" genes between species and "gene phylogeny" of "paralogous" genes within species.] To complicate matters further there are pseudogenes which are supposed to be non-functional relicts of members of gene families. And finally, some genes are composed of segments of numbers of other genes.

Gene constellations on several human chromosomes may be interpreted as indications of large regional duplications which took place during vertebrate evolution. Four groups of paralogous chromosomal regions can be recognized in both man and mouse, and may be the remnants of two or three rounds of tetraploidization that are likely to have occurred in the vertebrates (Lundin, 1993).

The problem of the identification of conserved segments in chromosomes labelled by unique markers is easier than the problems of aligning molecular sequences, written language, or bird song (Sankoff and Kruskal, 1983). If the markers cannot be uniquely labelled (doubt about gene family relationships) the problem becomes harder but is still soluble. We may expect relationships within multigene families to be clarified in some cases.

We can compare the gene order of two species by means of an Oxford grid (Edwards, 1991). Each row or column represents a chromosome, the larger the chromosome, the wider the row or column. Each homologous locus is plotted in the relevant cell, each cell being referenced by its chromosome number in each of the two species. To give a general impression of the similarity of two species, it is simplest to plot each locus as a point in the cell. A cell with a high point density denotes a large conserved segment of DNA between the species. For examples of this type of grid, see the human-ox (Figure 5.10) and human-mouse (Figure 5.11) grids. It is immediately clear that the number of chromosomal changes in the evolution of these species pairs differs considerably.

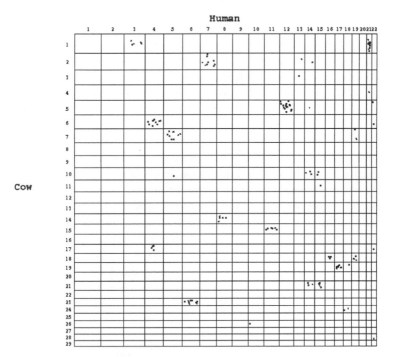

FIGURE 5.10 Oxford grid of human versus ox.

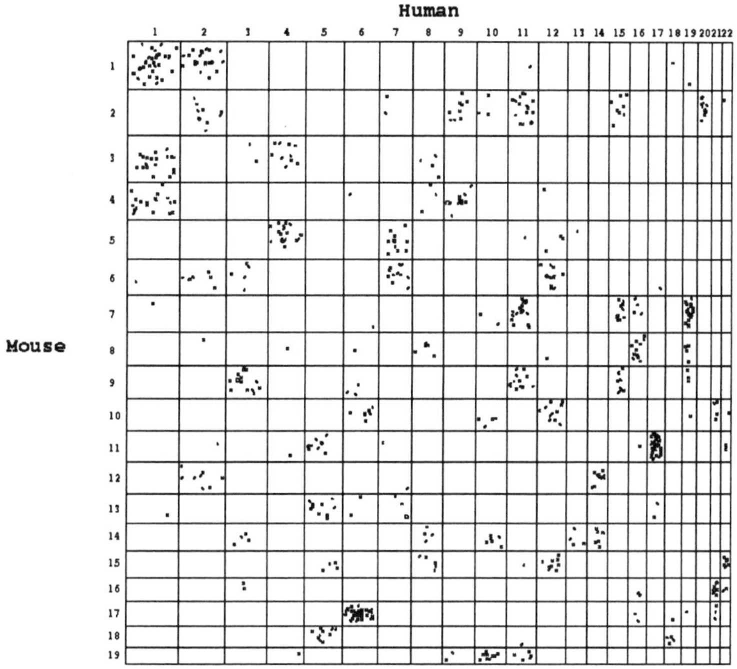

FIGURE 5.11 Oxford grid of human versus mouse.

For a more informative grid, when looking separately at each cell, having "zoomed in", we can draw diagonal lines, rather than individual points, the cells scaled so that the length of the line will directly show the length of the conserved chromosome segment. The orientation of the diagonal indicates if the segment is inverted or not.

Another useful form of display is to choose a chromosome of a first species and place it along the vertical side of a rectangle. The corresponding fragments of chromosomes of the other species are displayed along the horizontal and diagonals drawn as before. A complete diagonal should be produced when adequate data are available (orientation of the fragments can be flipped if necessary). The gene names should be included on the diagram and one would want to choose regions to zoom in and out. This is comparable to an alignment of sequences. Aligned maps of a chromosome of one species against fragments of others are provided by the Encyclopedia of the Mouse Genome (Figure 5.12).

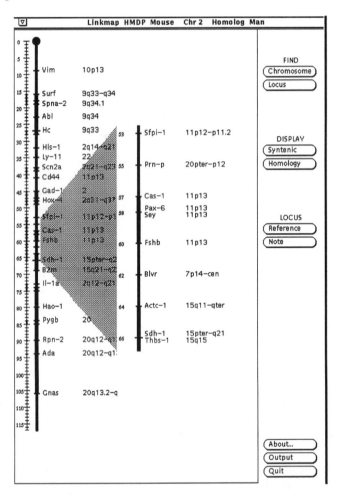

FIGURE 5.12 Comparison of mouse chromosome 2 with the cytogenetic locations of the corresponding markers on human chromosomes as displayed by the Encyclopedia of the Mouse Genome.

An important method is to calculate the minimum number of reciprocal translocations and inversions (whether pericentric or paracentric) required to convert one genome to another (simplest case - currently ignoring duplications, deletions and the very rare transpositions). This has already been done for a special case of the grid by Sankoff et al. (1990). They looked at the gene order for mitochondrial genomes. This problem corresponds to an Oxford grid with one cell. The extended case is obviously more complex although similar methods will be used.

Work is in progress on mammalian chromosomal evolution. The method of inference being used is maximum likelihood. Refined segment data will be produced after examination of the information with display tools which are being developed. Tree patterns and extent of divergence will be estimated from the segment data under the evolutionary models. The movement of chromosomal segments is framed in terms of a birth-death process of the links (compare Thorne et al., 1992). Validity of the models may be checked by Monte Carlo methods (Goldman, 1993).

5   Genome Sequencing

Genome sequencing is proceeding at quite a rapid pace, given the current technology, in a number of model organisms.

There a number of efforts to sequence *Escherichia coli*. The group of Fred Blattner is using a set of overlapping lambda clones from the wild-type strain MG1655. Initially they are sequencing the megabase spanning 80-100 minutes on the chromosome including the origin of replication oriC at 84 minutes. A report of progress is published in Daniels et al. (1992). In the 82-93 minute region more than 80% of the sequence consists of protein encoding genes (identified or as potential open reading frames (ORFs)). Four of the seven RNA operons are also within this region. Other features of interest include repeated sequences (Chi sites, REP elements and IRU sequences), as well as integration sites for lysogenic phage.

For yeast, chromosome III is complete (Oliver et al., 1992) and chromosomes II and XI are expected to be complete in 1993. So far, 346 ORFs have been detected on chromosome II and 369 ORFs on chromosome XI. Of these, 20% are known yeast genes, 20% are similar to known genes (from yeast or other organisms), 30% have only weak similarity to known genes and 30% are totally new.

In the nematode *Caenorhabditis elegans* it is planned to sequence 3 Mb as a pilot project by 1994 and to complete the entire 100 Mb genome in a few years from then. The first results have been reported by Sulston et al. (1992). To date, 1.2 Mb have been submitted to the public databases and 223 genes have been predicted, giving a density of 1 gene in 6 kb. About one third of the genes have matches to previous database entries. Comparison of the cDNA matches in the region (49) with the total known (3491) leads to an estimate of 16,000 genes in the nematode genome.

There appear to no major efforts to sequence human genomic DNA at present. The effort has been concentrated on sequencing cDNA. This strategy has led to the accumulation of 20,000 sequences (some from model organisms also) in dbEST. The cDNA strategy could go a long way to finding a large proportion of human genes (?80%) without having to sequence the genome. Genomic sequencing will be necessary to find all the genes in the human genome.

6 Comparative Sequence Studies

This is the subject of Chapter 7 and to some extent Chapter 8 so I am presenting a few miscellaneous topics not dealt with elsewhere.

6.1 Entrez

"Entrez: Sequences" is a retrieval system developed at the NCBI which provides an integrated approach for gaining access to nucleotide and protein sequence databases (GenBank, PIR and SwissProt databases), to the MEDLINE citations in which the sequences were published, and to a sequence-associated subset of MEDLINE. With Entrez, the user can rapidly search several hundred megabytes of sequence and literature data. The retrieval software and associated databases are distributed on a CD-ROM, but may be installed on a file server or local network if desired.

A key feature of the system is the concept of "neighbouring", which permits a user to locate related references or sequences by asking Entrez to "Find all papers that are like this one" (Figure 5.13) or "Find all similar sequences". The neighbours are pre-computed using algorithms developed at the NCBI that relate records within the same database (e.g. GenBank) by statistical measurements of similarity. In addition to neighbouring, there are also "hard links", which are very specific connections between entries in different databases. For each MEDLINE article, there are hard links to any protein or nucleotide sequences that were published in that article, and the cited protein or nucleotide sequences have reciprocal hard links back to the MEDLINE articles. Nucleotide sequences and the proteins derived from them by conceptual translation also have hard links to one another. The pre-computed neighbours and hard links are stored on the CD-ROM along with the databases and retrieval indices.

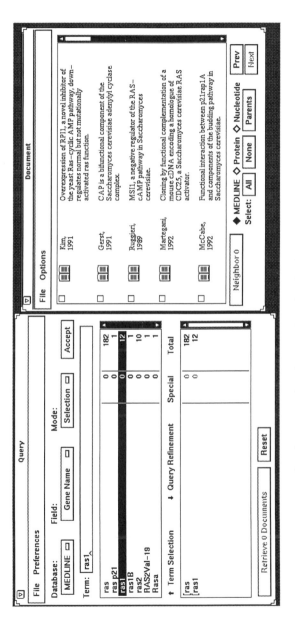

FIGURE 5.13 Entrez retrieval system showing results of selecting ras as a starting gene name and neighbouring on references relating to yeast.

The ability to traverse the literature and molecular sequences via neighbours and links provides a very powerful yet intuitive way of accessing the information in those databases. Given a record or sequence of interest, the user can switch to the appropriate entry in a different database for viewing the associated record or for neighbouring within that database.

6.2 Blocks

Blocks are short multiply aligned ungapped segments corresponding to the most highly conserved regions of proteins. A database of blocks has been constructed by successive application of the automated PROTOMAT system to individual entries in the PROSITE catalogue of protein groups keyed to the SwissProt protein sequence databank. The rationale behind searching a database of blocks is that information from multiply aligned sequences is present in a concentrated form, reducing background and increasing sensitivity to distant relationships. If a particular block scores highly, it is possible that the sequence is related to the group of sequences the block represents. Typically, a group of proteins has more than one region in common and their relationship is represented as a series of blocks separated by unaligned regions. If a second block for a group also scores highly in the search, the evidence that the sequence is related to the group is strengthened, and is further strengthened if a third block also scores it highly, and so on.

6.3 How Many Genes are Phylum Specific?

Approximately two thirds of the genes being discovered in the *E. coli*, yeast, nematode and human (cDNA) sequencing projects are new and unrelated to each other or to anything in the sequence databases. This suggests that the majority of genes with recognizable similarities across phyla are already known (Green et al., 1993). The number of these ancient conserved regions contained in SwissProt is presently 730, of which two thirds correspond to known conserved regions catalogued in the Blocks Database. The total number of such conserved families is estimated to be about 860.

The indications are that two thirds of genes are phylum specific or are evolving so rapidly that the distant relatives are no longer recognizable on the basis of sequence. Interpretation of human genome sequences will be greatly aided by sequencing the corresponding gene from other vertebrates such as the mouse or fugu. Inference of exon-intron structure and control regions will be much firmer based on three species rather than one. Fugu, the Pacific puffer fish, has a genome size of around 390 Mb and contains less than 10% or repetitive DNA. The dystrophin gene spans about 250 kb in man but a dystrophin-like region in fugu is only 22 kb. The coding sequence, intron-exon positions and exon organization are all highly conserved. Only one dystrophin-like gene has been detected in fugu and it is likely to be the gene which gave rise to both dystrophin and utrophin in man (Elgar and Brenner, 1993).

6.4   Models for Estimation of Phylogeny from Sequence Data

The earliest models for DNA sequence evolution (Felsenstein, 1981) were incomplete because they did not consider insertion and deletion. It should be possible to infer phylogenies and multiple sequence alignments from DNA sequences in a single operation. This goal has not yet been attained. Bishop et al., (1987) were pioneers in the inclusion of insertion and deletion into the model. Their method was much improved by the work of Thorne et al. (1991) who represented the insertion-deletion process as a birth-death process of imaginary links that separate single nucleotides. Thorne et al. (1992) made a further improvement by considering fragments of DNA being inserted or deleted rather than single nucleotides. These methods work for pairs of sequences and could be extended to joint estimates for multiple sequences.

DNA sequence data are going to provide raw material for investigation of these and many other statistical problems in the years to come.

7   Acknowledgements

I am grateful to Anthony Edwards, John Edwards, Nick Goldman and many other individuals for informative discussions on the topics discussed in this chapter.

8   References

Bishop MJ, Friday AE and Thompson EA (1987). Inference of evolutionary relationships. In "Nucleic acid and protein sequence analysis. A practical approach" (eds MJ Bishop and CJ Rawlings), pp. 359-385. IRL Press, Oxford.

Bickmore WA and Sumner AT (1989). Mammalian chromosome banding - an expression of genome organisation. TIG 5, 144-148.

Cannings C and Thompson EA (1981). "Genealogical and Genetic Structure". Cambridge University Press, Cambridge.

Carson HL and Kaneshiro KY (1976). *Drosophila* of Hawaii: systematics and ecological genetics. Ann. Rev. Ecol. Systematics 7, 311-345.

Daniels D, Plunkett G, Burland V and Blattner FR (1992). Analysis of the *Escherichia coli* genome: DNA sequence of the region from 84.5 to 86.5 minutes. Science 257, 771-778.

Edwards AWF (1972). "Likelihood". Cambridge University Press, Cambridge.

Edwards JH (1991). The Oxford Grid. Ann. Hum. Genet. 55, 17-31.

Elgar G and Brenner S (1993). Preliminary genomic sequencing and characterisation of the dystrophin/utrophin homolog in a small vertebrate genome. Abstracts of the meeting "Genome Mapping and Sequencing". Cold Spring Harbor Laboratory, New York.

Farr CJ and Goodfellow PN (1991). Hidden messages in genetic maps. Science 258, 49.

Felsenstein, J (1981). Evolutionary trees from DNA sequences: a maximum likelihood approach. J. Mol. Evol. 17, 368-376.

Fujii J, Otsu K, Zorzato F, de Leon S, Khanna VK, Weiler JE, O'Brien PJ and MacLennan DH (1991). Identification of a mutation in the porcine ryanodine receptor associated with malignant hyperthermia. Science 253, 448-451.

Gillard EF, Otsu K, Fujii J, Khanna VK, de Leon S, Derdemezi J, Britt BA, Duff CL, Worton RG and MacLennan DH (1991). A substitution of cysteine for arginine 614 in the ryanodine receptor is potentially causative of human malignant hyperthermia. Genomics 11, 751-755.

Goldman N (1990). Maximum likelihood inference of phylogenetic trees, with special reference to a Poisson process model of DNA substitution and to parsimony analysis. Syst. Zool. 39, 345-361.

Goldman N (1993). Statistical tests of models of DNA substitution. J. Mol. Evol. 36, 182-198.

Green P, Lipman DJ, Hillier L, States D, Waterston R and Claverie J-M (1993). Ancient conserved regions in new gene sequences and the protein databases. Science 259(5102), 1711-6.

Hillyard AL, Doolittle DP, Davisson MT and Roderick TH (1992). Locus map of mouse. Mouse Genome 90, 8-21.

Huntington's Disease Collaborative Research Group (1993). A novel gene containing a trinucleotide repeat that is expanded and unstable on Huntington's Disease chromosomes. Cell 72, 971-983.

Lundin LG (1993). Evolution of the vertebrate genome as reflected in paralogous chromosomal regions in man and the house mouse. Genomics 16, 1-19.

Lyon MF and Kirby MC (1992). Mouse chromosome atlas. Mouse Genome 90, 22-44.

Morton NE (1988). Multipoint mapping and the emperor's clothes. Ann. Hum. Genet. 52, 309-318.

Morton NE (1991). Parameters of the human genome. Proc. Natl Acad. Sci. USA 88, 7474-7476.

NIH/CEPH Collaborative Mapping Group (1992). A comprehensive genetic linkage map of the human genome. Science 258, 67-86.

O'Brien SJ (ed.) (1987). "Genetic Maps". Cold Spring Harbor Laboratory, New York.

O'Brien SJ, Seuanez HN and Womack JE (1988). Mammalian genome organisation: an evolutionary view. Ann. Rev. Genet. 22, 232-251.

Oliver SG, van der Aart QJ, Agostoni-Carbone ML, Aigle M, Alberghina L, Alexandraki D, Antoine G, Ballesta JP, Benit P et al. (1992). The complete DNA sequence of yeast chromosome III. Nature 357, 38-46.

Sankoff D and Kruskal JB (1983). "Time Warps, String Edits and Macromolecules." Addison-Wesley, Reading, MA.

Sankoff D, Cedergren R and Abel Y (1990). Genomic divergence through gene rearrangement. Methods Enzymol. 183, 428-438.

Searle AG, Peters J, Lyon MF, Hall JG, Evans EP, Edwards JH and Buckle VJ (1989). Chromosome maps of man and mouse. IV. Ann. Hum. Genet. 53, 89-140.

Sturtevant AH (1913). The linear association of six sex-linked markers in *Drosophila*. J. Exp. Zool. 14, 43-49.

Sulston J, Du Z, Thomas K, Wilson R, Hillier L, Staden R, Halloran N, Green P, Thierry-Mieg J, Qiu L et al. (1992) The *C. elegans* genome sequencing project: a beginning. Nature 356, 37-41.

Suzuki DT Griffiths AJF and Lewontin RC (1981). "An Introduction to Genetic Analysis." Freeman, San Francisco.

Thompson EA (1975). "Human Evolutionary Trees". Cambridge University Press, Cambridge.

Thorne JL, Kishino H and Felsenstein J (1991). An evolutionary model for maximum likelihood alignment of DNA sequences. J. Mol. Evol. 33, 114-124.

Thorne JL, Kishino H and Felsenstein J (1992). Inching toward reality: an improved likelihood model of sequence evolution. J. Mol. Evol. 34, 3-16.

White MJD (1973). "Animal Cytology and Evolution". Cambridge University Press, Cambridge.

Yunis JJ and Prakash O (1982). The origin of man: a chromosomal pictorial legacy. Science 215, 1525-1529.

CHAPTER 6

DNA Sequence Assembly on Unix Systems

*D. Stephen Charnock-Jones[1] and
S. A. J. R. Aparicio[2]*

[1] Department of Obstetrics and Gynaecology and
[2] Molecular Genetics, Department of Medicine, The
Clinical School, University of Cambridge, Cambridge
CB2 2QQ, UK
Internet: dscj1@mbui.bio.cam.ac.uk

1   Introduction

The determination of the sequence of nucleotide bases in a gene (or genome) is a complex process involving many steps, only one of which can legitimately be called DNA sequencing. The gene or region of interest usually has to be isolated in an appropriate cloning vector before any sequencing can be carried out. Once the gene has been successfully isolated, sub-cloning will almost certainly be required to obtain fragments which can be analysed. Current sequencing methods are limited by the need for electrophoretic separation of their reaction products. Excluding primer walking, (which is not applicable to large projects because of its high cost and slow speed) all methods rely on fragmenting a region of interest and assembling the complete sequence from the partial sequences of many fragments. These methods include mechanical shearing, frequent-cutter restriction enzymes and nested ExoIII deletions. We do not address here the biological problems of template preparation and the sequencing reactions, but seek to illustrate the process of assembling the whole sequence from the fragments obtained. Powerful and efficient software is required to handle the volume and complexity of information generated by all but the smallest of projects. Several packages with refined user interfaces exist for IBM-PC and Apple Macintosh computers, however none of these were developed for large (lambda-insert size and above) so that such packages do not offer the speed and accessibility of the Unix/X-windows equivalents. The software described was designed and written by Rodger Staden and colleagues for large projects using fluorescent sequencers (Staden and Dear, 1991), however much of what follows is directly applicable to smaller or radioactively based sequencing projects which, historically, provided the basis for developing sequence assembly programs.

2   Overview

The most efficient method of determining sequences over 3-5 kb in length is to use a "shotgun" approach. This implies that the sequence in question be mechanically sheared or cut with restriction enzymes and that the resulting smaller sub-clones are used as sequencing templates. This precludes any information a priori about the relative orientation of these clones, however if sufficient numbers are sequenced overlaps in sequences can be found which allow the sub-clones to be orientated with respect to each other. Once enough sub-clones have been sequenced the whole parent sequence can then be reconstructed. DNA sequencing performed in this way generates large amounts of data and a computerized system is essential for analysis and manipulation. Sequencing a 40 kb cosmid may generate 600 gel readings. All of these processes, referred to as sequence assembly or contig assembly, are carried out by the program xbap (X-windows big assembly program.)

The central concept of this program is that of the contig. A contig (derived from the word contiguous) is a set of gel readings or sequences which are related to each other by virtue of overlapping sequence. A contig is made up of one or more gel readings and all gel readings belong to a contig. Initially, as the first gel readings are entered into the database no overlaps are found and each gel reading is entered into a new contig. Eventually sufficient sequences will be entered such that new sequences overlap partially with existing gel readings and the incoming sequence is then entered into that contig. As the contigs grow in size, overlaps between contigs will be found and these contigs are joined, reducing the number of contigs in the database. Ultimately there will be only one contig which spans the region being sequenced and it will contain all the gel readings. The overall process of reconstructing a parent sequence is outlined in Table 6.1.

TABLE 6.1 The overall process of reconstructing a parent sequence

PROCESS	Software solution
(a) Data transfer to a Unix computer	(local)
(b) Removing poor quality sequence data	ted
(c) Screening for vector sequences	vep
(d) Assembling sequences and editing contigs	xbap
(e) Searching for internal joins, determining quality and designing walking primers to bridge gaps in the consensus	xbap

These processes have been automated to varying degrees and continuing software development aims towards the automation of the whole process once data transfer has been initiated. The programs described run in an X-windows environment on Unix workstations and although we assume some knowledge of this environment, an introduction is provided in Chapter 1. One important point to remember about this interface is that the arrow denoting the mouse cursor renders a dialogue box active only when it is positioned over that box. If, for example, a box appears prompting the user for a file name, the arrow or bar cursor must be over the box in order to type in the response.

3   Data Transfer

The fluorescent sequencers in current use, the ABI 373A and the Pharmacia ALF, have dedicated micro-computers attached for data capture. These data must be transferred to the Unix machine where the assembly is to be performed. The details of this process are network specific, however the following general points can be made. In the case of the ABI 373A, a sequencing run with 24 samples will generate approximately 2.5 Mb of data which require transfer. The physical link between micro-computer and Unix workstation is therefore important and in our experience Ethernet provides the best solution (as an example, we transfer the 2.5 Mb of data in less than 2 minutes using Eethernet). Software for effecting the transfer is widely available (we use AppleShare and the Columbia Appletalk Package) and can be FTP based or AppleShare based. Since files will be transferred to a Unix machine it is important to use file names which are legal in both environments - this means avoiding the characters ~`!@$%^&*()+={}[]|\'":;<,?/ and spaces, in the file names. Unix is also case sensitive; we keep all file names lower case to avoid confusion. In the case of the ABI 373A one can fill in the file names in the sample sheet, using meaningful names rather than the default Sample 01, Sample 02, etc. In the case of the ABI 373A two file types are generated for each clone. The key file is the chromatogram file which contains the fluorescent trace data for a given sample and has the file name as specified in the sample sheet, with no suffix. This file type forms the basis of the raw input to the trace editor TED. The second file contains the nucleotide sequence as plain text, and will have the file name given in the sample sheet with the suffix .Seq. This file is unnecessary since new sequence files will be written during the pre-processing steps. In order to reduce the amount of space taken up by the storage of the trace data and also to permit the analysis of sequence data derived from a wide variety of sources including both autoradiograph scanners as well as fluorescence based machines a standard file format has been defined by Dear and Staden (1992). Obviously xbap can read this (SCF) type of file.

4   Trace Editor (ted)

The output from a fluorescent sequencing run always contains data toward the end of the run which is of poor quality (i.e. it is inaccurate). There may also be some vector derived sequence at the start of the run. It is vital that the vector sequence be removed prior to contig assembly since it clearly would interfere with this process and it should never form part of the finished sequence. The sequence from later in the run where the quality is unacceptably low also needs to be removed. The program ted (Trace EDitor) was written to allow users to view the traces and edit them as they saw fit (Gleeson & Hillier, 1991). Thus after the data has been transferred from the Macintosh or PC, ted is run to process the data from each sequencing reaction. The program vep (see below) performs the vector pruning automatically so that ted is now mostly used to cut off poor quality data.

Ted may be invoked simply with the command

```
ted
```

Initially the editor window is empty. After clicking input, a dialogue box appears prompting for the trace file name. This dialogue also allow the format of the data to be read by ted to be set by the buttons which are marked ABI, ALF, SCF and plain. The strand to be read is set by the buttons "top" and "bottom". The trace is then displayed and the sequence can be examined. The name of the file being viewed is shown in the top right-hand corner of the ted window. The horizontal scroll bar moves the sequence to the left (left mouse button), the right mouse button moves the sequence to the right, and the middle mouse button causes the sequence to jump to the same relative position in the sequence as that of the cursor within the scroll bar. The magnification can also be altered with the "Scale up" and "Scale down" buttons. Two lines of bases are shown above the traces, the lower is the sequence as determined by the sequencing machine, the upper may be edited. However it is strongly recommended that the sequence is **NOT** edited at this point. The base-calling algorithms used by the machines are increasingly refined and if the machine calls an ambiguity then it is generally foolish to try to improve it based on the single gel read being viewed at the time. Once the gel reading has been entered into a contig there will be other overlapping gels which will allow resolution of the ambiguity and editing is best left until that stage.

ted allows the vector sequence or poor quality sequence at the left of the read to be cut off. This is done by selecting "Adjust left cut off". The pointer is placed to the left of the first base one wishes to leave in the sequence and the left mouse button pressed.

The entire sequence to the left of this point is dimmed and the background turned to grey (Figure 6.1).

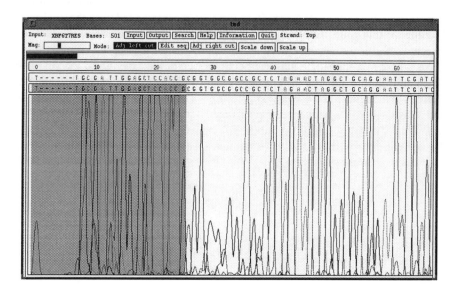

FIGURE 6.1 This figure shows a grey scale representation of a typical ted window. The menu options are displayed on the bar above the fluorescent trace data. Bases 0-25 have been "clipped" as they are vector derived. Although colour is not a strict system requirement, the colour coding of the peaks performed by xdap greatly aids manual identification of the bases.

If the majority of the sequencing is performed with the same vector and primer combination then the junction between the vector and the insert can rapidly be found using the search function, although vep has now rendered this largely unnecessary. If search is selected then a dialogue box appears prompting for either the nucleotide sequence or the base number (position) to be searched for. The cursor is then positioned at this point. The right cutoff is adjusted in a similar way but the choice of position is less easy to make. Clearly at the very end of the run the data will be poor but at some point in the run they will change from acceptable to unacceptable. It is prudent to be conservative and err on the side of caution by clipping off quite a lot of data. These data are not lost and can easily be incorporated into the growing contigs later. ted marks the clipped data from both ends but the entire sequence is passed to xbap and the cutoffs can be adjusted latter within this program. This feature of retaining the clipped (and therefore slightly less reliable data) for future possible inclusion into the contigs is an added benefit derived from the long runs obtained by fluorescent sequencing.

Once the cut offs have been selected an output file needs to be created. This is done by selecting "Output", which brings up a dialogue box prompting for the output file name. If a batch script is in use then the output filename will be inserted automatically, otherwise any name can be chosen but it is clearly sensible if it is related to the initial trace file name. There are two output file formats and the user is asked to select between them. One simply writes a plain text file containing only sequence between the cutoffs (if any were set). The second format "with header" contains the good data, and the clipped data in a format that allows xbap to make use of the cutoff data, if so desired. This latter format should always be selected if the data are to be used by xbap.

Besides standard X arguments (which allow you to specify the font used or the background colour for example) there are other ted specific arguments available. For example

```
ted -ABI myfile -baseNum 80 -mag 60
```

would open the ABI format file "myfile" with the caret positioned at base 80 with the magnification set at 60%.

There is also a help button which invokes the help screen. This is rather limited and somewhat out of date but gives some information on the arguments that can be used with ted.

Although the trace editor may be invoked by hand it is possible to automate some of the process by invoking the program repetitively using a shell script. A very simple shell example is given below, more complicated scripts exist with error checking and other features, however this script should work on any Unix system with the C-shell. A restriction of this script is that in the directory in which it is invoked, the only files should be chromatogram files. The commands should be typed into a file called (for example) abi2sun and the file given execute permissions using the Unix command chmod.

```
#!/bin/csh
# simple script for invoking ted repetitively on files within a directory
foreach file (*)
  ted -ABI $file -output $file.proc
  mv $file $fileRES
end

touch $cwd.files
ls *.proc >> $cwd.files

# end of script
```

The programs xbap and vep operate most efficiently when they are given a file containing the names of the actual data files to be processed. Although both programs can process individual files, the use of a file of file names removes much tedious typing for the user. The Unix command ls may be used to generate a file of file names.

When invoked, this script will process all the chromatograms in the directory and insert the output file name automatically into the ted dialogue box. The only action which the user needs to take is to set the cutoffs as required and then select output from the dialogue box and choose "output with header". The output file name will be automatically specified. Upon selecting quit, a new ted window appears with the next sequence. This process continues until all the files have been processed. A file of the output file names called "filelist" is generated. This file may be used as input to the vep and xbap programs.

5   Editing Out Vector Sequences

Although the xbap program contains a menu option allowing the user to screen against vector sequences, this is a tedious process. The program vep has been designed (by Rodger Staden) to automate this process. At the time of writing vep does not have an X-windows interface, however the degree of interaction required does not necessitate such an interface. Although the program is designed to be part of a script it can be invoked with the command

vep

The first request is for a file of file names which require processing. This can be created by the user manually, or the filelist output from the abi2sun script may be used. Next the vector sequence file name will be prompted for. This should be a file containing the user's vector sequence in Staden format. In its simplest form this is a sequence with no header line and sequence formatted to 60 characters per line. The program default option is M13mp18.seq. The 3' side of the cloning site is asked for (the start of the vector sequence is assumed to be position 1). Responding with 0 denotes that the vector was a cosmid. The next prompt asks for the relative position of the primer to the cloning site. The following three prompts allow the user to change the gap penalties and other matching parameters used by the program. In our experience, the default settings (obtained by pressing return to each question) are quite suitable. The final prompt is for a file name to store the list of passed file names. The program will search all the input files for partial or complete matches to vector sequence. Partial matches are edited out automatically by adjusting the cutoff sequences in the original files. Sequences judged to be completely vector are renamed to add a suffix which is the name of the vector sequence being used. So, for example, if the sequence file myseq1.sdn was a complete match to M13mp18.seq, the file would be renamed to myseq1.sdn.M13mp18. These files do not appear in the file of passed filenames. When searching has finished, a summary of sequences processed and the proportion of clean, partial vector or wholly vector containing files is printed.

6   Sequence Assembly - The xbap Program

6.1   Starting a New Project

When xbap is run (with the command **xbap**) three windows appear. They are labelled "Graphics" where any graphic output is displayed, "Output" for text output, and "Dialogue" is the window where commands are entered and prompts given. The "output" and "graphics" windows can be re-sized and any of the windows can be moved around or closed temporarily. There are three main menus in the "Dialogue" window which contain the various options. In addition the name of the function currently being executed is shown with the name and version number of the database in use. The contents of the pull down menu boxes are shown in Table 6.2.

TABLE 6.2 Contents of the pull down menu boxes in xbap

General menu	Screen	Modification menu
Open database	Clear graphics	Edit Contig
Display contig	clear text	AutoAssemble
List a text file	Draw ruler	Join Contigs
Redirect output	Use crosshair	Complement a Contig
Calculate a consensus	Change margins	Find Internal Joins
Screen against enzymes	Label diagram	Alter relationships
Screen against vector	Plot map	AutoEdit Contig
Check database	Plot single contig	Disassemble gel readings
Copy database	Plot all contigs	Extract Gel Readings
Show relationships		
Set parameters		
Highlight disagreements		
Examine Quality		

Rather than describe each of these functions in turn we shall illustrate their use in the order one would come across them if carrying out a sequencing project. There is also a button which toggles between execute and execute with dialogue. The "with dialogue" allows the use of alternate settings.

6.2   How Information is Stored by xbap

As already mentioned xbap utilizes a specialized database for the storage, manipulation and assembly of the DNA sequence data. On opening you will be prompted in the Dialogue box to "open existing database" or "start new database". Clearly the first time xbap is run a new database is needed. You will then be prompted for the name (this must be between 1 and 12 letters in length and must not contain a full stop; it is not case sensitive), the size of the database (this is the sum of the number of gel readings and the number of contigs to be entered into the database, but this can be altered later as necessary), the maximum gel reading length (this is initially set at 512) and finally whether the database is for DNA or Protein. (These latter two options may seem incongruous but this system can be used to generate multiple protein alignments, however this application is not discussed further here.)

The database is comprised of 5 files which are read by xbap and each database has a version number built into its file name. Thus for version 1 of the database "mygene" would be comprised of the files MYGENE.AR1, MYGENE.RL1, MYGENE.SQ1, MYGENE.TG1, MYGENE.CC1. The format of each of these files is precisely defined and therefore they should not be tampered with. In order to prevent multiple access to the database (this could occur if several people are working on the same project) which would corrupt the data, xbap writes a file with the name and version of the database <name>_BUSY<version>. This file is created each time a database is opened and is deleted when the database is closed down cleanly. In the above example this would be MYGENE_BUSY1. It is very important to leave the program by selecting "quit application" rather than killing the program, since unscheduled exits will at best fail to delete the lock file and at worst may leave one or more of the essential files corrupted and potentially unusable.

The contigs are not stored in the computer in the same way as they are presented on screen. The relationships file (MYGENE.RL1 above) contains sufficient information about each gel and its neighbourhoods (i.e. its length, which gels it overlaps and at what position) to allow the program to reconstruct the contig from the individual gel reads. The other files contain the sequences as they are modified (edited) during assembly, the list of original gel reading file names (the archive data) and information concerning the type, position and content of any added annotation (this includes the description of the clipped data). The system used for identifying each gel is also important. Each gel reading can be identified in one of two ways. Firstly by name, i.e. the file name as given when the data were written by ted. To denote that this is a name it is preceded by the slash "/" symbol (for example /outputfile.seq). The alternative is by number. This is how gels are identified by the program. Each gel as it is entered into the database is given a number (so the first gel is number 1, the second 2, etc.). Contigs are identified by the number of the left-most gel within them. (So for contig number 10 the gel that was entered into the database, 10th defines the extreme left end of this contig and uniquely identifies this contig.) If a new gel (number 54 for instance) is subsequently entered which extends contig 10 leftward then this contig would be identified as contig number 54. Some of the overlaps found will be in the opposite sense (in other words the reverse complement of a new sequence will match a contig already in the database). In this case the reverse complement of this new sequence will be entered into the contig and because the reverse complement was entered will be denoted by giving the gel a negative number (-14 for example). Thus all gels and contigs can be unambiguously identified by number and the sense of the original gel read inferred by the presence or absence of a minus sign.

Having now written the database files we are ready to begin entering the data. It is possible or even probable that some of the gel reads will contain some sequence derived from either the sequencing vector or the cloning vector. It is absolutely essential that these sequences are excluded from the database. This is frequently not done and vector sequences have been found in "real genes". Prior to the writing of vep, this process was carried out from within the xbap program by selecting "Screen against vector" and using a file of file names generated by the user. Although vector can still be searched for in this way, it is highly recommended that vep is used in preference since this performs the editing step automatically. If the xbap facility is used, then the user has the option to screen one file or a file of file names as with vep, but no editing is performed. A vector file must provided; this should be in Staden format and a limit of 500,000 nucleotides exists. File names which pass the screen are written to a new file of filenames nominated by the user.

A similar screening function is to "Screen against enzymes". This is useful if it is known that the cloned fragments do not contain certain restriction enzyme sites (for example if non-random cloning has been used to generate the sequencing templates). This function works in a very similar manner to that described above. The recognition sequences for the restriction enzymes are stored in a simple text file, one per line.

6.3   Assembling the Sequences

All the gel reads that passed the screening routines may be entered into the database and assembled into contigs. The function "Auto Assemble", under the Modification menu is used for this purpose. As with the screening functions, single gel read file names can be typed in, however it is much more efficient to use a file of file names.

Once initiated, any number of gel reads can be processed without any intervention. It is possible to run through the whole assembly procedure but not to permit entry of new data into the database; in this case alignments are produced and displayed in the Output window, however at the outset it is usual to permit entry and also the joining of contigs to start the contig building. The next option to confront the user involves choosing between "Perform normal assembly", "Put all readings into separate contigs" and "Put all readings into one contig". The latter is only really of use for producing multiple sequence alignments and will not be discussed further here. The usual choice is "Perform normal assembly". Following this selection, several different parameters are prompted which control how the searching and alignments are carried out, as follows:

1. The minimum initial match and minimum alignment block determines the stringency of the initial searches for overlaps.

2. The maximum number of pad characters which can be inserted into the gel reading and the contig, to improve the initial alignment.

3. The maximum percentage mismatch between two putative overlapping sequences when optimally aligned within the first two constraints.

Default values are offered for these and it is recommended that the user tries out small scale alignments to become familiar with the effects of changing these values. The percentage mismatch is especially critical when regions of repetitive DNA are being assembled; the default value is 8%, and the maximum permitted is 15%.

New gel readings that do not match an existing contig are entered into the database and form new single-gel contigs. Gel readings that do match are aligned with the contig in question and, provided the number of padding characters added to gel and contig and the percentage mismatch is not above the limits previously set, the gel is entered and added to the contig in the database. Gels that match two contigs without exceeding these parameters will automatically join these contigs. Gels which fail (for any reason) are not entered and they have their names written to a new file (specified by the user when prompted for "Filename for failed gels") of file names. These gels can then be further processed with different alignment conditions or separately entered into individual contigs which are then joined manually.

6.4   Assembly Strategy

The strategy employed for the contig assembly may vary slightly from gene to gene. In some cases the procedure will be as described above using the default values throughout, however there will be instances when highly repetitive sequences are being assembled and a slightly different approach is needed. The object is to avoid scrambling the contigs by incorrectly placing repetitive sequences which do not have enough unique information to be located correctly in a given contig. If, for example, the sequence contains many Alu (or any other) repeats it may be advisable to identify Alu containing gel readings and to enter these last. This can be achieved in several ways, for example, searching the fragments against DNA databases to identify repeats or by clustering the DNA sequences using programs such as ICAtools (Parsons et al., 1992). The latter produces pairwise local similarity groupings which allow abundant repeats to be identified. The GCG program "repeat" is also effective. If the repetitive element is known or suspected, the facility "Screen against vector" may be used, with a "vector" file that contains the sequence of the repetitive element. A new program (rep) which is similar to vep has been recently written to search for Alu type sequences. Once the unique sequences are in the database, the sequences containing repetitive **AND** unique sequence can be added. These may be selected by using "AutoAssemble" but not permitting entry. The alignments produced in the output window should be studied and the gels that extend the ends of contigs (into repetitive regions) identified. The remaining gels that are largely comprised of repetitive sequences can then be added using very stringent match criteria. Remember here that the clipped data obtained from the end of the run, while they will not be base perfect, may suggest their location if they contain unique sequences.

6.5   Editing and Joining Contigs

Having entered several gel reads into the database the next stage is to examine the contigs and with reference to the original data make edits to resolve conflicts. After editing there may be contigs that can be joined, and gels which failed automatic entry need to be entered manually. The key to these procedures is the contig editor. This is a fully functional screen editor and is the most impressive part of the program. It allows a contig to be viewed showing all the aligned gel reads and as either the consensus or individual gels are edited the consensus is continually updated. The fluorescent traces for each gel can also be viewed on screen (up to four at any one time) to allow the user to resolve ambiguities based on all the data available.

"Edit Contig" is selected from the Modification menu and the contig to be edited indicated by name or number (see below on using the graphics to find contig identities). A window similar to the one shown in Figure 6.2 will appear with the cursor positioned at the left end of the gel selected.

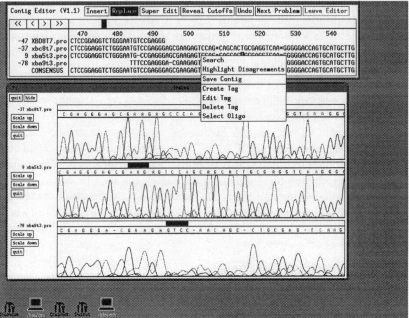

FIGURE 6.2 This figure is a grey scale representation of the contig editor, tag menu window and trace windows of xdap. Each window is identified in the bar at the top. The trace window was invoked by placing the cursor on a base and double clicking the middle mouse button. The tag window is invoked by holding control and the left mouse button over a region of the contig editor window.

Although the contig is most correctly identified by the number of its left-most gel the program will identify a contig by any gel contained with in it. The cursor can be positioned any where within the contig by use of the scroll buttons: "<" and ">" scroll left or right by a single character "<<" and ">>" scroll half a screen left or right. The mouse buttons can also be used for scrolling when the pointer is within the scroll bar. The left and right buttons scroll one screen forward and backward, and the middle button sets the editor position similarly to ted. The button marked "Find Next Problem" moves the cursor to the next padding character (*) or next ambiguity (-) in the consensus.

Editing can be in one of two modes, either "Insert" or "Replace". These are fairly self-explanatory, "Replace" allows the selected character to be replaced with another and "Insert" allows the insertion of one or more characters which are typed in from the keyboard. (The delete key will delete one character to the left of the cursor.) Insertions or deletions made to the consensus line also affect each gel reading in the contig at that point since all gels must remain in register. However, this can be over ridden using the "Super Edit" mode. When this button is highlighted, changes can be made to any position in the contig. This is potentially dangerous as alignments between gel readings can be altered, so this function should be used with caution. If an error is made the "Undo" button will undo the previous operation. Also no changes are made to the working copy of the database until you check "Leave Editor" and at this point the option to leave the editor without saving changes is offered. Thus no error is irreversible.

The key step when editing is the review of the original data. Previously this would have required painstaking examination and cross-referencing of large numbers of auto-radiographs. Since the fluorescent data are in a computer readable form they can be displayed on screen while editing. The mouse pointer is placed over the base of interest and the middle mouse button double clicked (pressed twice in quick succession). This will display a new window containing the original trace data. If the pointer is over the consensus line then all traces which overlap that region will be displayed. Up to four traces can be displayed at once; any additional traces displace those at the top of the trace display window. The trace can be scrolled in a similar way to the DNA sequence in the editor window using the mouse buttons. Each trace or the whole trace display window can be hidden or removed completely using the "hide" or "quit" buttons located to the left of each trace or in the top left-hand corner of the window. Thus it is possible to examine the sequencing data from a region containing a conflict and after consideration of these data to make the appropriate edits.

As the contigs build up there are likely to be regions of ambiguity in the consensus. Some of these will be easily resolved, for example if there are three reads covering a particular region and one is of poor quality but the other two are in agreement then editing the poor read is straightforward. However, there may also be regions where several reads of high quality disagree. In this case it is prudent not to make any changes without further data. Using a different sequencing method may help to resolve the differences (for example using dye-terminators rather than dye-primers may help). Regions of interest can be marked from within the contig editor using the tag facility described below.

6.6   Manual entry of Failures

The gels that fail entry into the database using "AutoAssemble" had their names written to a file of file names. These gels need to be entered. It is possible, with extreme caution, to use "AutoAssemble" again and to alter the alignment parameters (by increasing the number of pads allowed or increasing the percentage mismatch permitted). There is, however, a risk that during this operation non-contiguous sequences will be joined on the basis of poor matches. Then these contigs with poorer quality matches would need to be edited and the data become degraded. Some gels will match so badly that the alignment clearly is not genuine (for example if they contain a poorly conserved repeated sequence). These gels are best entered using "AutoAssemble" but selecting the option to put all gels in separate contigs.

6.7   Manually Joining Contigs

The automatic assembly process may fail to join overlapping contigs for a number of reasons. This situation may arise if gel readings have to be entered manually into separate contigs and it will also arise if a new gel read is entered into one contig (i.e. it matches well) and the other end of the same gel matches another contig but the quality of the match is too low to permit automatic joining. The position of such a possible join can be seen in the "Output" window and then the "Join Contigs" option selected from the modification menu. The program will prompt for the two contigs to be identified and then a window similar to the contig editor will appear. This window shows the two contigs, and all their gel reads, one above the other, with the positions where the two contigs disagree shown by a exclamation marks between them. Each contig can be scrolled to the left and right as in the contig editor. This means that they can be slid past each other until the best alignment is found. In practice it is easiest to move each of them to the position identified by "AutoAssemble". Remember at this point that "AutoAssemble" inserts padding characters to optimize the alignment, therefore the numbering of the bases will have changed slightly. However, moving one of the sequences in single base steps will rapidly reveal the correct alignment because most of the exclamation marks will suddenly disappear. Once the overlap has been found the two sequences can be locked together (by highlighting the "lock" button). When this is done the two sequences will scroll together as a single sequence with the relative positions of their left ends fixed. The overlapping region can then be examined and edited as appropriate. It is important to view the whole of the overlap before the join is finally made because once joined the two contigs cannot be moved independently. Selecting "Leave Editor" will give the percentage mismatch in the overlap and ask you to confirm that you wish to complete the join. As with the contig editor, no permanent changes are saved until this point.

6.8   Altering Gel Reading Cutoffs

The clipped data that were not initially entered into the database are often found to be correct and useful if compared with other (clipped) data from the same region. This is very easily done from within the contig editor. Normally the clipped data are not shown at the ends of contigs but if the "reveal cut offs" button is highlighted then this sequence is shown in grey and the consensus recalculated. If several gel readings cover the same region the clipped data may well show good agreement and therefore be worthwhile incorporating into the database. This can easily be done by positioning the cursor at the end of the gel reading and simultaneously pressing the meta key (a diamond on a Sun workstation), and using the right or left arrow to move the cutoff point. In this way the ends of contigs can be extended reliably.

6.9   Finding Internal Joins Automatically

As the number of contigs decreases it is very useful to be able to check that no joins have been missed. This is likely to happen since the clipped data are not used by "Auto Assemble". Search for internal joins under the modification menu performs this function. The basic principle of the program is that it uses sequences from the ends of each contig (say the last 100 bases, termed the "probe length" and selectable by the user) and searches, using both orientations, the consensus of all the contigs to the left (i.e. those with higher identifying numbers). If a match of sufficient quality is found it is displayed in the Output window. The user is then prompted, "Use Editor?". If the "Yes" button is activated then the standard contig joining editor is invoked with the two contigs already aligned on the basis of the suspected match.

The definition of this quality is expressed in terms of percentage match rather than percentage mismatch. 75% is the default value and is a reasonable figure to start with. Subsequent searches use the ends of the next contig to the left but search only the consensuses of contigs further to the left to ensure that matches are only displayed once. This function also has the facility to utilize the clipped data in searching for overlaps. If all the clipped data were to be used then this would contain some sequence of very poor quality. However, some will be usable (especially if the clipping was initially done conservatively). To distinguish between the two, a flexible definition of good data is employed. A window of fixed length ("Window size for good data scan"), is moved along the clipped data until too many dashes (- as base called by the automated sequencing machine) ("Maximum number of dashes in scan window") are found in the scan window. The additional sequence up to this point is then used and an extended consensus calculated for each contig. Since this function does not actually change anything in the database it is worthwhile investigating several different search conditions. If convincing overlaps are found then these contigs can be joined with the editor. Because the two contigs which may overlap are automatically aligned in the editor this process is very rapid and many potential joins may be examined. If clipped data are being used then some joins may be based solely on clipped (and therefore less reliable) data. Under these conditions it is wise to proceed with caution. One other point to be aware of is that clipped data will contain vector derived sequences and contigs should not be joined based on sharing these sequences. Sequences that are erroneously joined can be disassembled later from the alter relationships menu, although it is wiser to be cautious and get it right first time.

6.10   Tagging Regions of Special Interest

During a sequencing project it is inevitable that certain short sequences will take on special significance.   Some regions are particularly prone to compressions, making them difficult to sequence. Walking primers may be based on the existing sequence. Using xbap it is possible to "tag"" these special sequences. They can be colour coded and each colour can specify a particular type of tag (compression, walking primer or comment for example). These colours are defined in a separate file (TAGDB). Tags and their contents can then be searched for and used as landmarks within the sequence. Tags are created, using the contig editor, by selecting with the cursor the bases to be tagged and pressing the control key on the keyboard and the left mouse button together. This pops up a menu from which "Search", "Create tag", "Delete tag" and "Edit tag" can be chosen. The "Create tag" option evokes a tag editor where the tag type can be selected from a pull-down menu and a comment typed as desired. The editor works in a similar fashion and in both cases the changes are saved when the "Leave" button is used to exit the tag editor. To delete a tag simply position the cursor on the tag and select ""Delete tag" from the pop-up Tag menu. The "Search" option allows searching for specific sequences, positions, tag types and comments within tags. The search direction can be selected. This window remains active during normal contig editor function, which eases navigation around the contig.   The window can be removed by clicking the "Ok" button. If the search is successful the cursor moves to that position, if unsuccessful the terminal bell sounds.

6.11   Determining the Quality of the Sequence

As a sequencing project nears completion a considerable amount of time is spent examining each contig and trying to resolve conflicts and ambiguities within them. The vast majority of the of the sequence at this point will have been determined several times on both strands of DNA and thus be reliable. However, there will be regions which are much less reliable. If the total length of the contigs is more than a few kb then such regions may be easily overlooked.   The "Examine quality" function is designed to highlight the weaker data. In essence, each base in the defined contig is given a code according to how reliably it has been determined. The code is as follows:

```
0            well determined on both strands and they agree
1            well determined on the plus strand only
2            well determined on the minus strand only
3            not well determined on either strand
```

4   `well determined on both strands but they disagree`

The definition of "well determined" is the same as that used in the "Calculate a consensus" and "Display contig" functions. The calculation determines the score for each of the possible assignments at each point in the contig. The possible symbols assigned in the consensus are A, C, G, T * and - when none of these reaches a predefined threshold. This threshold value is set to 75% (by default) and is calculated as described below. The xbap program has the facility to encode bases that cannot be uniquely assigned from the gel by the use of "uncertainty codes". Thus "D" is interpreted as probably C but possibly CC and "R" means A or G. The other uncertainty codes are listed in "Help". This form of coding is only used when sequencing radioactively; the fluorescence based methods use N to denote an uncertain base.

The score for each assignment takes account of the uncertainty codes. The relevant uncertainty codes which contribute to the consensus assignments (those which could be an A for example) are summed with a weighting factor (to account for less reliably determined bases) and then divided by the total score for all bases:

$$\frac{(A, C, G, T, B, D, H, V, K, L, M, N, a, c, g, t) + 0.75\,(1, 2, 3, 4) + 0.1\,(R, Y, 5, 6, 7, 8)}{\text{total score}}$$

The weighting in this calculation means that the less well determined bases contribute less to the consensus. Since the score for each base is not simply divided by the number of times the sequence has been determined a dash in the consensus is less likely. This calculation is performed for each of the symbols used in the consensus and the value of the one which exceeds the cutoff is placed in the consensus line. If none of the values exceeds this cutoff then a dash is used. When the sequence quality is being specifically examined, the two strands are considered separately. In all other cases (for example when using the contig editor) quality is automatically determined taking both strands together.

The result of examination of the quality is summarized, and detailed base by base output (if requested) can be shown as text or graphically (example in Figure 6.3).

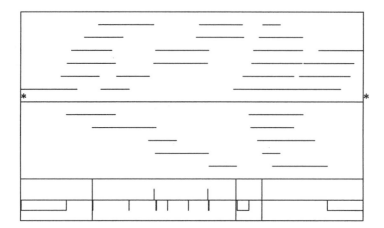

FIGURE 6.3 This figure shows the graphics window with two plots one above the other. The top box shows the gel readings from a single contig displayed in their relative positions and orientations, above and below the line with asterisks at each end. The quality plot (lower panel), produced by examining the quality of this contig, highlights the regions of conflict among the gel readings and the larger portions where the sequence has only been determined on one strand (the extreme ends for example).

The graphic display plots a graph with the x-axis representing the selected contig and the quality codes as rectangles on the y-axis.

```
Quality code 0 the rectangle extends from y=0 to y=0
Quality code 1 the rectangle extends from y=0 to y=1
Quality code 2 the rectangle extends from y=0 to y=-1
Quality code 3 the rectangle extends from y=-1 to y=1
Quality code 4 the rectangle extends from y=-2 to y=2
```

The ultimate aim is to achieve a single line with $y=0$ indicating the contig is well determined on both strands and there are no conflicts between the two strands. Any disagreements are represented by vertical lines (or rectangles) above or below the $y=0$ line.

6.12 Graphical Representation of Data in xbap

Apart from the window based displays of the trace and contig editors, the graphics menu allows the user to plot contig and quality information in the graphics window. It is possible to extract information from the graphics plots by using the crosshair function to a region of interest. There are three major uses of the graphics window, plotting sequence quality, plotting the relationships of all contigs and plotting the relationships of individual gel readings within a single contig.

The two functions "Plot all contigs" and "Plot single contig" under the "Graphics" menu both work in a similar manner and are most useful when used with the crosshair function. The first plots a line, at one of two heights (so that each contig can be distinguished from its neighbour) for each of the contigs in the database. The length of each line is proportional to the length of each contig. The order of the contigs as represented on screen bears no relationship to the actual relationship between each of the contigs. They are simply plotted from left to right in decreasing order of their identifier numbers. A text version of the contig relationships may be printed using the ""Show relationships" function from the general menu (see below). "Plot single contig" divides the plot frame into two portions (separated by a horizontal line with an asterisk at both ends). Each gel is then plotted; those that are in the complementary sense are below the line those that are unaltered are above. The length of each line is proportional to the length of the gel reading and the relationship of each gel to its neighbour is correctly shown. The information obtained from these plots is of a limited nature because the plots are simplifications of the data.

Further information can be obtained by using the crosshair function. When this is invoked from the graphics menu a small crosshair appears which can be positioned with the mouse over either the individual gels or contigs (depending on what was previously plotted). When positioned over a whole contig, pressing the left mouse button causes the aligned gel reads for 120 bp around the position corresponding to that of the crosshair to be displayed in the "Output" window. Use of particular keys on the keyboard selects various other options, the remaining keys simply exit from the crosshair function. The precise function of the special characters depends on the position of the crosshair, in particular which display box it is positioned in. Thus when in the "Plot all contigs" box, "Z" (zoom) causes a "Plot single contig" box to appear for the contig nearest to the position of the crosshair; "Q" (plot quality) gives a similar result to "Z" but in addition a quality plot is produced. When positioned in the "Plot single contig" box "Q" produces a quality plot for that contig and "Z" enlarge the plot contig box to fill the "Graphics" display. In all cases where "Plot all contigs" is shown the contig selected (by keyboard or mouse click) will be identified by a vertical line at the appropriate position. If the crosshair is near to a gel reading line and "I" pressed the nearest gel reading will be identified. If the display quality box is shown the "S" also functions as a special key, causing the aligned gel reads to be displayed at the crosshair position. It is important to realize that when the crosshair is active, the general purpose cursor will be deactivated and it is not possible to activate functions from the menus until the cross-hair is deactivated by pressing a keyboard character.

These functions allow the user to navigate through the data without having to remember all the numbers that identify the gel reads and contigs. Each contig can be graphically selected in turn, examined and, with the quality plot and aligned gel reads still on screen, the contig editor can be called and appropriate edits made. This completed, the editor is closed and the crosshair selected again and the next contig analysed. This graphic approach to navigation greatly speeds up the process.

6.13   Altering Relationships of Gel Readings and Contigs

On occasion it becomes apparent that a gel has been entered incorrectly in a contig and it is necessary to remove it. This may well break a contig into two smaller ones. This can occur if a single gel reading is derived from a co-ligation of two disparate fragments. The "Disassemble contig" function neatly allows one or more gel readings to be removed from the database. When selected, the user is prompted for the identifying numbers of the gels that define the left-most and right-most ends of the region to be disassembled. This may be only a single gel, or possibly several. These are removed from the database and the remaining gels and contigs renumbered. (The structure of the database requires that there are no gaps in the numbering.) The gels that have been removed have their names written to a file of file names, the name of which is prompted for. This list can then be edited (to remove the name of the co-ligated gel for example) and used in the "Auto-assemble contig" function. If the intention was merely to break a contig in two then it is simply used in "AutoAssemble" but disallowing joins to be made. *It is highly recommended that a copy of the database is made before using these procedures - it is relatively easy to scramble the relationships between sequences!*

6.14   Show Relationships

This function, available from the general menu, allows the user to list the relationships of gel readings in one or all contigs. The output lists the gel reading name, gel number, the length and relative position of each reading. Negative numbers next to the position indicate that the reading is on the opposite strand.

6.15   Calculate Consensus

This function uses the same method to calculate the consensus of either the whole database or a selected contig as the "Examine quality function". It automatically directs the output to a file. The cutoff score for this is set with the "Set parameters" function. It is initially set to 75%.

6.16 Miscellaneous Useful Functions

6.16.1 "Complement a Contig" (Modification Menu)

This function simply complements an entire contig (and obviously all the gel reads within it). This is used prior to the "Join Contigs" function when the user wishes to join manually two contigs where the match is between their opposite strands.

6.16.2 "Redirect Output" (General Menu)

This function, as its name suggests, redirects the output of another function ("Display contig" for example) to a file rather than the screen. The file name to be used is prompted for and the re-direction applies to the next selected function that would generate output in either the Output or Graphics window. The output will be sent to the file and when the "Redirect output" option is selected again, the file is closed and the output sent to the screen again.

6.16.3 "Check Database" (General Menu)

This function is used on occasion by other more complex functions to check that the database is logically consistent, i.e. there are no gaps in the numbering, no gel appears twice and there are no circular contigs. It can be invoked manually by selecting this option.

6.16.4 "Copy Database" (General Menu)

Initially when the database is set up the size is defined and this limits the number of gels and contigs that can be entered. This function will write a new copy of the database files and allow the size of the database to be increased. It prompts the user for a version number of the new database. The new files are named as described in Section 6.2 with the version number imbedded within the file names.

6.16.5 "Set parameters" (General Menu)

A variety of inbuilt parameters are required for xbap to function. Some of these are quite mundane and deal with window size and geometry. There is little need to alter these. The cutoff score used in the consensus algorithm can be altered with this function although the need for this will also be rare.

7 Conclusions

We have not attempted to describe exhaustively all of the features of the Staden X-windows assembly software but we hope that this overview will allow a novice user to explore the program and its capabilities. We would encourage users to experiment with small test projects in order to gain familiarity with the functions and their use - there is no doubt that practical experience produces a much deeper understanding of the processes involved in sequence assembly and the functions this powerful software can perform. Future enhancements include the automated use of the clipped data to fill in the single stranded regions, automated selection of oligonucleotides to extend the end of contigs (the sequences of the selected oligonucleotides and the appropriate templates are written to a file) and the use of a single script which automates every step from data transfer to assembly.

Further information about the distribution of these programs is available from Rodger Staden by e-mail. rs@mrc-lmb.cam.ac.uk

8 References

Staden R and Dear S (1991). A sequence assembly and editing program for efficient management of large projects. Nucl. Acids Res. 19, 3907-3911.

Dear S and Staden R (1992). A standard file format for data from DNA sequencing instruments DNA Sequence 3, 107-110.

Gleeson T and Hillier L (1991). A trace display and editing program for data from fluorescence based sequencing machines. Nucl. Acids Res. 19, 6481-6483.

Parsons JD, Brenner S and Bishop MJ (1992). Clustering of cDNA sequences. Comput. Applic. Biosci. 8, 461-466.

CHAPTER 7 Sequence Comparison

Michelle Ginsburg

Imperial Cancer Research Fund, Lincoln's Inn Fields,
London WC2A 3PX, UK

1 Introduction

The fields of molecular biology and genetics are faced with an accumulation of quantitative information at an increasing rate such that the unaided human mind cannot assimilate it or assess its significance (Bell, 1988). Comparing a newly determined sequence with one of the various sequence collections can be an important step in deriving useful information on function or structure. However, the point has long since been passed when this can be done without recourse to computer assistance. The aim of computer-aided sequence comparison is to take a pair of sequences and determine whether there is a match or alignment between an element or elements in the sequences. Part of the solution should be that there are the smallest possible number of changes such as insertions/deletions, compressions or substitutions. In other words, with two finite sequences what pattern of insertions or deletions makes the most plausible alignment between them. When this is performed against a collection of sequences such as one of the international sequence databanks in order to find any regions of alignment this is termed sequence database searching. Where the comparison is performed with a limited set of sequences (which may actually be many hundreds of sequences) with the aim of aligning part or all of the sequences to produce a common region or regions, this is termed multiple sequence alignment.

1.1 How Sequence Comparison is Performed

Constraints imposed by the rigour of the search versus the time taken to perform that search on a computer may compound the problems of determining the biological significance of a match. Whilst many search algorithms claim to be rigorous, much information is discarded and many compromises are made in order to save both computer time and disk storage space. Thus programs may save only a certain number of the highest scoring matches and may also report only one alignment per pair of sequences.

It is difficult for the naive user to determine which of the many programs available might be the best for a particular purpose. Although the literature will cite the nature of improvements, for example speed or sensitivity, there are few comprehensive benchmark studies for guidance. Under normal circumstances the laboratory scientist would include appropriate controls in any experiment performed. This is not always possible, especially with newly determined sequences. Therefore such studies are generally performed by using sequences whose features have been identified, and whose family members are known. However, this knowledge may pertain only to a particular point in time and a specific database release. As the databases increase in size the chances of finding random similarities increases (Collins and Coulson, 1990). With this caveat in mind is it then possible to ask whether a program accurately reports some or all of the information? In the case of database searching using a sequence whose family members are known one might ask whether all the family members have been identified, how much coverage is reported between any pair of aligned sequences and whether important features have been correctly aligned. Having determined the answers to such questions as these the user is then in a better position to say how a program might behave when using a newly determined sequence to search the database and, furthermore, how best to refine the search.

1.2 What Can Be Learned from Sequence Comparison

Searching sequence databases can provide much information about the structure, function and evolution of biological macromolecules. The databases can be a rich source of new knowledge (Doolittle, 1988). However, searching is not without its dangers and pitfalls. It has been pointed out that a run of 12 amino acids (or 30 bases) cannot have arisen by chance (Collins and Coulson, 1987). So, whilst it may be relatively easy to determine the significance of strong matches there may be a temptation to infer too much from a marginal resemblance.

There are a number of variables to be considered when embarking on a sequence search. These are the nature of the sequence to be used in the search, the database being searched and especially its size and quality (Doolittle, 1990), and the program and computer hardware being used to perform the search. If searching a database is like searching for a needle in a haystack then there is the danger that the searcher will not recognize the needle when it is seen, always assuming the haystack contains a needle in the first place.

2   Background to Techniques

2.1   String Matching

The basic technique of sequence comparison was originally derived from text or string matching techniques. Thus in Figure 7.1a asterisks are used to mark the positions of matching characters in the two strings being compared and Figure 7.1b shows what happens when one sequence is slid against another in order to find and align matching residues. Figures 7.1c and 7.1d show what happens when gaps are inserted into the character strings and how this may increase the number of matching residues.

Initially, scoring schemes were relatively simple, incrementing a running total for identical matches and decrementing it for mismatches or gaps. The results were compared with those derived from randomly ordered sequences of the same composition and the question was asked whether the search result was significantly better then that of a randomly ordered sequence. However, protein and DNA sequences are not collections of random characters, moreover, real proteins have regions of better local similarity then a random arrangement of the same residues (Collins and Coulson, 1987), and furthermore in protein sequences there are positional preferences of amino acids in secondary structure to consider (Argos, 1989). Moreover, macromolecules that are functionally equivalent can differ in sequence and structure.

```
a )                          c )
    ADVANCE                      ADVANC E
    * * *                        * * *      *
    ADVISE                       ADVANTAGE

b )                          d )
        ADVISE
        * * *                        ADV     ISE
    DISADVANTAGE                     * * *   * * *
                                 READVERTISE
```

FIGURE 7.1 Examples of string matching. A simple "probe" is aligned with target "sequences". In the simplest method two sequences are compared and all matching characters are marked (a) and in a more complex method gaps may be inserted to maximize the number of matching characters (c). In the second example (b) the matches are increased by sliding one sequence against another and in the fourth example (d) gaps are also included, and more characters match.

Functionally different sequences may also have developed from a common ancestor sequence whilst corresponding portions of related sequences may have similar biochemical functions. Sequences are often described as homologous when they show a high degree of sequence similarity. It is important to recognize the distinction between homology and similarity. Sequences inferred to be derived from a common ancestor are said to be homologous, whereas sequence similarity implies that sequences by some predetermined criterion resemble each other. The problem of homology inference may be compounded by such events as exon shuffling, or genome rearrangement. A rule of thumb (Doolittle, 1990) is that if sequences of 100 residues or more of a protein are 25% or more identical then there is almost certainly common ancestry.

2.2   Treatment of Gaps

When two sequences of equal length (N) are compared and if no gaps are inserted then the time taken to perform the comparison is proportional to N^2. In order to maximize the number of matching residues between a pair of sequences it may be necessary to insert gaps of varying lengths. If this were performed for every position in each sequence there would be a further $2N$ calculations. Uncontrolled insertion of gaps will have a large effect on the sequences being aligned and some comparisons would produce nonsensical results. Clearly there must be a method of controlling the number of gaps inserted between sequences being aligned.

A number of ways to treat insertions and deletions have been described. Generally a score is applied to the gap, which might be a penalty subtracted from the overall score produced by aligning the sequence pair. Since an apparent deletion in one sequence is an apparent insertion in the other the gap can be treated the same in either case and both will score identically. In this case one scores for the gap irrespective of size, that is, no penalty is applied for the size of the gap. An alternative method is to apply a penalty for opening a gap, and then apply a second but lower penalty for maintaining or extending the gap. In this instance not all gaps are considered equivalent and this tends to penalize large gaps, possibly producing short chunky alignments. In order to overcome the effect of such a penalty and obtain a long alignment the sequences being aligned must contain a large number of matches. Some authors have found that a length dependent gap penalty is not required in order to obtain the best alignment (Barton and Sternberg, 1987).

Although the gap penalty is applied equally over the whole length of a sequence this is a simplistic approach. For example, there is a greater tolerance of insertions/deletions in loop regions linking core secondary structures of proteins than in secondary structures themselves. It is likely therefore that gap penalties should be varied within regions of an alignment according to local secondary structure (Argos and Vingron, 1990). Ideally there should be different penalties for gaps at the end of sequences as opposed to internal gaps. Difficulties arise in the use of such end-weighted gaps where the relationship between the query and potential hits in a search is unknown. Until a relationship is known, such penalties should be used with caution or reserved for a second round of searches.

2.3   Dot Matrix Comparisons

A dot plot or matrix comparison simultaneously displays all possible sequence comparisons. If one considers a matrix where sequence (i) is arrayed as a row, and (j) represents a second sequence placed in the columns the simplest form of matrix comparison places a dot in each cell of the matrix where (i) and (j) match (Figure 7.2).

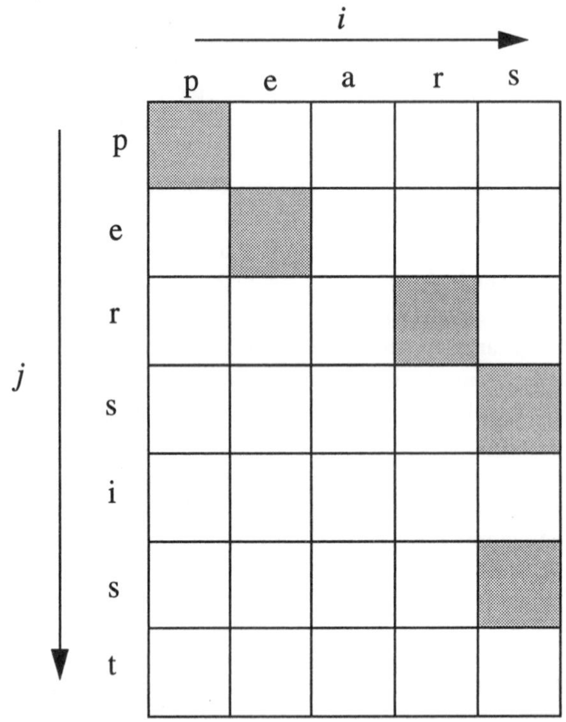

FIGURE 7.2 A simple matrix comparison. Matching characters are marked with stippling. The beginnings of diagonal lines can be seen with the second diagonal offset due to an insertion/deletion.

Where the sequences match, a diagonal line will build up. This tends to produce a plot with many dots scattered over the matrix, especially where there is a low similarity between the sequences and a large amount of random matching. In practice some form of filtering must be applied (Figures 7.3 and 7.4).

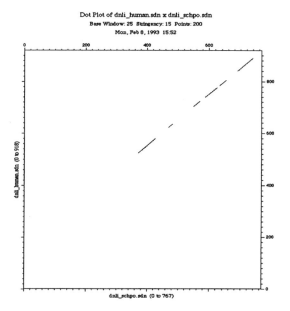

Dot Plot of dnli_human.sdn x dnli_schpo.sdn
Base Window: 25 Stringency: 15 Points: 200
Mon, Feb 8, 1993 15:52

FIGURE   7.3 Dot matrix comparisons. The effects of changing window size and stringency are shown in the panels of dot matrix plots. The human DNA ligase I is compared with the DNA ligase from *Schizosaccharomyces pombe*. Here a stringency of 15 and a window size of 25 are used.

This can be done by only placing a dot where the local density of a match equals or exceeds some set threshold, called the stringency. Consider a window W which is a diagonal path of this length in the matrix. If the stringency is set to s then a dot is only placed in a window if s out of W residues match. The best representation can be achieved if a dot is placed at each matching residue rather then each matching window when a window passes the filtering threshold. The maximum signal will be the length of the smaller sequence and the window size chosen should be a reflection of the purpose of the comparison. Thus a small window should be chosen for promoters or active sites whilst larger ones would be used for structural elements or exons.

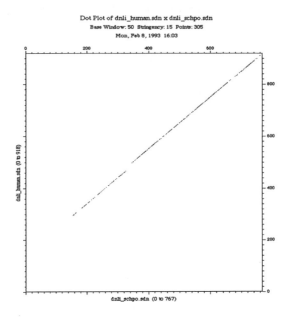

Dot Plot of dnli_human.sdn x dnli_schpo.sdn
Base Window: 50 Stringency: 15 Points: 305
Mon, Feb 8, 1993 16:03

FIGURE 7.4 Details as for Figure 7.3 except that the stringency is maintained but the window size is increased to 50.

Another way to find points of similarity is to search for short perfect matches of some set length, referred to as "words". The word comparison between two sequences is many times faster than the window/stringency match described above, but loses in sensitivity since it requires that the sequences contain short perfect matches for any similarity to be found (Wilbur and Lipman, 1983). The word length is referred to as a "k-tuple".

We have already stated that where two sequences are identical or similar (depending on the scoring scheme in use) this will be seen as diagonals within the matrix, the most significant diagonal representing the best aligned sequence. Insertions or deletions will cause diagonals to be offset in relation to the main diagonal (Figure 7.4). The appearance of lines perpendicular to the main diagonal will represent palindromic sequences whereas lines parallel to one of the matrix axes represent stretches of single residues or bases (e.g. oligo-A or poly proline).A simple matrix comparison. Matching characters are marked with stippling. The beginnings of diagonal lines can be seen with the second diagonal offset due to an insertion/deletion.

2.4 Sequence Alphabets and the Signal to Noise Rratio Problem

It might appear that because of their great size more information may be gained by searching DNA databases alone. Whilst it is true that the majority of protein sequences "known" today are inferred from their DNA sequences it is less effective to search DNA because of signal to noise ratio problems.

Consider a DNA sequence and assume that it consists of "text" built up of characters derived from an alphabet. Then the alphabet forming that text is small, comprising four letters, and when two sequences are compared the chances of random matching are very high (lots of noise and not very much signal). The problem is compounded by the fact that significant text in DNA can vary dramatically in length. DNA sequences are frequently very long (consider genes, introns, exons) whilst some conserved regions or signals may be short (restriction sites, transcription factor binding sites, etc.).

In the case of proteins the "text" is derived from a larger alphabet of 20 letters, hence the chances of random matching are much lower (more signal and less noise). In addition, protein sequences have chemical properties which determine structure and function. The sequences tend to be shorter and methods are generally more amenable to refinement.

3 Scoring Schemes and the Treatment of Gaps

3.1 Identity Scoring

Probably the simplest similarity scoring scheme to understand is one where a positive score is given for every identical match and a negative score for every gap. Mismatches can be scored either with a zero or negatively. Scores for gaps and mismatches are then decremented from the running total. Termed identity scoring or identity matrix, this type of scheme is considered to be an appropriate system for scoring DNA matches but not for proteins. If one considers that amino acids may substitute for one another with little alteration in chemical properties of a protein then clearly this property cannot be reflected in an identity scoring scheme. Since some amino acids may substitute for each other chemically then an identity scoring scheme would represent a loss in sensitivity since amino acids performing a similar function would not be recognized as such. Thus some other system must be used for maximal sensitivity in protein searches.

3.2 Reduced Alphabets

How is it possible to make a scoring scheme more sensitive? If we consider the case of proteins then we know inherently that not all amino acids are functionally dissimilar. Thus one can use the idea of chemical similarity to reduce the alphabet. For example all hydrophobic residues could be counted as equivalent, similarly for positively charged residues and so on. A number of different alphabets have been described using just such methods (Jimenez-Montano and Zamora-Cortina, 1981; Miyata et al., 1979). However, the problem then arises that if the alphabet is reduced too much, for example as a reduction to hydrophobic and hydrophilic residues only, then the number of random matches and hence the noise level will rise.

3.3 PAM Tables

PAM is an acronym for Point Accepted Mutation. This is an exchange of one amino acid for another accepted by natural selection. To be accepted the new amino acid side chain must function in the same way as the old (Dayhoff et al., 1978). PAM tables were derived from the pattern of substitutions observed in proteins at short evolutionary distances and used to predict the pattern at longer distances. Taking a collection of pairs of sequences which differ at no more than 15% of residues, it may be assumed that no multiple changes have taken place at any one position. Values were then derived for the probability that a residue of given type should mutate to any other type or not in an evolutionary interval where one nucleotide point mutation was accepted per 100 residues, i.e. 1 PAM. Longer distances are derived from multiplying the matrix of values by the appropriate number of times. The similarity score is the log of the odds that a particular pair of amino acids has arisen by mutation rather than by chance.

This type of scoring is more sensitive to the actual information encoded and should produce biologically interesting alignments since conservative substitutions will score highly. The original PAM matrix is still widely used. However, it is likely that the values for hydrophobic residue substitutions are inaccurate. Early protein sequences were mostly derived by amino acid sequencing of globular protein and so those rich in hydrophobic residues such as membrane proteins were under-represented in early collections. Since most protein sequences are now inferred directly from the DNA sequence this is no longer true. Amino acids have mutational properties which do not depend on the proteins in which they are found. Many of the changes expected from single point mutations are seldom observed; they probably occur but are not preserved. A further point to consider is that the original model assumes that all sites will mutate with equal frequency regardless of the position of the site within the protein (George et al., 1990). It is now known that this is not true and that sites within a proteins may show quite different levels of variability.

4   Algorithm Types

4.1   Dynamic Programming

For a rigorous sequence comparison with a database the task can be viewed as performing comparisons of pairs of sequences where one of the pair is the probe sequence and the other of the pair is always from the database. Modern sequence comparison methods have computerized this task, sometimes using specialist hardware architecture in order to maintain speed and sensitivity. The term dynamic programming will frequently be seen in association with computerized database searching programs. The term implies a model where all possible events are calculated and then some are rejected based on a number of criteria. The method keeps a table containing all previously computed events and their results. For database searching, a matrix comparison will provide all possible alignments between a pair of sequences. The matrix would then be examined and most alignments rejected. The process of revealing a best alignment is to compute each matrix element moving forward and then through the matrix to find the best path through it which corresponds to the alignment.

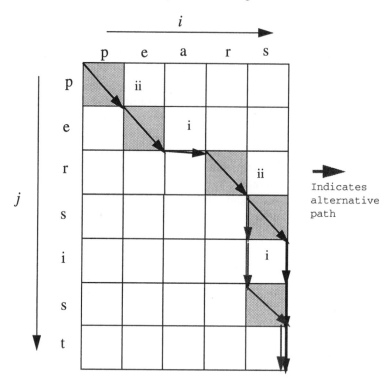

FIGURE 7.5 A score matrix. The stippled boxes indicate a matching character in the comparison matrix. The arrows in the matrix correspond to matches (ii), or an insertion or deletion in one sequence relative to the other (i).

4.2   Needleman-Wunsch Algorithm

This is often cited as an early example of a dynamic programming algorithm applied to a biological problem (Needleman and Wunsch, 1970). All possible matches are reported and weights are assigned to every residue pair, reflecting their similarity. Penalties are assigned to insertions/deletions and the sum subtracted from the number of matches. The algorithm constructs a two dimensional array, and a path is then found in which the sum of weights assigned to matching residues is maximal. The best alignment is found by extending shorter ones tracing back through the matrix from the cell with the highest value.

4.3 Total Alignment

Collins and Coulson (1987) call this type of alignment a type I alignment (Figure 7.5a). In this method a score matrix has dimensions $(n+1, m+1)$ and has an extra column and row to allow for initial insertions and deletions. All alignments between the two sequences can be represented by paths through the matrix. There are a number of ways to move through the matrix (Figure 7.5) and the score at each point is generated by considering the scores along the three paths which lead to it. These generate new scores by subtracting penalties for transitions associated with gaps (insertions/deletions) and adding bonuses for those transitions associated with matches. This process is continued until the score of the final cell in the matrix is known. A best alignment is then obtained by examining all the paths through the matrix; this is performed by backtracking through the matrix. There may be more than one path with the best score. There may be sub-optimal paths which are biologically meaningful.

4.4 Best Location

The best location (Figure 7.6b) or type II search (Collins and Coulson, 1987) also uses a matrix to consider every location in a long sequence as a potential starting point for a match with a shorter sequence and every location in the bottom row is a potential exit point. All unmatched residues in the longer sequence attract no penalties if they precede the first character in the short sequence. Paths from some starting points will not reach the bottom but will be cut off before they reach it by better paths. A number of alignments may be produced but the exit paths do not contain information about any path other than the best. Backtracking is again used to find the best path through the matrix. This type of alignment is good for detecting a short consensus such as a control region or restriction site (Collins and Coulson, 1987).

4.5 Best local similarity

In this alignment (Figure 7.6c), type III of Collins and Coulson (1987), every cell in the matrix is considered a starting point and no penalties attach to overhangs of either sequence. At any cell where the score falls below zero the current path is stopped. The score is reset and the cell treated can then be treated as a new starting point for a region of local similarity. Regions of greatest similarity are identified by backtracking. The type III alignment is good for functional or structural analogies. Where sequences are highly similar over a long stretch a local alignment will tend to become a global alignment.

(a)

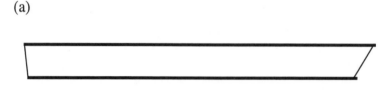

(b)

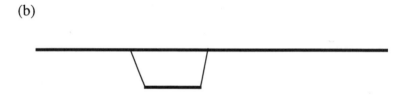

(c)

FIGURE 7.6 Types of alignment. (a) Represents a total alignment, (b) represents a best location and (c) represents a best local alignment.

4.6 Smith-Waterman Algorithm

Used in conjunction with different scoring matrices and methods of gap treatment, dynamic programming algorithms can be very sensitive when applied to database searching. The Smith and Waterman algorithm implements type III alignment and is regarded as a satisfactory solution to the sequence searching problem (Collins and Coulson, 1990). It is used in many database searching programs.

5   The Programs

5.1   FASTA

The program written by Lipman and Pearson (1985) firstly focuses on groups of identities between two sequences. A look-up table of positions is constructed for each word (in the query sequence) (the values aa (ktup=1) or aa pair (ktup=2) are used in protein sequence searches). The initial search finds local regions of identities between the sequences using the look-up table; mismatches are scored but insertions or deletions cannot be detected. The difference in position for each matching word is calculated and is called the offset; this is the same for residues on a diagonal line in a dot matrix. The score is increased for each match and decreased for each mismatch. The highest scoring regions by this method are re-scored using a PAM table. Finally an optimization is performed allowing for insertions and deletions.

Three scores are calculated: *init1*, which is derived when joining nearby contiguous stretches of similarity, *initn* when similar regions of nearby diagonals are joined into longer stretches and *opt,* which is derived after performing a dynamic programming step on the highest scoring regions. There is also a separate program for searching DNA databases with a protein sequence (TFASTA). The program is available as part of the GCG package, as a stand-alone program for a number of hardware platforms and as an e-mail server.

5.2   BLAST

The BLAST algorithm is a heuristic for finding un-gapped locally optimal sequence alignments (Altschul et al., 1990). There are in fact a number of programs. BLASTN compares a DNA sequence against a DNA sequence databases, and uses a positive score for matching residues and a penalty for mismatches. The other programs are BLASTP, which compares an amino acid sequence against a protein database, BLASTX, which compares a DNA sequence translated in all reading frames against a protein database, and TBLASTN, which compares a protein sequence against a DNA database translated in all frames, and all three use a substitution matrix. The programs are available for a number of hardware platforms and as an e-mail server.

The output of the algorithm is a unit called the HSP or High-scoring Segment Pair. Each segment pair is a run of contiguous residues where the score of the aligned segment exceeds a positive cut-off value. The HSP consists of one segment from the query and one from a database sequence. In addition an MSP or Maximal-scoring Segment Pair has also been defined. This is the highest scoring of all possible segment pairs on all diagonals and is defined by a pair of sequences and a scoring scheme.

There are number of user definable parameters which are set before the search. E is set a value which approximates to the number of HSPs that will be found purely by chance. It has a default value of 10 and a range of 0-1,000. S is the cut-off score for reporting an HSP. Usually it is calculated from E but may be set explicitly. Anything scoring below the value of S will not be reported. It should be noted that the calculated value of S will be different when searching databases of different lengths because the values for E and S are affected by the length and residue composition of the query, the length of the database and the hypothetical composition of the database and the scoring scheme used. In order to normalize the statistics when databases of different length are used a parameter called Z is set to a constant value.

5.3 Specialized Architecture Computers

5.3.1 PROSRCH on the DAP

The DAP or Distributed Array Processor is a SIMD machine (Single Instruction Multiple Data) with processing elements arranged in 32×32 (DAP 510) or 64×64 (DAP 610) arrays. The PROSRCH program is based on an extension of the Smith and Waterman algorithm (Collins et al., 1987). This finds and reports all paths in the two dimensional comparison matrix. There are some constraints such as only one path may be reported from each starting point and paths must be non-intersecting. The program incorporates user selectable PAM scoring tables and applies an indel (gap) penalty. This may be selected from a range which depends on the PAM table in use. The user may opt for stringent or relaxed treatment of gaps.

5.3.2 BLAZE on the MasPar

The MasPar machine is a massively parallel computer and the MP1 has 4,096 processors in a 64×64 array. The full version of BLAZE searches DNA and protein databases for sequence similarity and reports the alignment score, percentage of match, and statistical significance of each database sequence. Queries can include stop codons and IUPAC codes. BLAZE is based on a modification of the Smith and Waterman algorithm (Smith and Waterman, 1982; Gotoh, 1982). The scoring system uses PAM matrices and gaps are penalized using an affine (gap extension) penalty. The program is available on the IntelliGenetics time sharing system.

5.3.3 MPSRCH on the MasPar

This is an implementation of the Smith and Waterman algorithm for the MasPar family of massively parallel machines (S. S. Sturrock and J. F. Collins, personal communication). The program has recently been made available via the BLITZ e-mail server at EMBL.

Query sequences may be up to the present maximum of 10,000 residues in length. There are separate values for indels and gaps; a gap is one or more adjacent indels and the implementation used guarantees to minimize the number of gaps while maintaining the correct score for the Smith and Waterman algorithm. The program can use PAM tables between 1 and 500. Indel or gap penalties are usually in the range 5 to 30. The program can also "suggest" a suitable value based on the PAM table used and this is set if the user fails to set one or sets an illegal value. Where the BLITZ e-mail server is used then the number of results may also be requested (between 30 and 100). Only one match per database sequence is reported.

5.4   Search Results

Although some of the programs described are available as e-mail servers, as separate programs in the public domain or as components of commercial packages, the searches for this chapter were all performed at the UK Human Genome Mapping Project Resource Centre. The facilities included access to a DAP 510 running PROS-RCH and a MasPar MP-1 running MPSRCH and BLAZE. The SwissProt database (release 23) was used and for all programs the default settings were used unless otherwise stated.

In order to illustrate the differences between database searching programs two protein sequences have been used. These are both human sequences, the first being the human ATP dependent DNA ligase I and the second being the large subunit of the human ribonucleotide reductase. The sequences have been chosen because they are members of families with prokaryotic and eukaryotic representatives. They also display interesting features, some of which are well conserved and some of which show considerable variation. Both sequences are reasonably long and may be presumed to contain more then one functional domain. This allows the sensitivity of the searching programs to be estimated in several ways.

The human DNA ligase I is an ATP dependent DNA ligase with a sequence length of 919 residues. The active site has been characterized by experimentation (Tomkinson et al., 1991). The sequence is considerably longer than that of any DNA ligase characterized to date (ATP dependent DNA ligases vary from approximately 350 for bacteriophage ligases to the 919 of the human ligase I). The enzyme may be involved in DNA replication and is suspected of being involved in at least one human disease syndrome. The large subunit of the key enzyme ribonucleotide reductase is the first unique enzyme in the DNA synthetic pathway. In viruses the enzyme is considered a determinant of pathogenicity. In anti-viral therapy and chemotherapy the enzyme is considered to be a valid target. The large subunit of the ribonucleotide reductase contains an allosteric effector site and may also be involved in the redox reaction by contributing SH_2 groups at the interface between subunits.

5.5 Results Using the Human DNA Ligase

In ATP dependent reactions the site of adenylylation is a lysine. The sequence around the active site has been shown to be conserved, with the most conserved residues being KxDG (Tomkinson et al., 1991). The position of the active site lysine is almost constant, being some 320 residues from the carboxy-terminus. Therefore it was possible to ask not only if when the human sequence was used as a probe it found other DNA ligases, but also how much coverage was there between the sequences pairs and finally whether the active site had been correctly aligned.

It was observed that for all programs the coverage for the top 3 sequences was almost identical (Table 7.1), and in addition each had correctly aligned the active site.

TABLE 7.1 Coverage results from searches with human DNA ligase I. The coverage is the length of probe sequence which has been aligned against a hit sequence. In this case only the most conserved region of the human ligase has been used, i.e. from about residue 500 to the carboxy-terminus of the sequence, giving a sequence of similar size to the average ATP dependent DNA ligase molecule. nd means not detected in the search. Figures in parentheses represent the actual percentage of residues aligned when gaps are not considered.

Sequences in database	Program			
	PROSRCH	MPSRCH	FASTA	BLAST
Sch. pombe	99.2%	99.2%	99.7%	95.7% (93.5%)
Saccharomyces cerevisiae	96.1%	96.6%	96.1%	94.7% (90.9%)
Vaccinia virus	81.6%	81.6%	90.7%	81.6% (30%)
T6 phage	85%	nd	nd	nd
African swine fever virus	57.6%	nd	31.9%	nd
T3 phage	49.5%	21%	nd	nd
T4 RNA ligase	nd	nd	56.1%	nd

A potential problem with the output produced by BLAST is that whilst the coverage overall is almost identical to that of the best programs, the program has reported the sequence alignments as several chunks. This reflects the property of the program that it is looking only at un-gapped alignments although the interval between each chunk may represent a small or short gap. The more interesting results happen further down the hit list where only the program PROSRCH finds most of the potential ATP dependent DNA ligases. Interestingly, FastA reports instead an RNA ligase which also preserves some elements of the conserved active site motif. FastA fails however to correctly align the active site for the African swine fever enzyme. This protein differs in that an aspar-agine residue has been substituted in the active site sequence in place of aspartic acid.

The apparent success of PROSRCH in finding nearly all available DNA ligases and producing long alignments could be attributed to a number of factors. The program has used a 100 PAM table with fairly lenient use of gap penalty. In the case of MPSRCH the default penalty applied is actually quite harsh. By focusing initially on identities the FASTA program excludes some of the potential alignments because the number of iden-tical residues is low and subsequent rounds of extension and optimization cannot over-come this. A similar problem faces the BLAST program, in that there are some regions where large gaps would be encountered and the segments would not therefore be reported as part of the highest scoring segments. In the case of the vaccinia virus align-ment the number of matching residues is 30% even although this potentially covers regions represented in 80% of the sequence.

5.6 Results Using the Human Ribonucleotide Reductase

Results from the second search again show that there is relatively little difference in the order or coverage of the aligned sequences (Table 7.2). A modification of the cover-

TABLE 7.2 Coverage results from the human ribonucleotide reductase probe. In this case the results are expressed as a percentage of the sequence aligned. The first column under the heading PROSRCH uses a gap penalty of -7, the second column uses a penalty of -14. The column marked No. in the case of the BLAST alignments refers to the number of fragments making up the percentage coverage. Figures in parentheses represent the actual percentage of residues aligned when gaps are not considered

Sequences in database	Program						
	PROSRCH		MPSRCH	FASTA	BLAST	No.	BLAZE
Mus musculus	100%	100%	100%	99.8%	100%	1	100%
Vaccinia virus	95.7%	95.7%	95.7%	95.7%	95.7% (94.5%)	3	95.7%
S. cerevisiae	95%	95%	95%	95.4%	95% (92.9%)	5	95%
African swine fever virus	88.7%	86.8%	84.9%	43.2%	84.9% (70.5%)	10	88.7%
Herpes simplex virus-2	78.4%	57.3%	60%	85.8%	53.9% (43%)	6	78.4%
Escherichia coli	82.3%	77.7%	77.7%	88.3%	77.7% (46%)	8	82.3%
Varicella zoster virus	79%	61.3%	61%	93%	57.8% (43%)	8	79%
Epstein-Barr virus	91%	23.7%	23.7%	42.9%	57.3% (35%)	6	91%
Human cytomegalovirus	67%	14.8%	14.8%	73%	nd		67.4%

age definition has been introduced in order to take into account the BLAST results. The coverage in this instance is calculated from the overall length represented by the fragments rather then the summed length of the individual fragments. The number of fragments required to make up the alignment is shown in the table. However, as the further examination makes clear there are significant differences proceeding down the results. BLAST appears to be the worst in terms of total coverage and members of the protein family recovered, since it failed to find the human cytomegalovirus protein altogether. The percentage coverage results were consistently poorer.

Both PROSRCH and BLAZE perform identically in this instance, with MPSRCH showing much poorer coverage. Use of different gap penalties will change the coverage dramatically. In the instance of PROSRCH, use of the more stringent -14 indel (gap) penalty alters the coverage from 91% to 23.7% in the instance of the human protein versus the Epstein-Barr virus protein. Thus the apparently poor performance can probably be related to the fairly stringent gap penalty which is offered as a default setting.

In most instances the FASTA program performs well. However, when the Epstein-Barr virus alignment is considered the program reports a much reduced coverage. Further analysis of the sequence such as performing a dot matrix comparison between the probe and target sequence shows that the Epstein-Barr virus sequence has an apparent insertion relative to the human which coincides with the end of the aligned sequence. The size of this insertion is about 35 residues. The FASTA program does not permit gaps in excess of 32 residues and does not report more then one alignment between a pair of sequences.

5.7 Overall Conclusion

It is clear that not all searching programs will produce the same results even where apparently similar methodology is employed (i.e. the same algorithm or scoring table). The user should be aware of this and try to understand the algorithm or limitations of the program in use. Special points to consider in running the program are the treatment of gaps, whether identity scoring or another scoring method such as PAM scoring tables is used, and whether the algorithm itself is attempting to produce a local or global alignment.

When examining the search results the user should try to collect as many as possible and visually inspect them. When considering the results the user should ask whether the hits are sifted or optimized in any way. Some programs will only report the best hit from each sequence and therefore the user may expect to see only one alignment between a pair of sequences. In this case some further analysis such as a dot plot may be necessary.

The user should never just perform one run with default settings and rely on this but having examined the results, should repeat the search. It is possible to vary the parameters in a logical fashion (Figure 7.7).

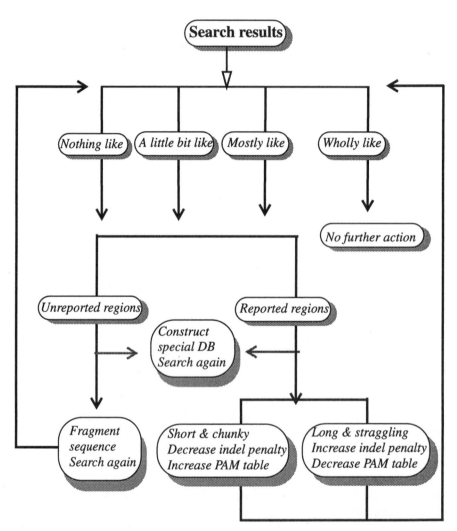

FIGURE 7.7 An outline strategy for database searching. The model program is in this case PROSRCH. Some options such as building a limited subset of the databases may not be easy with certain programs. However, refining parameters in a similar fashion and using parts of the sequence for which no results have been reported is possible to do with all programs.

If the sequence has repeat regions or runs of residues or bases that are composed of one or two types, then search without those regions. With long sequences especially, the likelihood of finding regions for which no alignment is reported is increased. Therefore the user should run the searches with shorter overlapping segments, especially removing regions for which some information has already been garnered. It may also help to enrich a meaningful result by building a sensible subset of the database and searching against this.

6 Multiple Sequence Alignment

6.1 What Can Be Llearned from Multiple Sequence Alignment?

Multiple sequence alignment can be used to display relationships between groups or families of sequences. It has a role in protein modelling and structure prediction and is also a precursor to studies on molecular evolution. The alignment of apparently similar sequences is widely used in the detection and characterization of sequence motifs (Chapter 8). Bearing in mind such caveats as conserved residues which may have different spacing even in closely related sequences, the technique is not without its difficulties. As with database searching it may not be possible to include appropriate controls when performing new multiple alignments. If a family of newly or poorly characterized sequences is being aligned then it may be unclear which if any features are preserved or are important to structure or function.

6.2 Background to Technique

Comparing all possible sequence pairs in order to perform a multiple alignment will rapidly become computationally intractable as the number of sequences to be aligned increases. Most programs therefore use a progressive pairwise approach and do not guarantee to produce an optimal alignment. Difficulties also arise where sequences are vastly different in length or where unrelated sequences are included in the alignment. Since the aim is generally to produce a global alignment, either of the aforementioned conditions will degrade the quality of the final result. Some of the algorithms are sensitive to the order in which the sequences are to be aligned and therefore it is necessary to produce some kind of guide by determining the most related sequence pairs. A number of automated programs are available, which provide facilities for export to multiple sequence editors. The user edits the sequences to "improve" some or all of the aligned regions.

6.3 CLUSTAL

The method used in CLUSTAL is based on the algorithm of Feng and Doolittle (1987) whereby sequences are aligned in larger and larger groups. Once having introduced a gap in a pair of aligned sequences, the method always maintains that gap. Thus if a gap is introduced between a pair of closely related sequences it is not removed when trying to align against less closely related sequences.

In the method of Higgins and Sharp (1988), each pair of sequences is compared and a crude measure of similarity derived. This is used to produce a dendrogram which will guide the final alignment. The similarity measure is calculated using the Wilbur and Lipman algorithm. At each alignment step the algorithm of Myers and Miller (1988) is used.

For protein sequences the user may select between identity, PAM 100 or PAM 250 scoring matrices. The last is the default matrix. Two gap penalties are used, a fixed and a floating gap penalty, the default value for both is 10 but the range varies from 0 to 100. Although DNA sequences have not been considered in the examples used here, DNA transitions will be weighted more strongly than DNA transversions.

6.4 ALIEN

This program (A. J. Bleasby, personal communication) is externally similar to CLUSTAL. It firstly calculates an optimal pairwise alignment using the Wilbur and Lipman algorithm. However, it differs in a number of key features from CLUSTAL. It also allows the use of a user definable scoring table. Furthermore, the user may select a matrix threshold cut-off; this allows fewer diagonals to be considered in the alignment. All gaps attract a fixed penalty (range 1-100) and in a multi-gap segment a floating gap penalty is also applied (range 1-100). Although DNA sequences have not been used as examples an option for weighting or unweighting C/T and G/A transitions is an option. Using the weighting gives transitions a score intermediate between identities and mismatches. A k-tuple of 1 or 2 may specified.

6.5 PileUp

PileUp also uses the Feng and Doolittle (1987) algorithm to align up to 300 sequences of maximum length 5,000. Firstly it compares all sequence pairs to produce a clustering order. This can be represented as a dendrogram. The clustering method is the unweighted pair group method. The method used is similar to the method described by Higgins and Sharp (1988).

The multiple alignment is produced by making a pairwise alignment of the two most similar sequences. This is then aligned to the next most related sequence or pair of aligned sequences. This process continues until a final alignment is achieved. The pairwise alignments include increasingly dissimilar sequences until essentially all sequences have been included. The pairwise alignments are produced using the Needleman and Wunsch (1970) algorithm. Before the alignment is produced the sequences are first clustered by similarity to produce a tree representation of relationships. It is this tree or dendrogram that directs the order of the subsequent pairwise alignments. The information from the tree producing process is not used to produce the alignment but only to ensure that the most similar sequences are aligned first. Furthermore, the tree produced is not a phylogenetic tree. The vertical branch lengths are, however, proportional to the similarity between the sequences.

The scoring table for protein alignments is based on the Dayhoff table (Dayhoff et al., 1978). The values are normalized and perfect matches are set to 1.5 with no matches scoring better than perfect matches. The treatment of gaps is considered to be arbitrary and indeed an equally satisfying alignment may be produced simply by different distributions of gaps. The program can be made to exaggerate this by shifting the gaps in the sequences to the left or right. The penalty applied to gaps is divided into a gap weight and a gap length weight. In addition it is also possible to weight gaps at the ends of the sequence in the same way as interior gaps rather then not penalizing them.

6.6   Other Methods

In considering multiple alignment, Barton and Sternberg (1987) took families of proteins where at least two members had a structure solved by X-ray crystallography. They then compared the aligned tertiary structures against alignments produced by a Needleman and Wunsch alignment. They found that if a significance score between two sequences was greater than 5 standard deviations then the alignment was probably aligned correctly over most of the core secondary structure. The alignment strategy for the resultant program, AMPS, is that it performs all pairwise comparisons. From this can be derived an order in which to align the sequences starting with the most similar pair and then the next similar pair and so on. Optionally, the alignment may be refined by re-aligning each sequence with the completed alignment.

7   Results

7.1   Results Using the ATP Dependent DNA Ligase Sequences

Interest in performing a multiple alignment for the ATP dependent DNA ligases centres around the search for conserved lysines. It is the lysine residue that is important in the adenylation reaction. Experimentation has since shown that the cluster of residues containing an apparently conserved lysine may not actually be the active site (Barker et al., 1987; Smith et al., 1989). A lysine has been identified by adenylation of the human DNA ligase I which occurs nearer to the amino-terminus and is conserved in all of the ligases. In the alignments produced by the programs under consideration, three regions containing apparently conserved lysines have been used as a test for the quality of the alignment. Because of the quite considerable difference in length between the sequences, multiple sequence alignment is less straightforward than usual.

In the case of PileUp the effects of altering the gap penalty settings was most extensively studied. Where the full length sequences were used the default settings seemed to give the best results, correctly aligning the three sites shown in Figure 7.7 in all cases. Increasing the gap length weight (from 0.1 to 1) reduced the overall number of large gaps between the sequence but also had the effect of misaligning the active site for the African swine fever ligase. The program has an option to allow the same weighting for internal and end gaps. The effect of this was to degrade badly the region 1 alignments where the full length sequences were used.

CLUSTAL and ALIEN had problems in producing an alignment where all three regions were correctly aligned. With ALIEN where full length sequences were used, initial attempts using the default settings produced alignments with large gaps and only the most similar sequences aligned for region 1 (i.e. human, *S. cerevisiae, Sch. pombe* and vaccinia virus). Region 2 was the most successfully aligned, with all but the African swine fever sequence being misaligned. Region 3 was misaligned in the same fashion as region 1. CLUSTAL performed better, with only region 1 being misaligned (Figure 7.8).

```
                              Region properly aligned   Region aligned by CLUSTAL
Region 1
  Human              CEYKYDGQR..AQIHALEGGE    CEYKYDGQRAQIHALEGGE
  Sch.pombe          CEYKYDGER..AQVHFTEDGK    CEYKYDGERAQVHFTEDGK
   S. cerevisiae     SEYKYDGER..AQVHLLNDGT    SEYKYDGERAQVHLLNDGT
  Vaccinia virus     AEVKYDGER..VQVH.KNNNE    -EVKYDGERVQVH-KNNNE
  Bacteriophage T3   ADCKYDGVR..GNIVVDNVAE    ----FHLTNVPTKLTPKG-
  Bacteriophage T4   AQLKADGARCFAEVRGDELDD    ------NKSLKGTISEKEA
  ASF virus          ALSKYNRHARQKRGAHTNRGM    ------LDNIKKELKQ---

Region 2
  Human              EGLMVKTLDV.DATYEIAKR     EGLMVKTLDV--DATYEIAKR
  Sch.pombe          EGLMVKMLEGPDSHYEPSKR     EGLMVKMLEGP-DSHYEPSKR
   S. cerevisiae     EGLMVKMLEGPESHYEPSKR     EGLMVKMLEGP-ESHYEPSKR
  Vaccinia virus     EGLVLKDINGV...YEPGKR     EGLVLKDINGV----YEPGKR
  Bacteriophage T3   EGLIVKDPQGI...YKRGKK     EGLIVKDPQGIYKRG-----K
  Bacteriophage T4   EGIILKNIDGL...WENARS     EGIILKNIDGLWENA-----R
  ASF virus          EGAIVRNANGPYEPGYNNYH     EGAIVRNANGPYEPGYN-NYH

Region 3
  Human              SHNWLKLKKDYL            SHNWLKLKKDYL
  Sch.pombe          SRHWLKVKKDYL            SRHWLKVKKDYL
   S. cerevisiae     SRNWLKLKKDYL            SRNWLKLKKDYL
  Vaccinia virus     ..RWLKIKRDYL           --RWLKIKRDYL
  Bacteriophage T3   ..GWWKLKPEC.           KSGWWKLKPEC-
  Bacteriophage T4   ..NLYKFKEVI.           SKNLYKFKEVI-
  ASF virus          PHLAKLKPLL.            SPHLAKLKPLL-
```

FIGURE 7.8 Regions of conserved lysine residues in DNA ligases. The figure shows three regions where there is an apparent conservation of lysine. Region 1 is where the adenylated lysine found by experimentation is located. ASF virus is African swine fever virus.

The use of different scoring tables produced some dramatic effects. Changing from a unity score matrix to a PAM 100 or PAM 250 table without any alteration in gap penalties produced alignments with large numbers of gaps. Although this might be predicted where sequences of disparate sizes (e.g. the full length ligase sequences) are used this would not have been generally predicted where truncated sequences were aligned. Careful choice of both the gap penalty and the extension penalty would seem to be necessary in order to produce a reasonable result. In the case of CLUSTAL where the PAM 100 table was used with full length sequences, regions 1 and 2 were correctly aligned, but region 1 was only partially aligned. The overall effect on the sequences was to produce very short regions separated by, in some instances, gaps of 30 to 40 residues. Raising both gap penalties reduced the number and extent of unaligned regions but also failed to preserve the alignment of the target regions.

Comparing the use of the standard matrix with PAM 100 and using PAM 250 as the scoring matrix and default gap penalties for ALIEN saw an improved region 1 alignment although there was a failure to align the African swine fever virus properly, and a failure to align regions 2 and 3 in any except the vaccinia, human and yeast sequences. The alignments generally had fewer gaps where the truncated sequences were used and the higher PAM table was used. Where the full length sequences were used, only region 2 was properly aligned. Since there are few gaps anyway in the truncated sequence alignment, increasing the gap penalty does not improve the alignment. Indeed, increasing the floating gap penalty has a detrimental effect on the truncated sequence alignments.

7.2   Results Using the Ribonucleotide Reductase Sequences

It was shown relatively early in the study of ribonucleotide reductase that redox-active thiols are involved in the catalytic reaction (Thelander, 1974). Therefore the identification of invariant cysteines is important as a prelude in determining which might involve the catalytic reaction. Most of the work has been done using the *E. coli* enzyme and four different cysteines have been chemically labelled in experiments to locate redox-active thiols (Lin et al., 1987). Thus there are a number of criteria for determining how good an alignment is. Again the test sequences are of somewhat different lengths and this had an effect on the final quality of the alignment. In particular the additional 450 amino acids at the amino-terminus of the herpes simplex virus (HSV) large subunit are apparently unrelated to reductase function. Performing alignments which incorporate this sequence caused problems for all the programs used. In the instance of CLUSTAL and ALIEN the alignments started with the initiator methionine and then included many gaps as the programs attempted to align the sequences globally. Figures 7.9a and 7.9b show the results when a large unrelated sequence is included in the alignment. Although the regions shown are considerably downstream of the protein start, the alignment has been degraded. The results can be improved by removing the offending region and rerunning the program (Figure 7.9b), giving a much more plausible alignment. With the program PileUp, because of its ability to weight end gaps differently to internal gaps, the large amino-terminal domain causes fewer initial problems.

(a)

```
RIR1_HSV11    MESVFQMYTRIAGFLACRATRGMRHIALGREGS----WWEMFKFFF
RIR1_EBV      FCGRVSIKSLMFSIVNCAVKAGSPFILLKEACNAHF-WRD------
RIR1_HUMAN    THASPTLF-----------------------NAGTNRPQLSSCFL
RIR1_MOUSE    THAPPTLF-----------------------NAGTNRPQLSSCFL
RIR1_YEAST    THASPTLF-----------------------NAGTPLPQMSSCFL
RIR1_VACCC    THASPTLF-----------------------NAGTSRHOMSSCFL
RIR1_VZVD     LESLCQFFLRLAATVTTEIVNLPKIATLIPGINDGYTWTDVCRVFF
RIR1_HCMVA    RDGQLSLSTFTMSTVGFDRVPQYDFLISADPFSRDASWAAMC----
```

(b)

```
RIR1_HSV11    EGS----WWEMFKFFFHRLYDHQIVPSTPAMLNLGTRNYYTSSCYL
RIR1_EBV      ARPEIESDMEVFDYYFEHLTSQTVCCSTPFMRFAGVENSTLASCIL
RIR1_HUMAN    HKEDIDAAIETYNLLSERWFTH----ASPTLFNAGTNRPQLSSCFL
RIR1_MOUSE    HKEDIDAAIETYNLLSEKWFTH----APPTLFNAGTNRPQLSSCFL
RIR1_YEAST    HGSDIESVLKTYNLMSLRYFTH----ASPTLFNAGTPLPQMSSCFL
RIR1_VACCC    HQWDIDSAIETYNLLSEKWFTH----ASPTLFNAGTSRHOMSSCFL
RIR1_VZVD     GINDGYTWTDVCRVFFTALACQKIVPATPVMMFLGRETGATASCYL
RIR1_HCMVA    PARELPSDRNALWREMDTVSRHSAGLGSFRLFQLIMRHGPCLIRHS
```

FIGURE **7.9** Multiple sequence alignments - degradation of the alignment. The figure shows degradation of the alignment when a long sequence is included (the alignment has been performed using the program ALIEN). In this case the amino-terminus of the herpes simplex virus protein has sequences which are unrelated to its function as a reductase and do not have counterparts in the other sequences used. The regions underlined show the effect of removing this sequence. In this instance the *E. coli* sequence was not used in the alignments.

Table 7.3 shows the comparative performance of the programs when the invariant cysteines are considered. The table shows the number of cysteines aligned correctly in relation to the *E. coli* sequence.

TABLE 7.3 Alignment of invariant cysteines. "Full length" and "Truncated" refers to the herpes simplex virus sequence with its additional amino-terminus. In these particular alignments 9 sequences were used and the results are therefore given as a x/9. 0/9 means that no other cysteines were aligned to the *E. coli* sequence, 2/9 means that one other cysteine was satisfactorily aligned and so on*

Program	Full length					Truncated				
Position	225/ 761	439/ 761	462/ 761	754/ 761	759/ 761	225/ 761	439/ 761	462/ 761	754/ 761	759/ 761
CLUSTAL	8/9	9/9	9/9	2/9	8/9	9/9	9/9	9/9	2/9	8/9
ALIEN	5/9	7/9	0/9	0/9	8/9	8/9	8/9	0/9	6/9*	8/9
PileUp	8/9	8/9	9/9	0/9	0/9	8/9	8/9	9/9	3/9*	0/9
PileUp (all gaps the same)	8/9	8/9	9/9	6/9*	8/9	8/9	8/9	9/9	6/9*	8/9

* In this instance cysteines were aligned, but not against appropriate the E. coli residue.

From a consideration of these results it can be seen that where full length sequences are used there is quite considerable variation in the apparent reliability of the programs, with CLUSTAL performing the best overall. When truncated sequences are used then PileUp performs better but still fails to achieve the alignment of the final conserved cysteine. This can be attributed to the end weight option of this program as previously discussed. In this instance where the sequences of interest are actually at the extreme carboxy-terminus the alignment is lost when differential gap weighting is allowed, unlike the case with the DNA ligases. When end gaps are weighted the same as internal gaps, then the carboxy-terminal cysteines are aligned. It should be noted that the cysteines corresponding to C754 in the *E. coli* sequences are not aligned with it.

Where specific residues are considered then there is a marked difference between the programs. However, if the overall alignment is looked at then it becomes more difficult to assess the quality of the results produced. ALIEN and CLUSTAL when run with default parameters and full length sequences produce alignments with many short, chunky but well aligned regions. There are many gaps of differing sizes and most notably all the alignments start with the initial methionine of the test sequences. This leads to an attempt to align the amino-terminus of the sequences with the unrelated amino-terminus of the herpes simplex sequence. In the instance of PileUp this does not happen and for the bulk of the sequences there is no alignment made until the equivalent of residue 360 (approximately) in the herpes simplex sequence. This highlights another instance of the advantage of this kind of score weighting. Generally the PileUp results have fewer gaps and longer contiguous stretches.

7.3 Strategic Considerations

In performing the multiple alignments it becomes clear that a certain amount of thought prior to running any particular program could be useful. A simple examination of the lengths of sequences under consideration might reveal length discrepancies for example. These should prompt the user to consider the existence of novel or unrelated domains. The relative positions of such domains can be simply revealed by using a dot matrix comparison program. As previously discussed, the presence of insertions and deletions as well as repetitive regions can also be visualized in this manner. This should suggest to the user whether or not truncating parts of the relevant sequences might improve the potential alignment. Where there are a number of sequences which are not very different throughout the whole length, this can also cause some problems by biassing regions strongly. The user may wish to consider whether fewer representatives of such sequences may be more appropriate in producing the initial alignment. Again an understanding of the scoring scheme and the treatment of gaps will be useful in determining an appropriate strategy to follow once an initial alignment has been produced.

Finally the ability to use a multiple sequence editor after the automated alignment has been produced should also be taken into account. LineUp, for example, which is part of the GCG suite of software can be used after PileUp. This program accepts sequences in GCG's multiple sequence format (MSF format) and can accept up to 30 sequences simultaneously. Alignments from ALIEN can be edited in the program SOMAP. At the very least, judicious use of a text editor where no alternative exists should be considered, especially for small regions.

8 Overall Conclusions

In using these programs whether for database searching or multiple sequence alignment certain common factors have emerged. Firstly there is probably no best program to perform any particular task. Many programs will perform adequately under most circumstances. However, there will be times when the peculiar features of a sequence or set of set sequences will cause a program to fail in some way. The user should be aware that this can happen and by careful examination of the results and knowledge of the sequences in question arrive at a plausible reason for this failure and a strategy to deal with it. Judicious changes in program parameters will have an effect on the results. Too small a change will have little or no effect and too large a change may be potentially fatal. There will be instances when a sequence is apparently unique and fails to align plausibly with any other sequence. In this case much can still be learned by using other methods such searching the sequence with one or other of the motif exploration programs and a database such as the PROSITE database (Chapter 8). In any case, once the user feels that no more information can be derived from further refinements of the database search, other methods of sequences analysis should be brought in to play. The search is a beginning and not an end to sequence analysis. Multiple sequence alignment can be a powerful technique and variants of the methodology designed to build profiles or motifs (for example the PROFILE series of programs within the GCG suite or the Motif Exploration Program of the Staden suite of software) can be used to derive further information.

9   Where to Find the Programs

The programs used to run the database searches were all available at the UK Human Genome Mapping Project Resource Centre. Searches were run against release 23 of the PIR protein database. Some of the programs such as BLAST (blast@ncbi.nlm.nih.gov), PROSRCH (dapmail@ed.ac.uk) and MPSRCH (blitz@embl-heidelberg.de) are available as e-mail servers. In addition BLAST and FASTA can be obtained from several anonymous FTP sites for local installation. FastA is also part of the GCG suite of software.

The multiple sequence alignment programs were performed using the Seqnet resource. CLUSTALV (Higgins et al., 1992) can be obtained from one of the anonymous FTP sites. ALIEN was written by A. J. Bleasby and PileUp is part of the GCG suite.

10   References

Altschul SF, Gish W, Miller W, Myers EW and Lipman DJ (1990). Basic local alignment search tool. J. Mol. Biol. 215, 403-410.

Argos P (1989). In "Protein Structure: A Practical Approach" (ed. TE Creighton), pp.169-190. IRL Press, Oxford.

Argos P and Vingron M (1990). Sensitivity comparison of protein amino acid sequences. Methods Enzymol. 183, 352-365.

Barker DG, White JHM and Johnston LH (1987). Molecular characterisation of the DNA ligase gene, CDC17, from the fission yeast *Schizosaccharomyces pombe*. Eur. J. Biochem. 162, 659-667.

Barton GJ and Sternberg MJE (1987). A strategy for rapid multiple alignment of protein sequences. Confidence levels from tertiary structure comparisons. J. Mol. Biol. 198, 327-337.

Bell GI (1988). In "Computers and DNA" (ed. GI Bell and TG Marr), pp 3-11. Addison-Wesley, New York.

Collins JF and Coulson AFW (1987). In "Nucleic Acid and Protein Sequence Analysis: A Practical Approach" (eds. MJ Bishop and CJ Rawlings), pp. 323-358. IRL Press, Oxford.

Collins JF and Coulson AFW (1990). Significance of protein sequence similarities. Methods Enzymol. 183, 474-486.

Collins JF and Coulson AFW and Lyall A (1987). Protein and nucleic acid sequence database searching: a suitable case for parallel processing. Comp. J. 30, 420-424.

Dayhoff MO, Schwartz RM and Orcutt BC (1978). In "Atlas of Protein Sequence and Structure" (ed. MO Dayhoff), Vol 5. Suppl. 3, p. 345. National Biomedical Research Foundation, Silver Spring, MD.

Doolittle RF (1988). In "Computers and DNA" (eds. GI Bell and TG Marr), pp. 21-32. Addison-Wesley, New York.

Doolittle, RF (1990). Searching through sequence databases. Methods Enzymol. 183, 99-110.

Feng D-F and Doolittle RF (1987). Progressive sequence alignment as a prerequisite to correct phylogenetic trees. J. Mol. Evol. 25, 351-360.

George DG, Barker WC and Hunt LT (1990). Mutation data matrix and its uses. Methods Enzymol. 183, 333-351.

Gotoh O (1982). An improved algorithm for matching biological sequences. J. Mol. Biol. 162, 705-708.

Higgins DG and Sharp PM (1988). CLUSTAL: a package for performing multiple sequence alignment on a microcomputer. Gene 73, 237-244.

Higgins DG, Bleasby AJ and Fuchs R (1992). ClustalV: improved software for multiple sequence alignment. Comput. Applic. Biosci. 8, 189-191.

Jimenez-Montano M and Zamora-Cortina L (1981). In "Proceedings of the VII International Biophysics Congress".

Lin AN, Ashley GW and Stubbe J (1987). Location of the redox-active thiols of ribonucleotide reductase: sequence similarity between the Escherichia coli and Lactobacillus leichmannii enzymes. Biochemistry 26, 6905-6909.

Lipman DJ and Pearson WR (1985). Rapid and sensitive protein similarity searches. Science 227, 1435-1441.

Myers EW and Miller W (1988). Optimal alignments in linear space. Comput. Applic. Biosci. 4, 11-17.

Miyata T, Miyazawa S and Yasunaga T (1979). Two types of amino acid substitutions in protein evolution. J. Mol. Evol. 12, 219-236.

Needleman S and Wunsch C (1970). A general method applicable to the search for similarities in the amino acid sequence of two proteins. J. Mol. Biol. 48, 443-453.

Smith GL, Chan YS and Kerr SM (1989). Nucleic Acids Res. 17, 9051-9062.

Smith TF and Waterman MS (1981). Identification of common molecular subsequences. J. Mol. Biol. 147, 195-197.

Thelander L (1974). Reaction mechanism of ribonucleoside diphosphate reductase from *Escherichia coli*. Oxidation-reduction-active disulfides in the B1 subunit. J. Biol. Chem. 249, 4858-4862.

Tomkinson AE, Totty NF, Ginsburg M and Lindahl T (1991). Location of the active site for enzyme-adenylate formation in DNA ligases. Proc. Natl Acad. Sci. USA 88, 400-404.

Wilbur WJ and Lipman DJ (1983). Rapid similarity search of nucleic acid and protein data banks. Proc. Natl Acad. Sci. USA 80, 726-730.

CHAPTER 8

Sequence Functional Inference

Luciano Milanesi[1], Nicolay Kolchanov[2], Igor Rogozin[2], Alexander Kel[2] and Igor Titov[2]

[1] Istituto di Tecnologie Biomediche Avanzate, Consiglio Nazionale delle Richerche, Milan, Italy
[2] Institute of Cytology and Genetics, Siberian Branch of the Russian Academy of Sciences, Novosibirsk, Russia

1   Introduction

With the recent development of a systematic approach to mapping and sequencing the genomes of man and other mammals there is a need for computer based methods for the interpretation of the sequence data produced during these projects. The requirement is to identify the coding parts of newly discovered genes and the regions regulating DNA replication, transcription, RNA maturation and translation.

2   Organization of Mammalian Genes

The mammalian genome is diploid and it exceeds the *E. coli* genome by a factor of 10^3 (Saenger, 1984). A considerable portion of the eukaryotic genome consists of non-coding DNA. In man, for example, coding DNA comprises approximately 20% of the genome (Lewin, 1980).

The organization of the eukaryotic gene is very complex and the mosaic pattern of alternating introns and exons is remarkable. Exons correspond to the coding fragments of the genes; introns are the non-coding regions that are removed from mRNA by the splicing mechanism at acceptor and donor sites during RNA maturation.

The non-coding regions of the eukaryotic genome cannot be regarded as functionally inert. Portions of the non-coding DNA comprise regulatory gene regions which are very long and saturated with functional sites providing transcriptional control (Karlin, 1989). This is manifest in long extensions of the 5'-regulatory regions and also in the large variety of functional sites interacting with the regulatory proteins in those regions (Libermann et al., 1990). The non-coding portion also includes introns which contain different kinds of sites involved in the regulation of gene expression. The great majority of eukaryotic genomic DNA is involved in interaction with histones and other proteins to form chromatin.

In contrast to the prokaryotic genome, the eukaryotic genome has three types of genes served by different RNA polymerases. RNA polymerase I transcribes ribosomal genes. RNA polymerase II transcribes genes coding for proteins and some low molecular weight nuclear RNAs (e.g. U1, U2, U5, etc.). RNA polymerase III transcribes tRNA, 5S RNA, other low molecular weight RNA genes.

There is also a need for developmental stage or cell specific expression of eukaryotic genes provided by regulatory elements (Karlin, 1989). Their regulation is extremely complex since multicellular eukaryotic organisms contain from several tens to hundreds of differentiated cell types (Winnacker, 1989).

Transcription of each of the above gene groups has unique features. During the formation of gene products at each period of the cell cycle the appropriate concentrations of gene products are achieved by means of differential initiation and termination of transcription, RNA processing, and differential initiation of translation.

High saturation with different types of repeats is a characteristic feature of the mammalian genome (Schmid and Shen, 1985). There are two large groups of repeats: one tandemly clustered, the other dispersed throughout the genome. The first group includes satellite DNA (Willard and Waye, 1987) and clusters of isofunctional genes belonging to different isofunctional families. The second one includes Alu, B1, B2, L1, which are subdivided into two classes, short (SINE) and long (LINE).

The copy number of Alu is $(5-9) \times 10^5$ per haploid human genome. Alu-like repeats were also found to occur in the genomes of primates, rodents, and ungulates. Repeats of the L1(KPN1) type are members of the Line group, 5,000-7,000 bp long, present in the genome in 10,000-100,000 copies in both marsupial and placental mammals.

3 Functional Sites in DNA and RNA Sequences

3.1 Recognition of the Promotor Regions of Eukaryotic Protein Encoding Genes

Transcription of the protein encoding genes is controlled by RNA polymerase II in conjunction with various types of regulatory factors such as proteins and protein-ligand complexes (Winnacker, 1989). These regulatory factors specifically interact with particular regions of DNA molecules called signal sequences. The available databases contain information concerning the promotor regions of the eukaryotic genes, the various transcription factors and signal DNA sequences (Bucher, 1989; Faisst and Meyer, 1992; Prestridge, 1991; Wingender, 1988).

3.1.1 The Eukaryotic Promotor Database (EPD)

EPD (Bucher, 1989) provides information about eukaryotic promotors available in the EMBL Data Library. EPD contains the promotors recognized by eukaryotic RNA polymerase II.

An example of a promotor entry is shown in Figure 8.1.

```
//
FP              Hs c-myc        P2+:+S          EM:HSMYCC
1+              2490;           11148.053 010*2
XX
DO              Experimental evidence: 4,4#,<2>
DO              Expression/Regulation: +mitogen
RF                              Cell34:779      EMBOJ2:2375
MCB7:1393       MCB7:2988
//
```

FIGURE 8.1 Example of an entry from EPD.

The FP line is the start of each promotor entry. It contains a position reference to a transcription initiation site. The FP line contains the following fields and sub-fields: description (name of promotor, initiation site type), functional position reference (database, promotor entry code, position number), identification of alternative promotor (number of the gene, the number of initiation site). Characteristics such as the group of promotors, circular or linear type of sequence, type of strand (+ or -) are also included in the FP line.

Two DO lines are assigned to each entry. The first DO line refers to the transcript mapping experiments that define the promotor, the second DO line contains information about regulation and expression of the promotor. A hierarchical classification system is used for arranging the entries of EPD.

3.1.2 Databases of Transcription Factors and Signals

The database of Faisst and Meyer (1992) is a compilation of the transcription factors of vertebrates. It contains information about transcription factors and the relative consensus sequences. The fields of this compilation are as follows:

1. Factor - name of the transcription factor;
2. Synonyms/homologies - alternative name;
3. Binding sequence - DNA sequence interacting with the factor;
4. M_r (kDa), domains - molecular weight of the factor and name of factor domains;
5. Tissue specificity - list of tissues where the factor is active;
6. Inducers/repressors - components affecting the factor action;
7. Features - characteristics of the binding factor.

Some examples from the database compiled by Faisst and Meyer are given in Table 8.1.

The Transcription Factor Database (TFD) (Ghosh, 1990) contains a large body of transcription related sequence information and is organized in a relational manner. The compilation includes information concerning eukaryotic transcription factors. The database contains over 1,800 binding sites (Prestridge and Stormo, 1993).

The relational model incorporates one-to-one and one-to-many relationships between the different types of information about the function and interaction of factors at different steps of gene expression. The database is organized so as to allow the incorporation of all the major classes of information about the eukaryotic transcription machinery. The body of information is subdivided into 5 interrelated tables:

1. SITES - information about sequences recognized by the transcription factors;
2. DOMAINS - information concerning amino acid motifs in the protein factors;
3. FACTORS - general information about the factors;
4. CDNAS - sequences of transcription factor cDNA;
5. ELEMENTS - sequences of functional elements such as promotors and enhancers containing the mentioned signals.

The central part of the database is the SITES table. It contains: nucleotide sequences recognized by the transcriptional factors; name of the promotor or gene from which the sequence originated; the position of the sequence relative to the transcription start.

TABLE 8.1 The examples from the database of transcription factors compiled by Faisst and Meyer (1992)

1	2	3	4	5	6
Factor[1]	Synonyms homologues	Binding sequence	M (kDa) domains[2]	Tissue specificity	Inducers (repressors)
AP1[h,m,r,c,h]	PEA1[m]	TGA G/C T C/A A	v-Jun: 65 c-Jun: 39 v-Fos: 55/75 c-Fos: 55-65 bZIP (Ph)	Ubiquitous	TPA, EGF, Ha-ras, raf, v-mos, IL-2, NGF, TGFBeta, ConA, picrotoxin, Py-mt metrazole, serum
CP2[h]	NF-Y[m]	C/T AG C/T N$_3$ A/G R CCAATCN$_3$ G/A			v-src, serum
EF-1A[h,m,r]		CGGAAGTG		Ubiquitous	
PPAR[m]		AGGTCA	52.4 zinc f.	Liver, kidney, heart, brown adipose tissue	Peroxisome, proliferators

1	7
AP1	Homodimer of Jun or heterodimer between members of the Jun and Fos or Jun and ATF families. Positive or negative regulating factor of various cellular and viral promoters. Fos down-regulates immediate-early gene expression via CArG boxes. DNA-binding is inhibited by IP1 (30-40 kDa) which may interact with the Jun/Fos bZIP
CP2	CCAAT box binding factor
EF-1A	Binds cooperatively to two binding sites. May be related or identical to E4TF1
PPAR	Member of steroid hormone receptor superfamily. Important for triglyceride and cholesterol homeostasis. May play a role in the development of liver tumours

[1] The species in which a factor has been identified is given in superscript letters (b, bovine; c, calf; ch, chicken; f, frog; h, human; ha, hamster; m, murine; r, rat; s, :simian).

[2] bZIP, leucine zipper protein containing a basic domain; (Ph), phosphoprotein; zinc f., zinc finger.

3.1.3   Computer Analysis of Transcription Signals Based on Weighted Matrices

The results of experiments and of computer studies both demonstrate that not one of the identified transcription signals is invariant with respect to all the promotors of RNA polymerase II. Signal sequences such as the TATA box, cap site, CCAAT and GC boxes are the most frequently occurring in the promotor regions. Detailed computer analyses of these signal sequences have been carried out (Bucher, 1990; Bucher and Trifonov, 1988).

In analysis of these signals in 502 unrelated eukaryotic promotors Bucher (1990) has used his method based on iterative weight matrix refinement.

Let us consider a set of aligned signal sequences of length l corresponding to the functional signal under consideration.

Then $F = |f_{ij}|$, (i= $(1, ..., 4)$, j= $(1, ..., l)$) is the nucleotide frequency matrix, where f_{ij} is the absolute frequency of occurrence of the i-th type of the nucleotide out of the set $\{A, T, G, C\}$ at the j-th position of the above alignment. The weight matrix of the functional site $W = |w_{ij}|$ can be constructed, where the element w_{ij} is calculated as follows:

$$w_{ij} = \ln\left(\frac{f_{ij}}{e_{ij}} + \frac{s}{100}\right) + c_i \qquad \textbf{(EQ 8.1)}$$

Here, e_{ij} is the expected frequency of the nucleotide of the i-th type at the j-th position, c_i is the column-specific free constant and s denotes the so-called smoothing percentage.

These optimized weight matrices can be used to search for functional signals in the nucleotide sequences. For any nucleotide fragment of length l in an analysed sequence, which is tested for assignment to the proper functional signal, a matching score can be calculated as follows:

$$x = \sum_{j=1}^{l} w_{ij} \qquad \textbf{(EQ 8.2)}$$

The match percentage can be used for estimation of the similarity between the analysed nucleotide fragment and the weight matrix:

$$match = 100\frac{x - x_{min}}{x_{max} - x_{min}} \qquad \textbf{(EQ 8.3)}$$

where

$$x_{max} = \sum_{j=1}^{l} \max{}_i w_{ij}$$

and

$$x_{min} = \sum_{j=1}^{l} \min{}_i w_{ij}$$

By scanning a nucleotide sequence with the definite cut-off matching score value (i.e. threshold match to the corresponding weight matrix) all the potential functional signals (motifs) of the given type can be revealed.

Bucher's (1990) method for weight matrix construction allows a large variation in signal location with respect to the transcription start site. Comparison of promotor sequences can reveal a local region of preferential occurrence of a definite signal. The quantitative measure of local over-representation is used as an optimization criterion for constructing the weight matrix. Table 8.2 gives the frequency and weight matrices for the cap site.

TABLE 8.2 Characteristics of the cap site (Bucher, 1990)

	-2	-1	0	1	2	3	4	5
A	49	0	288	26	77	67	45	50
C	48	303	0	81	95	118	85	96
G	69	0	0	116	0	46	73	56
T	137	0	15	80	131	72	100	101
A	-1.14	-5.26	0.00	-1.51	-0.65	-0.55	-0.91	-0.82
C	-1.16	0.00	-5.21	-0.41	-0.45	0.00	-0.29	-0.18
G	-0.75	-5.26	-5.21	0.00	-4.56	-0.86	-0.38	-0.65
T	0.00	-5.26	-2.74	-0.29	0.00	-0.36	0.00	0.00
	T	C	A	G	T	C	T	T
	G		T	T	C	T	C	C
			C	A			G	

A short degenerate consensus (Table 8.2) and a rather rigidly conserved location are the characteristic features of the cap site. The consensus cap site was present only in 60% of the analysed promotors. Because of the high background occurrence frequency of the cap site, its potential for promotor recognition is insignificant (Bucher, 1990).

The variation range of the distance between the cap site and initiation codon is fairly large (Kozak, 1989).

Table 8.3 gives a characterization of the TATA box consensus built with the use of the same method. The identified consensus is 16 bp long. The consensus TATA box is observed in 78% of the analysed promotor regions, the remaining 22% includes several promotors of the nuclear RNA genes. It is present in much larger numbers in the promotors of the protein encoding genes than the cap site. The TATA box is the most over-represented and conserved signal sequence among eukaryotic promotors. A certain variation in location is characteristic even of this signal (Figure 8.2) and it extends from -36 to -20 bp upstream from the transcription start site.

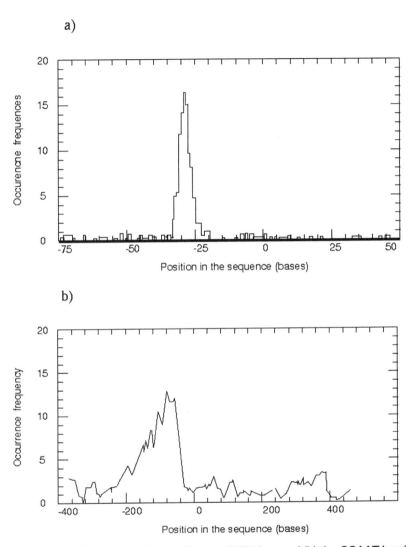

FIGURE 8.2 The positional distribution of (a) the TATA box and (b) the CCAAT box in the sample of vertebrate promotor sequences. The value on the graph corresponds to the percentage of promotors which have the named box in the current position (Penotti, 1990).

The characteristic features of the CCAAT and GC boxes are high degeneracy of the consensus (Table 8.3), large variation in location (Figure 8.2) and low occurrence fre-

TABLE 8.3 Characteristics of three eukaryotic promotor signal sequences (Bucher, 1990)

Signal sequence	Consensus
TATA box	G T A T A A A A G G C G G G G C T T T T A C G C C C C Preferred Region: centred between -36 and -20
CCAAT box	T C T A G C C A A T C A C T C G A T A G G Preferred Region: centred between -212 and -57
GC box	A A G G G G C G G G G C T T T G T A T A T A T T C G A A T Preferred Region: centred between -164 and +1

quencies. For example, the CCAAT box was found only in 30% of the examined promotors, and its location varies in the -212 to -57 range upstream from the transcription start site (Bucher, 1990).

High degeneracy of the consensus sequences of the transcription signals and the variations in their location decrease the diagnostic value of the individual signals in promotor recognition. These signals and other elements of the context can be useful in recognition of transcription initiation sites when taken together.

3.1.4 Transcription Signal Analysis Based on the Discrimination Energy Model

Additional information about the structure of the promotor signal sequences may be derived from the discrimination energy model developed by Berg and von Hippel (1987).

Protein-DNA recognition is based on the DNA sequence dependent pattern complementary to the binding site of the protein. This functional property is treated in terms of binding strength. The initial assumption is that one of these DNA patterns may be represented as a consensus consisting of base pairs occurring most frequently at certain positions of a functional site. It is also assumed that the consensus corresponds to a pattern most tightly binding to protein. Each functional signal is characterized by a certain affinity for protein, and the nearer the signal is to the consensus, the higher is the binding affinity.

The aim is to compute the free energy of binding of a signal taking into account the contribution of each signal position to the total binding energy.

The main postulates of Berg and von Hippel are as follows:

1. Recognition sites are selected in evolution so that binding affinity values for a certain protein fall within a useful range.

2. The number of sequences that can be used in this affinity range is large. If selection is based on affinity, mutational "neutral sequence drift" will ensure an equal probability for all the possible sequences.

3. Each possible base pair at every position in a site contributes independently and, therefore, additively to the binding free energy (specific activity) at that site.

With these assumptions, one can find the relationship between the frequency of occurrence of base pair B at the position l in the site, f_{lB}, and its contribution $e_{lB}kT$ to the total binding energy. e_{lB} are dimensionless numbers and only relative changes are of interest. Representing the four possible base-pairs A-T, T-A, G-C, C-G by the number set $B = \{0, 1, 2, 3\}$, let us denote $B = 0$ as the consensus base pair (i.e. the most frequent) at each position l and set $e_x = 0$. Thus, e_{lB}, which is called the discrimination energy per base pair, is a non-negative value, and it represents the change in binding free energy that results when the consensus base pair ($B=0$) is replaced by another base pair B. The sum of the base pair contributions gives the total discrimination energy for a particular sequence, and it has to be zero for an "ideal" signal sequence corresponding to the consensus and positive for other signals. Thus, the discrimination energy characterizes the binding activity of the corresponding signal.

Of course, detailed experimental knowledge of the corresponding biochemical processes is needed to establish a better agreement between the discrimination energy and the actual free energy change.

Now let us assume that all the four canonical base pairs are equally probable in the genome and consider a population of all possible signal sequences. In a real case, this population can be expected to form a very small subset of all random sequences.

It is suggested to estimate the occurrence frequency of the base pair B at the l-th position of a signal as follows:

$$f_{lB} = \frac{n_{lB} + 1}{N + 4} \qquad \text{(EQ 8.4)}$$

where n_{lB} is the number of occurrences of the base pair B at the position l in the sample of signals used for consensus construction and

$$N = \sum_B n_{lB} \qquad \text{(EQ 8.5)}$$

is the number of signals in the sample.

At large N values,

$$f_{lB} = \frac{n_{lB}}{N} \qquad \text{(EQ 8.6)}$$

At small N values, this estimate minimizes the error due to the "small sample" effect. This effect may be observed as the low occurrence frequency of certain base pairs at certain positions $n_{lB} \ll (N/4)$.

The best estimation of the local discrimination energy can be obtained as follows:

$$\varepsilon_{lB} = \lambda^{-1} \ln \left(\frac{n_{l0} + 0.5}{n_{lB} + 0.5} \right) \qquad \text{(EQ 8.7)}$$

where λ is a scale parameter of no importance in determining the relative affinities.

At large n_{l0} and n_{lB} values, the expression under the logarithm is the ratio of nucleotide occurrence frequencies.

From the observed base pair frequencies, the best estimation for the information contained at the position l in the signal can be derived as

$$I_{seq}(l) = \left(\sum_{B=A}^{T} \frac{n_{lB} + 1}{N + 4} \right) \ln \left(4 \frac{n_{lB} + 1.5}{N + 4.5} \right) \qquad \text{(EQ 8.8)}$$

The standard deviation of ε_{lB}, as well as of I_{seq}, can be calculated in this way.

With this approach, profiles of the information content for the TATA box and cap site were built (Penotti, 1990). The profiles confirmed the local nature of these signals and also that there are no additional conserved nucleotides upstream and downstream from the TATA box and cap site (Figure 8.3). It was found that for the human promotors the total information content is 9.8 bits for the TATA box and 2.7 bits for the cap site. This difference reflects the more important role of the TATA box than the cap site in determining the exact starting point of transcription. However, the information content of the cap site may be quite sufficient for correct choice of the transcription initiation site in the local DNA region downstream from the TATA box after it has been recognized by the nascent transcription complex. Considerable increase in computer recognition accuracy may therefore be achieved by taking into account the key steps of signal sequence recognition by the transcription complex.

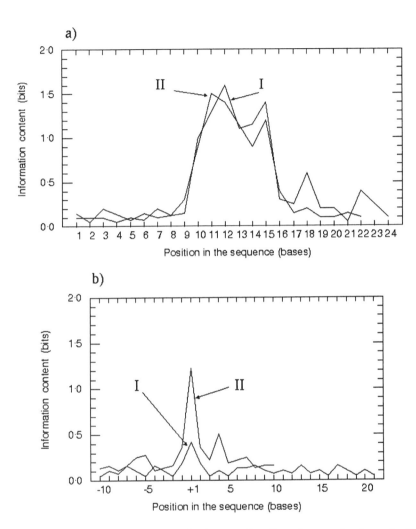

FIGURE 8.3 The informational content for human (line I) and general eukaryotic (line II) (a) TATA boxes (position 10 in the sequence corresponds to the first T in the canonical TATAAA consensus hexamer) and (b) cap sites (position +1 in the sequence is the first transcribed nucleotide (Penotti, 1990).

3.1.5 Role of Conformational Characteristics in Transcription Signals

The application of Calladine-Dickerson rules demonstrates the significance of the conformational parameters for recognition and function of promotors and enhancers. Nussinov (1991) has noted the important role of the following characteristics of DNA in recognition of signal sequences by regulatory proteins: (a) geometry of the DNA structure; (b) anisotropic DNA flexibility; (c) DNA thermodynamic stability; (d) hydrogen bonding patterns.

In particular, analysis of the CCAAT and TATA boxes and DNA spacer between them in vertebrate promotors demonstrates that purine-purine and pyrimidine-pyrimidine are frequent in the upstream region, near the CCAAT signal sequence. At the same time, purine-pyrimidine and pyrimidine-purine are abundant near the TATA box (Nussinov, 1992).

Analysis revealed that the downstream part of the DNA spacer is rather flexible, whereas the upstream part is rigid, both with respect to the geometry of the DNA structure. This property was revealed in the analysis of 100 individual sequences and is statistically significant ($p < 10^{-5}$).

It has been suggested that this distribution of flexibility may provide proper spatial juxtapositioning of the CCAAT and TATA signals and, hence, correct interaction of the basal transcription factors related to these signals (Nussinov, 1992).

It should be emphasized, however, that we know very little about the conformational parameters of the DNA involved in the interaction of protein factors with signal sequences. For this reason these conformational characteristics can be applied only very cautiously in recognition of signal sequences.

3.2 Computer Programs for Recognition of Transcription Signals

The large body of signal sequences specifically binding to the regulatory factors of transcription stored in sequence databases has made possible their use for the analysis of raw sequencing data (Ambrose and Bina, 1990; Ghosh, 1990; Bucher, 1990; Prestridge, 1991; Prestridge and Stormo, 1993; Wingender et al., 1991).

3.2.1 Recognition of Transcription Signal by Homology Search

One of the approaches to the search of potential transcription signals in nucleotide sequences is based on the SIGNAL SCAN program (Prestridge, 1991; Prestridge and Stormo, 1993). With this program, regions with homology to the signal sequences in the TFD are searched. The output information of the SIGNAL SCAN is the list of potential transcription factor binding sites (signals) represented in the standard format (Figure 8.4).

```
HUMHSP.seq: 113 base pairs
Signal database file: mammal.dat
---------------------------------------------------------------------
  Factor or Site name     Loc. Str.  Signal sequence          TFD S#
---------------------------------------------------------------------
  hat-indf                  6   (+)  CTGGAATATTCCCG           S00774
  HSTF                      6   (+)  CTGGAATATTCCCG           S01248
  CAP-site        ┌─────┐  26   (+)  CANYYY                   S00089
  T-Ag            └─────┘  28   (-)  GAGGC                    S00973
  CP1                      41   (-)  YNNNNNNRRCCAATCANYK      S01306
  GATA-1                   43   (-)  MYWATCWY                 S00477
  CTF/CBP                  45   (+)  GATTGG                   S00777
  ........                 ...       ..........
  TFIID                    85   (+)  TATAWAW                  S01540
  T-Ag                     92   (-)  TGGGC                    S01375
  SV40.11         ┌─────┐  93   (+)  CCCAG                    S01003
  T-Ag            └─────┘  97   (+)  GGGGC                    S00974
  PEBP2                   104   (-)  GACCGC                   S00053
  H4TF-2                  106   (+)  GGTCC                    S00742
```

FIGURE 8.4 Output of the SIGNAL SCAN program. Analysis of human 70 kDa heat shock (hsp 70) gene promotor region (Prestige,1991). The sequences were scanned using the mammalian database. Loc. is the signal location in the sequence. Str. is the DNA strand where the signal is revealed (+/-). TFD S# is the TFD site number.

Shachmuradov et al. (1986) suggested the method for searching functional sites based on statistical estimation:

1. The IUPAC-IUB standard (Table 8.4) for ambiguous nucleotides is used to describe the consensus.

2. It is assumed that a consensus of length L may have M strictly conserved positions.

3. The remaining L-M positions of the consensus are variable.

4. It is assumed that violations of homology between the consensus and the segment of length L belonging to the sequence of interest may occur only at L-M variable positions.

5. To test the statistical significance of the homology between the consensus of the region of the examined sequence, the following parameters are calculated:

   a) The expected number $\bar{T}(L, K)$ of fragments (L, K) of length L in the examined sequence differing from the consensus in K positions and having all the other positions matching the consensus. The calculation of the expected number is based on the frequencies of nucleotides in the examined sequence and also on the nucleotide types in the consensus.

b) The confidence level $T_0(L, K)$ for the expected number $\bar{T}(L, K)$ of fragments in a random sequence.

TABLE 8.4 The IUPAC-IUB characters used for certain nucleotide groups

Number	One-letter code	Nucleotide group	Interpretation
1	A	A	Adenine
2	T	T	Thymine
3	G	G	Guanine
4	C	C	Cytosine
5	R	G or A	puRines (large)
6	Y	T or C	pYrimidines (small)
7	M	A or C	aMino (positive charge)
8	K	G or T	Keto (negative charge)
9	W	A or T	Weak interaction
10	S	G or C	Strong Interaction
11	B	T or G or C	not A
12	V	A or G or C	not T
13	H	A or T or C	not G
14	D	A or T or G	not C
15	N	A or T or G or C	aNy

If the observed number of homologous regions $T(L, K)$ meets the condition

$$T(L, K) \geq T_0(L, K) \qquad \text{(EQ 8.9)}$$

the homology revealed between the consensus and sequence fragments is not random. Figure 8.5 illustrates the application of this method to search for a transcription signal such as the CCAAT box, CREB binding element and TATA box in the promotor region of the human gene for histone H2B.

In the case of the TATA box, for length of homology $L=15$ with $K=1$ mismatches, the expected number of homologous fragments $\bar{T}(L, K) = 0.017$; the upper confidence limis $T_0 = 1$ and the observed number of homologous fragments is $T=1$. If condition (8.9) is met, the revealed homology may be regarded as non-random.

```
[ Search for motifs in sequences "MOTIF"]
*********************************************************************
Promoter of Human histon H2B
Sequence length =   326
=====================================================================
CREB-binding element
TGACGTYW
------------------- (+) strand --------------------
Expectet number: .019; coinf.interval: 0; found:   1; mismatches:  0
start:  224; end:  231; sequence:TGACGTTA
=====================================================================
CCAAT-box
HYYRRCCAATSR
Conservative positions in consensus:   4  6  7  8
------------------- (+) strand --------------------
Expectet number: .052; coinf.interval: 0; found:   1; mismatches:  1
start:  164; end:  175; sequence:TTCAACCAATAG
------------------- (-) strand --------------------
Expectet number: .036; coinf.interval: 0; found:   1; mismatches:  1
start:  214; end:  203; sequence:TCTGCCCAATCA
=====================================================================
TATA-box
STWTAWADRSSSSSS
Conservative positions in consensus:   3  6
------------------- (+) strand --------------------
Expectet number: .017; coinf.interval: 0; found:   1; mismatches:  1
start:  294; end:  308; sequence:CTATATAAAAGCGCC
------------------- (-) strand --------------------
Expectet number: .019; coinf.interval: 0; found:   1; mismatches:  1
start:  109; end:   95; sequence:TTATAAAAAGCGCCG
=====================================================================
```

FIGURE 8.5 Output of the MOTIF program (Shachmuradov et al., 1986). Analysis of the promotor region of the human gene for histone H2B.

Staden (1989) suggested another method for calculating the a priori probability of finding functional signals or their combinations (patterns) based on the probability-generating functions. Formulas were obtained for calculating the probability of observing at random nucleotide sequences of the following motif types:

1. Exact match to a short defined sequence.
2. Percentage match to a defined short sequence.
3. Match to a definite sequence using a score matrix and cut-off.
4. Match to a weight matrix with cut-off score.
5. Inverted repeats or stem loops and some other types.
6. Search for individual transcription motifs with the above approach yielded a large number of false positive matches. To decrease overprediction, the probability of finding patterns, i.e. combinations composed of a certain set of signals (Staden, 1989), can be calculated. Table 8.5 contains the results

of the search of the pattern composed of three transcriptional motifs in the human β-globin gene using the above approach. As Table 8.5 shows, only three patterns with the overall probability cut-off of 0.7×10^{-6} were revealed and only one of these is located in the 5' region.

TABLE 8.5 Search for patterns composed of three transcription motifs in the 5'-region of human β-globin gene (Staden, 1989)

| Number of pattern | Location of signal | | | Probability |
	CCAAT box	TATA box	Cap site	
1	28	71	99	0.16×10^{-9}
2	1070	1100	1134	0.44×10^{-9}
3	1251	1286	1311	0.6×10^{-9}

3.2.2 Search for Transcription Signals Based on Weight Matrices

The search for functional sites in the promotors can be based on weight matrices. By scanning a nucleotide sequence with a given cut-off matching score, one can find the oligonucleotide fragments most similar to the weight matrix of the functional signal. The data in Table 8.6 present some of the results which Bucher (1990) obtained using weight matrices for the recognition of promotor sequences in the adenovirus type 2 genome. Being well studied, this small genome is a useful model for the recognition of eukaryotic signals of transcription.

The virus has nine transcription start sites. Of these, 7 have the TATA box and two (EIIa and IV2) lack it. Only two of the three additional signals (the cap signal and GC box) were found in three promotors containing the TATA box (EIb, protein IX and EIV). Finally, two promotors with the TATA box (EIa and EIII) contain only an additional signal each. Of the two promotors lacking the TATA box, one, IVa2, contains three additional signals, and the other, EIIa, has none of the above mentioned signals.

The results obtained illustrate the variation in the composition of the eukaryotic promotors when initiation of transcription requires different combinations of known signals or the presence of signals we do not know yet recognize (as in the case of the promotor EIIa). It is premature to state the conditions necessary and sufficient for accurate computer recognition of eukaryotic promotor regions when reliance is placed on signal sequences. Another drawback of predictions of the promotor regions made with reliance on local signals is high overprediction with recognition of false positive signals. As the data of Table 8.6 show, of the 11 TATA boxes with maximum scores, only 5 are real promotors.

TABLE 8.6 Some results of promotor signal recognition in the adenovirus type II genome using weight matrices (Bucher, 1990)

Rank	Predicted TATA box		Initiation Site		Positionally correlated elements		
	Score	Location	Location	mRNA	Cap signal	CCAAT	GC box
1	-0.910	+6,010	+6,039	Major late	+	+	+
3	-2.310	+1,671	+1,700	EIb	+	-	+
4	-2.600	+32,036			-	-	-
5	-2.740	+35,636			-	-	-
6	-2.940	+3,547	+3,547	Protein IX	+	-	+
7	-3.170	+31,811			-	+	-
8	-3.270	+17,646			-	-	-
9	-3.380	+34,957			-	-	-
10	-3.570	-35.639	-35,611	EIV	+	-	+
11	-3.950	+469	+498	EIa	+	-	-
....							
154	-7.730	-25.983	-25,954	EIIa-late	+	+	+
163	-7.890	+27.582	+27,610	EIII	-	-	+

3.3 Analysis and Recognition of Sites at the 3' End of Pre-mRNA Processing

The nature of signals providing termination of transcription in the eukaryotic genes transcribed by RNA polymerase II remains unclear. As a rule, transcription stops in regions hundreds to thousands of base pairs away from the end of the coding part of a gene (Wickens, 1990). The resulting pre-mRNAs are subjected to 3' end cleavage.

The next step is polyadenylation of the cleaved 3' end by poly(A) polymerase, which synthesizes a poly(A) tract approximately 200-300 bp long (Manley, 1988). Cleavage and polyadenylation are performed by a specific complex referred to as the poly(A)some, spanning 67 bp, 33 before and 34 after the cleavage point (Proudfoot, 1991).

The results obtained with point, deletional and insertional mutagenesis, as well as with chemical modification of nucleotides (Humphray et al., 1987; Montell et al., 1983; Conway and Wickens, 1987), agree in demonstrating the presence of a specific nucleotide context in the vicinity of the poly(A) site. Furthermore a number of signals were revealed and one of these, AATAAA, located upstream of the RNA cleavage point is required for correct cleavage/processing (Gil and Proudfoot, 1987).

The characteristic features of the region downstream of the RNA cutting point is the presence of U-rich and GU-rich oligonucleotides with variable composition and location (Taya et al., 1982; Brinstiel et al., 1985). Using a representative sample of mammalian pre-mRNAs, McLauchlan et al. (1985) have studied the region downstream of the poly(A) site. As a result, the presence of the consensus YGTGTTYY was revealed generally located 20-30 bp 3' of the poly(A) site. This study, however, has demonstrated that only 67% of the examined sites have this consensus. Consequently, the nature of poly(A) sites is variable, and this complicates their recognition relying on the "conventional" consensuses. The method of recognizing poly(A) sites based on a generalized consensus (Kondrakhin et al., 1993) will now be described.

Let us examine a sample of poly(A) sites of length ω each and phased with respect to the RNA cleavage site.

Let $Z = \{z_i\}$ be the set of all the possible oligonucleotides of length d, $i = 1, ..., 4^d$. Then $Q = |q_{ij}|$, where $j = 1, ..., (w - d + 1)$, is the matrix of the generalized consensus, where element q_{ij} is equal to the occurrence frequency of a oligonucleotide of the i-th type at the j-th position in the sample of functional sites.

The suggested matrix of oligonucleotide frequencies has obvious advantages over the conventional mononucleotide frequency matrix because it allows us to take into account the correlations between neighbouring nucleotides. Each line of the matrix describes the distribution of a concrete oligonucleotide of length d along the site (see Figure 8.6). Using Smirnov's criterion of the Ω^2-square type, it was shown that the most pronounced non-uniformity of the distribution of poly(A) sites is characteristic of triplets (17 triplets are non-uniformly distributed at the 0.005 significance level).

Non-uniform distribution of triplets UUU and AAA along the polyadenylation site for a sample of 63 poly(A) sites is illustrated in Figure 8.6. A peak of triplet concentration at the 3' end of the poly(A) sites and a minimum near the AAUAAA signal are characteristic of the triplet UUU distribution pattern (the one representing the location of the GU- and U-rich elements). In contrast, a peak near the location of the AAUAAA signal and a minimum near the location of GU- and U-rich elements are characteristic of the triplet AAA pattern. As for the GGG, there is a peak at the 3' end of the poly(A) site and a near-zero concentration in all the other regions.

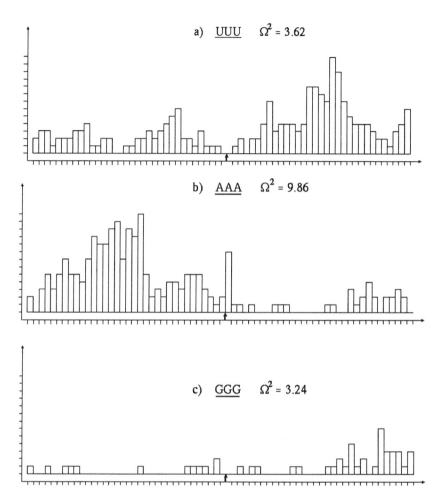

FIGURE 8.6 Non-uniform distribution of trinucleotides along poly(A) sites (Kondrakhin and Shamin, 1993). (a) UUU value of the statistics $\Omega^2 = 3.62$; (b) AAA of $\Omega^2 = 9.86$; (c) GGG of $\Omega^2 = 3.24$. The abscissa is the position of the fragment (0 to 65), the ordinate is the number of triplets observed for the given position. The arrow indicates the cleavage/polyadenylation point.

Based on the observed non-uniform distribution of oligonucleotides, a method was designed for recognizing poly(A) sites. For the nucleotide fragment $X = (x_0, x_1, ..., x_{\omega-1})$ of length ω the proximity to the poly(A) sites is described by the following score value:

$$\mu(X) = \prod_{j=0}^{\omega - d} \overline{\overline{P_{ij}}} \, \overline{\overline{q_{ij}}} \qquad \text{(EQ 8.10)}$$

where

$$\overline{\overline{q_{ij}}} = \begin{pmatrix} q_{ij}, \, q_{ij} > 0 \\ 1, \, otherwise \end{pmatrix}$$

and

$$\overline{\overline{P_{ij}}} = \begin{pmatrix} 1/m, \, q_{ij} > 0 \\ 1/(m+1), \, otherwise \end{pmatrix}$$

This is a measure of the degree to which the fragment X is similar in oligonucleotide distribution to the functional site set. If $\mu(X) > \mu^*$ the fragment X may be regarded as a polyadenylation site (where μ^* is the cut-off score).

Table 8.7 gives examples of the method tested on the control data (a set of nine poly(A) sites in the adenovirus type II genome). The optimal relationship between the first and second order errors made when recognizing poly(A) sites was attained at $\mu^* = 5.8 \times 10^{-107}$.

TABLE 8.7 Errors of the first and second orders made when recognizing poly(A) sites in the adenovirus type II genome (Kondrakhin et al., 1993)

μ^*	Errors	
	First order	Second order
1.5×10^{-107}	0	0.033
3.1×10^{-107}	0.11	0.027
5.8×10^{-107}	0.22	0.023
5.8×10^{-107}	0.33	0.002
4.6×10^{-107}	0.66	0.0004
3.6×10^{-107}	0.77	0.0002

3.4 Splice Site Analysis and Recognition

Splicing of introns is part of a multistage process of RNA maturation which takes place in the nucleus to generate mature mRNA molecules for transport to the cytoplasm. The following intermediate steps are significant for splicing:

1. Assembly of a large ribonucleoprotein complex on the pre-mRNA.
2. A lariat intermediate, i.e. a branched RNA molecule with a 2'-5' phosphodiester bond between the 2'-OH of the "branched nucleotide" is formed. A

short branch point signal containing the adenosine residue is involved in the lariat structure formation.

3. At the final step of the splicing process two exons are joined and the intron is released as lariat RNA.

This process involves several factors such as snRNP (small nuclear ribonucleoprotein particles) and hnRNPs (heterogeneous nuclear ribonucleoprotein particles). This complex assembly is called the spliceosome. U1 snRNP recognizes the donor splice site, U2 snRNP presumably recognizes the branch site and U5 snRNP interacts with the acceptor one (Figure 8.7). Most introns start with GT at the 5' end and terminate with AG at the 3' end and almost always follow the "GT-AG rule" (Maniatis and Reed, 1987).

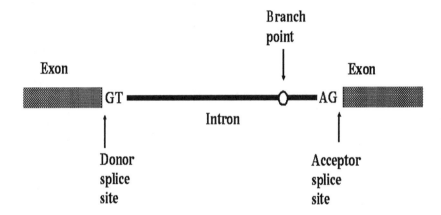

FIGURE 8.7 A scheme of splice sites in the exon/intron structure of genes.

The splicing process requires correct recognition of a number of signal sequences considered below.

3.4.1 The Donor Splice Site

We owe credit to Mount (1982) for the first catalogue of the splice site sequences of the nuclear protein-coding genes. A 9 nucleotide consensus (A,C)AG/GT(A,G)AGT (Figure 8.8a) was derived for the donor splice sites.

```
                exon              intron
Posi-  -3  -2  -1    +1 +2 +3 +4 +5 +6
tions
-------------------------------------------
(a)     C   A   G  /  G  T  A  A  G  T
        A                  G
-------------------------------------------

(b)
-------------------------------------------
            A   G  /  G  T  A
                /  G  T  A  A  G  T
            R   G  /  G  T  G  A  G
            A   G  /  G  T  N  N  G  T
-------------------------------------------

(c)
-------------------------------------------
A     28  59   8  /   0   0 54 74  5 16
C     40  14   5  /   0   0  2  8  6 18
G     17  13  81  / 100   0 42 11 85 21
T     14  14   6  /   0 100  2  8  4 45
```

FIGURE 8.8 Description of the donor splice sites: (a) consensus sequence from Mount (1982); (b) four sequences from Iida and Sasaki (1983); (c) percentage of each nucleotide for the human donor splice site positions (Senapathy et al.,1990).

With this consensus, correct localization of splice sites in the sequences is not consistently achieved because the predictive capability of the consensus is low.

Iida and Sasaki (1983) have constructed a set of four sequence patterns for donor splice sites (Figure 8.8b). They found that most donor sites correspond to one of the sequences and that such patterns rarely occur in exons.

The idea was developed further by incorporating the method of functional site classification (Kolchanov et al., 1991; Rogozin et al., 1993; Kudo et al., 1992). This was an improvement because the method takes heterogeneity into account. A set of consensuses is constructed instead of a single consensus describing the site. The results of donor site classification (Rogozin et al., 1993) are given in Table 8.8. A heterogeneous set of 20 consensus sequences was revealed. The number of sites corresponding to a particular consensus varies from 3 to 255.

TABLE 8.8 Consensus sequences of donor splice sites (Rogozin et al., 1993)

N	Number of sites corresponding to a certain consensus	Consensus
1	255	nnnnnnnnnnAG/GURAnnnnnn
2	182	nnnnnnnnnnnG/GURAGnnnnn
3	101	nnnnnnnnnnnn/GURAGUnnnn
4	93	nnnnnnnnnMAG/GUnnGnnnnn
5	71	nnnnnnnMnnnG/GUAnnnnnnn
6	29	nnnnnnnnnSAn/GURnGnnnnn
7	20	nnnnnnnnnnnG/GURnGUnnnn
8	16	nnnnnnCnnMnn/GURMRBnnnn
9	8	nnnnSnnnnnRG/GURSnSnnGn
10	12	nnnnnnnnnnnn/GUAAGnnnnn
11	10	MKnYnnSnVnRG/GUnnnnnnnn
12	9	nnnnnnnnHnRG/GUAnDnnnnn
13	9	nnnnnSAnnnRn/GURnDBnBnn
14	4	nBnAnnCnHnnG/GUnnnRnnnn
15	5	nnnnnnnnUnnR/GUnnGnRnYn
16	7	nBnnnnnnMnMn/GURRnnnnHY
17	4	nnUnnnKnnnnG/GYnRGWnnnn
18	3	nnCnnCnnnnnn/GUnnGnnnnn
19	3	CKKnYnRnnnnn/GUnnnnnnnn
20	3	nnRMAKnnnnnn/GUnnnnAnn

It should be noted that all the consensuses may be assigned to two large groups. The first group 1-5 describes the majority of the donor site population (83%). Consensuses of this group are compatible with the highly conserved donor consensus AG/GURAGU, but each contains only certain positions of the above consensus.

Group 6-20 describes 17% of the donor splice site population and is considerably different from consensus AG/GURAGU. These consensuses reflect the high heterogeneity in the donor splice site population.

A set of frequency matrices has been derived from analysis of a large sample of donor splice sites (Senapathy et al., 1990). The heterogeneity of the human donor splice sites is high as the matrix in Figure 8.8c shows. The results of recognition of the human donor splice sites with the use of this matrix are given in Table 8.9. In many cases the real splice sites have high scores, being at or near the top of the list.

TABLE 8.9 Splice site ranks for three GenBank entries (Senapathy et al., 1990)

Entry	Intron	Donor site			Acceptor site		
		Rank	Score	Sequence	Rank	Score	Sequence
HUMMH							
	1	12	75.1	GC/GTGAGT	7	91.4	CTCCTCGCTCCCAG/G
	2	2	88.4	CG/GTGAGT	>100	61.7	CGGGGGCGGGCCAG/G
	3	>100	60.8	GG/GTACCA	8	91.0	CTCTTTCCCGTCAG/A
	4	3	87.6	GG/GTAAGG	11	87.6	CCCCCTTTTCCCAG/A
	5	1	95.4	AG/GTAAGG	4	93.8	TTTTCTTCCCACAG/A
	6	4	87.6	AA/GTAAGT	3	95.8	TTATTCTACTCCAG/G
RATCTRPB							
	1	1	92.8	TG/GTAAGT	3	94.3	TATTCCCTTCCAG/G
	2	2	89.5	AG/GTGAGA	6	92.4	TTCGTCCTCCCAG/G
	3	5	84.4	AA/GTGAGT	>100	72.5	GTCTCAATACCTAG/G
	4	71	67.2	AG/GTACAC	1	95.9	TCTTGTCCCCACAG/G
	5	3	89.5	TG/GTGAGT	14	87.6	CTGTATCCCTGCAG/C
	6	>100	68.3	TG/GTACAG	2	95.6	ACCTTTCTCTGCAG/G
RABMHI191							
	1	2	94.8	GG/GTGAGT	8	87.3	CCTGTCGCCCGCAG/G
	2	5	92.3	CG/GTTCGC	>100	59.6	CGGGGCGGGGCCAG/G
	3	30	75.1	AG/GTTCGC	7	86.9	AATCTTTCCCTCAG/A
	4	>100	63.6	GG/GTAGAG	11	86.2	CCTTCCCTTCTCAG/A
	5	12	83.3	AG/GTAGGG	2	92.7	TTTTCTTCTCACAG/A
	6	1	98.3	AG/GTAAGT	1	96.0	TTTGTTCACCCCAG/G

However, some sites are ranked very low. If we chose the score to be 70 for example, of the 18 real donor splicing sites, 1 will be misclassified. By lowering the limit the number of false splice sites classified as potential splice sites will increase. These results improved by using the discriminant energy method (Gelfand, 1989). But an accurate prediction of donor splice sites remains an unachieved goal.

3.4.2 The Acceptor Splice Site

The short consensus CAG/G, which is preceded by a region of pyrimidine abundance (polypyrimidine tract), is a characteristic feature of acceptor sites. The consensus for the acceptor splice sites of primates is shown in Figure 8.9a, and Figure 8.9b demonstrates the frequency matrix for these sites (Senapathy et al., 1990). Acceptor splice sites are as difficult to predict as donor splice sites.

		intron													/ exon
	−14	−13	−12	−11	−10	−9	−8	−7	−6	−5	−4	−3	−2	−1	/ +1
(a)	T	T	T	T	T	T	T	T	T	T	N	C	A	G	/ G
	C	C	C	C	C	C	C	C	C						
(b)															
A	10	8	6	6	9	9	8	9	6	6	23	2	100	0	28
C	31	36	34	34	37	38	44	41	44	40	28	79	0	0	14
G	14	14	12	8	9	10	9	8	6	6	26	1	0	100	47
T	44	43	48	52	45	44	40	41	45	48	23	18	0	0	11

FIGURE 8.9 Description of the acceptor splice sites: (a) consensus sequence; (b) percentage of each nucleotide for the position of the human acceptor splice sites (Senapathy et al.,1990).

There are some other possible signals upstream of the 3' splice site. With only 2% exception, there is no AG in the 10 nucleotides preceding the AG at the intron/exon junction. Also, lack of GA and GG nucleotides in the region upstream of the intron/exon boundary indicates that this may be a significant feature for the acceptor splice site (Senapathy et al., 1990).

3.4.3 The Branch Point Signal

The branch point signal is located within the range 10-50 bases upstream from the acceptor splice site (the lariat region).

The location of the functional branch sites is experimentally demonstrated in only a small number of cases. A pentanucleotide consensus sequence CT(G,A)A(C,T) (Figure 8.10a) was derived. Figure 8.10b demonstrates the nucleotide frequency matrix for the branch point signal derived from plant, rat, human, chicken and drosophila sequences. Analysis of the above consensus distribution along gene sequences demonstrates that the potential branch point sites are: (1) nearly randomly distributed in exons and introns and (2) more than 50% of the introns have no sequences similar to the consensus in the lariat region. Thus, the problem of branch point signal prediction remains open. A further consensus, which is not similar to CT(G,A)A(C,T), may perhaps also determine the branch point signal (Senapathy et al., 1990).

	Positions				
	-3	-2	-1	0	+1
(a)	C	T	G A	A	C T
(b)					
A	1	0	39	99	11
C	76	8	15	1	45
G	2	0	42	0	6
T	21	91	4	0	38

FIGURE 8.10 Description of the branch point signal: (a) consensus sequence; (b) percentages of each nucleotide for human, rat, chicken, plant, and drosophila branch point signal positions (Senapathy et al.,1990). 0 indicate the position of the "branched nucleotide".

3.4.4 Neural Network Method for Splice Site Prediction

The neural network approach reproduces the natural process of human learning and attempts to simulate what occurs in the nervous system during neural processing.

A neural network consists of layers of identical units (neurons) and the connection pattern between them (Figure 8.11). The pattern is denoted by the pair $\{T, W\}$, where T is the topology of the connection between the units, and W is the network weights (including connection strengths between the units and their threshold).

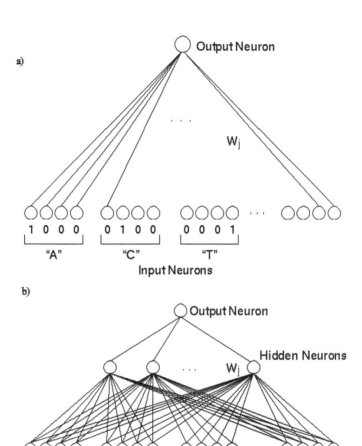

FIGURE 8.11 (a) A first order neural network (Perceptron). Base representation is used. Each symbol is encoded by 4 bits. The lower line of circles represents the input neurons which assume the value of 0 or 1. The state of the output neuron (upper circle) is determined by the input neuron states and after training they should have a value near 1 for the case of the YES class and near 0 for that of the NO class. (b) An example of a neural network with one layer of hidden neurons.

The neural network is organized hierarchically so that the number of units increases with each ascending level of hierarchy.

Each unit operates independently and in parallel with the others. A unit receives inputs from the other units to which it is connected. The unit integrates these inputs and generates an output if a signal exceeds the threshold. This output is then propagated to the other units of the network. It was established that learning takes place in such a model through adaptive modification of connection strengths and thresholds which are the parameters optimized by learning.

The neural network can be regarded as a computational device capable of automatically learning from training samples. Once a network has been trained (i.e. the network weights have been optimized) for a given training set, it can serve as a straightforward procedure for recognition.

The neural network method was applied to the recognition of the human splice sites (Lapedes et al., 1990). This procedure was used for three lengths of a window of bases surrounding the exon/intron and intron/exon junctions. The input of the neural network is formed by two sets of sequences. One set contains the splice sites (class YES), the other contains the sequences that do not perform splicing (class NO). Table 8.10 shows the results obtained.

TABLE 8.10 Prediction accuracy of recognition of the human donor splice sites by the neural network method (Lapedes et al., 1990)

DNA segment length (bases)	Prediction accuracy (%)
11	94.5
21	94.5
41	91.3

3.4.5 Other Approaches to Splice Site Prediction

The problem of splice site recognition remains an open issue in spite of the abundant evidence we have for splicing signals. There is a gap in our knowledge of what is going on during fundamental steps of the splicing process. The role of the secondary structure of the pre-mRNA in recognition of the splicing sites by a spliceosome is also not clear.

By examining a mutation effect on the splicing machinery, one may get an idea of how intricate splicing may be. At the human *hprt* locus, a large proportion of mutations produce aberrant splicing of corresponding mRNAs; 34 such mutations have been revealed (Steingrimsdottir et al., 1992). Mutations at the acceptor splice sites located at the 5' ends of introns 4, 6 and 7 result in aberrant splicing observed as loss of the downstream exons. In contrast, mutations at the acceptor sites of introns 1, 5, or 8 give rise to a "cryptic" site. Mutations at the donor site of introns 1 and 5 have resulted in the utilization of a downstream "cryptic" site. As for the other introns, the upstream exons are spliced out.

The most salient findings were for the set of mutations in the middle of exons 3 and 8 which resulted in cutting off a corresponding exon in a part of the mRNA population.

To achieve an increase in the prediction accuracy of splicing sites, a combined approach was proposed (Shapiro and Senapathy, 1987; Nakata et al., 1985). The original method was based on the use of information about potential splice sites in conjunction with the coding potential.

3.5 Translation Initiation Sites of Eukaryotic mRNAs

The scanning ribosome mechanism of translation initiation of mRNAs has gained wide acceptance. The postulated steps involve the initial binding at the capped 5' end of the mRNA, subsequent linear scanning along the mRNA, the ribosome stalling at the first AUG codon in a sequence context favourable for translation initiation. Analysis has demonstrated that translation in 95% of all mRNAs starts at the first AUG triplet. There are experimental data consistent with the scanning ribosome model (Kozak, 1989).

The data on RNA translation may be interpreted according to the "ribosome skipping" model or the "internal initiation" model. The former assumes that a ribosome may skip over certain regions of a leader sequence before it starts interacting with the initiator codon (Gough et al., 1985), and the latter assumes recognition of certain mRNA regions near the AUG codon as an initiation site by the ribosome (a recognition mechanism which may be the same as postulated for the translation initiation sites of prokaryotic mRNAs; Jackson et al., 1990).

Analysis of the translation initiation sites of eukaryotic mRNAs has disclosed features in their context which can be applied for recognition. The leader region is rather short, judging by estimates of the distance between the cap site to the initiation codon for vertebrate mRNAs. In fact, for 90% of the leader sequences the distance between the cap site and initiation codon does not exceed 200 nucleotides (Kozak, 1987). In this investigation of databases (including 699 vertebrate mRNAs), Kozak came to the conclusion that (GCC)GCC^A/$_G$CCAUGG is the expanded consensus sequence for initiation of translation in higher eukaryotes. This feature of nucleotide context is conspicuous near codon AUG with respect to purine (R), position -3, and G, position +4. AACAAUGGC, the consensus sequence for initiation of translation in plant mRNAs, is different from that found in vertebrate mRNAs (Lutcke et al., 1987).

High occurrence frequencies were evident for nucleotide G at positions -9, -6 and -3 (Kozak, 1984). A similar periodicity in occurrence of G has been also demonstrated for the coding part of the genes (Trifonov, 1987). It has been suggested that the periodicity of G residues facilitates ribosome retention in the correct frame during translation. A mechanism of this kind can switch on immediately upstream from the initiation codon (Kozak, 1984).

The weight and frequency matrices built for vertebrate, plant and animal mRNAs have been efficiently used for recognizing the initiation translation sites (Kozak, 1987; Stormo, 1987). An illustrative nucleotide frequency matrix for the translational initiation site of vertebrate mRNAs (Kozak, 1987) is given in Table 8.11.

TABLE 8.11 Nucleotide percentage frequency matrix for translation initiation sites of vertebrate mRNAs (Kozak, 1987)

Position	-12	-11	-10	-9	-8	-7	-6	-5	-4	-3	-2	-1	+4
A	23	26	25	23	19	23	17	18	25	61	27	15	23
C	35	35	35	26	39	37	19	39	53	2	49	55	16
G	23	21	22	33	23	20	44	23	15	36	13	21	46
T	19	18	18	18	19	20	20	20	7	1	11	9	15

Another method for recognition of initiation translation sites uses the computation of the weight matrices taking into consideration the unequal representation of different homologous gene families in the set of translation initiation sites (Guigo et al., 1992).

In recognition of the translation initiation sites with the assistance of the "GeneID" tool (Guigo et al., 1992), the distribution of the length of the leader untranslated mRNAs in vertebrate genes is also taken into account.

4   Prediction of Coding and Non-Coding Gene Regions

There are a number of computer programs based on statistical methods with biological constraints to investigate the presence of potential genes in newly determined DNA sequences. We will describe only some of the more commonly used methods.

4.1   Search by Context for the Gene Coding Regions

The main methods for predicting gene coding regions are based upon evaluating statistical constraints imposed by protein composition on the coding regions. These characteristics are specific for these regions and are different from random sequences or other functionally significant gene regions (like introns, functional promotor regions, etc.). Various methods have been developed for recognition of the gene coding regions by using the different coding potentials, i.e. the functions that indicate the closeness of the context characteristics of the considered genome region to those typical for the gene coding regions (Gelfand, 1990a).

4.1.1 Uneven Positional Base Frequencies Method

This method is based on the assumption that the protein coding regions are statistically less random for the positional base composition than non-coding regions. This method is part of the NIP, NIPL and XNIP programs (Staden, 1990).

Let us consider the sliding window of length n and let N_{ij} be the number of the i-th base occurrence (i=A, T, G, C) in the j-th position of a codon (j=1, 2, 3) for definite location of this window in the sequence under consideration.

An expected number E_{ij} of the i-th base in the j-th position (assuming an even distribution) is equal to

$$E_{ij} = (N_{i1} + N_{i2} + N_{i3}) / 3 \qquad \textbf{(EQ 8.11)}$$

The absolute difference between the expected and observed positional base frequencies can be calculated as follows:

$$D = \sum_{i,j} |E_{ij} - N_{ij}| \qquad \textbf{(EQ 8.12)}$$

By calculating D for each position of sliding window (with one codon step) in the analysed sequence, one can reveal regions where the maximal uneven distribution of bases within the three positions of codon is characteristic. This distribution was used for choosing the threshold values of D for coding region discrimination (Staden, 1990).

A typical output is shown in Figure 8.12. In this example we use the sequence containing the polymorphic epithelial mucin (PEM) gene (Lancaster et al., 1990) taken from GenBank (EntryName HUMPEM) or EMBL (EntryName HSPEM).

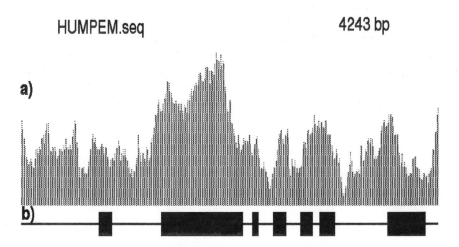

FIGURE 8.12 Coding potential for the sequence of the human polymorphic epithelial mucin (PEM) gene: (a) uneven positional base frequencies method; (b) location of exons in the gene.

4.1.2 TestCode Method

TestCode is an algorithm for identification of the coding regions by measuring the non-randomness of the composition at every third base in a codon (Fickett, 1982). It is

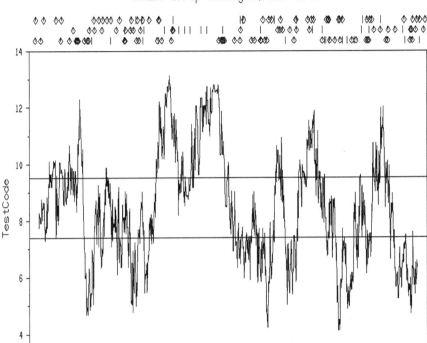

based on a similar methodology to the uneven positional base frequencies method. An example of output for the PEM gene is shown in Figure 8.13.

FIGURE 8.13 Coding potential for the sequence of the human polymorphic epithelial mucin (PEM) gene (TestCode method) (Fickett, 1982). Genetics Computer Group (Devereux et al., 1984).

4.1.3 Codon Usage Method

This method, suggested by Staden and McLachlan (1982) is based on the fact that specific codon frequencies are common to the majority of genes. This method measures the closeness of each reading frames codon composition to an expected set of codon.

Let $f(abc)$ be the frequency of codon abc characteristic of the given taxonomic group (or defined region on the genome).

Let us consider the nucleotide fragment of length 3 $(n+1)$ bases. It can be represented as

$$a_1 b_1 c_1 a_2 b_2 c_2 a_3 b_3 c_3 \ldots a_n b_n c_n a_{n+1} b_{n+1} c_{n+1} \qquad \text{(EQ 8.13)}$$

If we assume that the identity of nearby triplets is independent, it is possible to estimate the probability of observing each of the three potential reading frames:

Frame 1 $p_1 = Q_1 f(a_1 b_1 c_1) f(a_2 b_2 c_2) \ldots f(a_n b_n c_n)$

Frame 2 $p_2 = Q_2 f(b_1 c_1 a_2) f(b_2 c_2 a_3) \ldots f(b_n c_n a_{n+1})$

Frame 3 $p_3 = Q_3 f(c_1 a_2 b_2) f(c_2 a_3 b_3) \ldots f(c_n a_{n+1} b_{n+1})$

$$\text{(EQ 8.14)}$$

where Q_1, Q_2 and Q_3 are fractions of the triplets which are read in frames 1, 2 and 3, respectively.

By using Bayes' statistics it is now possible to estimate the probability of a particular reading frame being the coding sequence:

$$P_1 = \frac{p_1}{p_1 + p_2 + p_3}$$

$$P_2 = \frac{p_2}{p_1 + p_2 + p_3}$$

$$P_3 = \frac{p_3}{p_1 + p_2 + p_3} \qquad \text{(EQ 8.15)}$$

Considering a window of L triplets, we can estimate P_1, P_2, P_3, and for each position of the window within the sequence under consideration. The results of this method depend on the codon usage table chosen.

Figure 8.14 shows the result of this method for the analysis of the human PEM gene. One can see a good match between the location of most exons and the expressed maximum in one of the three reading frames.

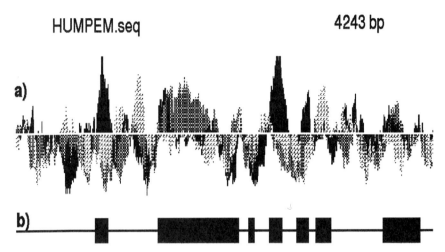

FIGURE 8.14 Coding potential for the sequence of the human polymorphic epithelial mucin (PEM) gene: (a)codon usage method; (b) location of exons in the gene.

4.2 Comparison of the Context Characteristics for Exons and Introns

Since the exon/intron structure of the eukaryotic genes was discovered, the problem of functional significance of introns remains to be fully elucidated. The absence of context features in introns makes their effective recognition problematical. The data available provide evidence that introns can not be considered as random sequences.

4.2.1 Contrast Words Method

The investigation of contrast words (Beckmann et al., 1986) represents one of the most effective methods for description of the global features of nucleotide context.

Let us consider oligonucleotide $s = N_1N_2...N_b$. In according with this method it will be considered as a word of the sequence if

$$std(s) = \left| \frac{f(s) - E(s)}{max(\sqrt{E(s)}, 1)} \right| > 3.0 \qquad \text{(EQ 8.16)}$$

where $E(s)$ and $f(s)$ are expected and observed frequencies of s in the sequence (or set of sequences) under consideration.

The expected frequency of s can be estimated as follows:

$$E(s) = E(N_1 \ldots N_n) = \frac{f(N_1 \ldots N_{n-1}) \times f(N_2 \ldots N_n)}{f(N_2 \ldots N_{n+1})} \qquad \text{(EQ 8.17)}$$

Using Equation 8.16 a comparative analysis of human introns and exons (Beckmann et al., 1986) was carried out. Analysis of distributions of the std-values for all triplets, tetramers, pentamers and hexamers revealed that these distributions are significantly different from the corresponding distributions of std values obtained for random sequences. Introns have a specific non-random vocabulary composed of short contrast words $(n \leq 5)$. It is interesting to note that the intron vocabulary contains a greater number of the mirror and symmetrical words, i.e. words of the structure $N_1 N_2 N_3 (N) N_3 N_2 N_1$. The authors believe that the major feature of the mirror symmetrical sequences is a very low potential to form hairpin loops. Positive selection towards mirror and symmetrical words is assumed to lower the probability of the formation of local hairpin structures in the RNA transcripts of introns.

4.2.2 k-tuple Method

The interpretation of introns as gene regions with specific nucleotide context was also examined in the work of Claverie et al. (1990).

Let us consider a sequence $S = \{s_i\}$ of length L with $s_i \in \{A, T, G, C\}$; $i = 1, \ldots, L$. It can be transformed into a sequence of k-tuples (i.e. oligonucleotides of length k):

$$W_k = \{W_{k,i}\}$$

$$(i = 1, \ldots, L - k + (1) ; W_{k,i} \in \Omega) \qquad \text{(EQ 8.18)}$$

Here $\Omega = \{W_{k,i}\}$ is the set of all the possible oligonucleotides W_k of length k. In this way, it is possible to construct a table F with the occurrence frequency $F(W_k)$ for all possible k-tuples of the set of sequences $\{S\}$ having the function of interest.

Let us consider two sets of sequences $\{S^{(1)}\}$ and $\{S^{(2)}\}$ with mutually exclusive functions (e.g. intron or exon). In this way it is possible to calculate the k-tuple frequency tables F_1 and F_2 for these two sets of sequences. The difference in frequencies between these tables can be used for discrimination.

To analyse the test sequence using the F_1 and F_2 tables, the following local discriminant index is calculated for the i-th position:

$$d(i) = \frac{F_1(S_{k,i})}{F_1(S_{k,i}) + F_2(S_{k,i})} \qquad \text{(EQ 8.19)}$$

Then the value $d(i)$ is smoothed using an averaging window of $2w+1$ consecutive positions:

$$D = \sum_{j=i-w}^{i+w} d(i)$$

(EQ 8.20)

Figure 8.15 represents application of this approach with $k=6$ for discrimination of exons and introns in the PEM gene (dicodon usage method). Regions of the plot above the threshold line are more similar to exons and those below the line are more similar to introns, respectively. Here one can see that most exons correspond to a marked vertex in the plot. Again there can be also seen a number of lesser additional vertices not corresponding to real exons (false positive signals).

HUMPEM.seq   4243 bp

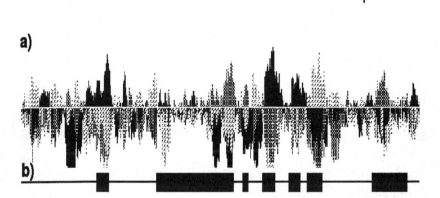

a)

b)

FIGURE 8.15 Coding potential for the sequence of the human polymorphic epithelial mucin (PEM) gene: (a) dicodon usage method; (b) location of exons in the gene.

5   Computer Programs for Exon/Intron and Gene Prediction

The different methodologies for revealing splice sites and coding regions in nucleotide sequences alone are not able to predict the gene structure. The exon prediction methods miss most of short exons and cannot reliably define the exon/intron boundaries, while the splice site prediction discovers some real splice sites along with a great number of false sites. In order to increase the reliability in the prediction methodology, various authors suggested the use of a combination of methods (Shapiro and Senapathy,

1987; Nakata et al., 1985; Kolaskar and Reddy, 1985; Staden, 1984), and several computer systems for coding region prediction were created (Guigo et al., 1992; Gelfand, 1990b; Hutchinson and Hayden, 1992; Mural et al., 1992; Fields and Soderlund, 1990; Milanesi et al., 1992; Snyder and Stormo, 1993). In the following sections we describe some of these computer systems attempting to predict coding regions and exon/intron structure.

5.1 SORFIND

SORFIND (Hutchinson and Hayden, 1992) is a computer tool for prediction of internal exons in sequences of the human genome. Potential coding exons are stratified according to the reliability of their prediction from confidence level 1 to 5.

The program first reads the input file and tries to determine the sequence format. For a GenBank formatted file the feature table is analysed to determine the coding regions of the sequence which is later used to compare results of the program with real exon/intron structure.

5.1.1 Algorithm

After reading the sequence from file, the program scans it from left to right, stopping at each AG dinucleotide. It rejects those sites with another AG less than 11 bp upstream. The site is then scored according to the method of Berg and von Hippel (1987), and accepted if its score is over the threshold for acceptor sites. The position of the first downstream stop codon in each of the three reading frames is then noted, and all GT dinucleotides that are at least 60 bp downstream and within this window are located. Each potential donor site is scored, and the site is accepted if its score is over the donor threshold value. If a given sequence segment passes the selection procedure it must consist of at least one open reading frame (ORF) with 60 bp or more, bracketed by acceptor and donor splice sites. Such a structure is defined as a Splicable ORF or SORF. The program then calculates three separate variables, based upon codon usage, for each SORF. The algorithm is first to look upstream and sum the individual codon usage scores within a set window for the immediately adjacent regions of potential introns, then subtract this value out of an equal window just downstream of the acceptor site within the SORF, giving the 5' codon usage difference. It is expected that true acceptor splice junctions will separate good and poor regions of codon usage, corresponding to exon and intron, and a large, positive codon usage difference results. A similar value, the 3' codon usage difference, is calculated for the donor site, and a codon usage average is then calculated for the entire SORF. There are separate thresholds set for these three values, and if a SORF falls below the threshold for two or more, it is rejected.

SORFs passing through the filtration procedure may be in conflict with others, either by overlapping them, or by being less than a minimum distance away (corresponding to the expected minimum length of an intron). The ilustrated results use a minimum intron length of 70 bp. A mediation procedure reveals those SORFs that are in conflict, and passes them on to an arbitration step. This step chooses the best candidate among the conflicting SORFs based upon a score which linearly combines the five values described above.

After the confidence level 1 analysis the thresholds are relaxed. The confidence level 2 analysis is then conducted with these new threshold values. Depending upon the number of confidence levels requested by the user the procedure above is repeated. Analysis will avoid regions already containing a successful SORF and its surrounding minimum introns.

5.1.2 Output

An example of the output is shown in Figure 8.16. The output is a list of potential internal exons, ordered by the confidence level, including start and stop positions, length, splice and codon usage scores, 5' and 3' phase and amino acid translation. The 5' phase is defined as the number of nucleotides required from a previous exon to put the current SORF into its correct reading frame. Similarly, the 3' phase is defined as the number of nucleotides from the current SORF carried over to the next exon. If the input is an annotated file in GenBank format, the output also includes a line for each SORF identifying its relationship to the exons described in the feature table.

```
SORFIND   Version 1.5.1

Start Run: Tue Jun 23 15:30:25 1992

SORF:     201..295      Length: 95
Confidence: 3
Phase  5': 0    3': 1
Acceptor:    cttggctttctccaagg Score:  6.51
Donor    :        agggtgggg Score:  4.32
Codon Usage            5'difference: 4.307
                       3'difference: 0.235
                       Average    : 0.032

Amino Acid Translation:
EGTQAAGKSGWGGDCGFRGERGVERDRERLE

SORF:     395..498      Length: 104
Confidence: 5
Phase  5': 2    3': 0
Acceptor:    ggccgctctgcttcagt Score:  7.76
Donor    :        cacgttagt Score:  5.93
Codon Usage            5'difference: 0.604
                       3'difference: -0.108
                       Average    : -0.039

Amino Acid Translation:
DPGRAGKWSGRPRGGLPDLAVQDLDLAGFVPHPH


. . . . . . . . . . . . . . . . . . . . . . . . . . . . . . . . . . . . . .


SORF:     3735..3903      Length: 169
Confidence: 2
Phase  5': 1    3': 0
Acceptor:    ttttccttccacccagg Score:  2.72
Donor    :        ctggtgagc Score:  2.49
Codon Usage            5'difference: 5.322
                       3'difference: 0.135
                       Average    : 0.041

Amino Acid Translation:
FLQVMVAAASLTQTQQWQPLLPTCRGTSPAELSGQPVPFHSTQVLQGQSPCTLFGL


Input File: orfj.seq      4243 bp
GC Content: 0.59
```

FIGURE 8.16 Example of output from the SORFIND system for the HUMPEM sequence. Only part of the file is shown.

The program was written in C++ for PC DOS or SunOS.

5.1.3 Testing the System

14 genes in a control set were analysed. 70 out of 80 internal exons greater than 60 bp in length were identified (87.5%), with 47 completely and 23 partially matched. SORFs that partially match true internal exons share at least one splice site with the exon, or share both splice sites but were revealed in an incorrect reading frame. Specifi-

city (the percentage of SORFs that correspond to true exons) varied from 91% at confidence level 1 to 16% at confidence level 5. An overall specificity is 35-40%.

5.2 GRAIL

GRAIL (Mural et al., 1992) (Gene Recognition and Analysis Internet Link) is an computer system which attempts to predict the exons in DNA sequences of the human genome.

The GRAIL system is able to analyse the sequences received by the e-mail address "grail@ornl.gov". The input file includes the registration number, the name and the sequences in FASTA format (length not less than 100 bp and not more than 100 kb).

5.2.1 Algorithm

GRAIL is based on a Coding Recognition Module (CRM) which consists of seven sensor algorithms, each designed to provide an estimation of the probability that a given fragment of sequence is a coding region. The program performs the scanning of the sequence by using a window (e.g. 100 bp long) advancing 1 bp each time. The seven statistical tests (frame bias matrix, Fickett statistic (Fickett, 1982), fractal dimension, coding 6-tuple words, in-frame 6-tuple words (Claverie et al., 1990), k-tuple commonality, repetitive 6-tuple words) are calculated for each window. Each algorithm constitutes one input node to the neural network, which combines all the statistical data on the sequence.

5.2.2 Output

An example of the output is shown in Figure 8.17. For each sequence the following information is returned:

- SCORE. The score for the coding potential for each position analysed on each strand (the f-(forward) strand represents the sequence as received by e-mail, and the r-(reverse) strand is the reverse compliment). These scores range from 0.0 to 1.0 and a score greater than 0.5 identifies potential coding regions.
- FRAME. The system calculates the reading frame with the maximum value of the coding potential in the window over which the calculation is done and this information is returned for regions with scores over 0.5.
- ORF. The positions between which the frame with the maximum value of coding potential is open (without stop codons) are returned for windows with scores over 0.5.

The second part of the output is the interpretation of raw data. This output gives the limits of the extent of the coding exons, the most likely strand for the exon with a probability of the correctness of the strand assignment, the preferred reading frame for the exon and a quality assessment (excellent, good and marginal).

```
>HUMPEM.seq, len = 4243

pos    f-strand frame     orf      || pos    r-strand frame      orf
                                    ||
.........................................................................
.........................................................................
 871   0.166    -       - - -      || 3371   0.149    -        - - -
 881   0.062    -       - - -      || 3361   0.021    -        - - -
.........................................................................


.........................................................................
3921   0.000    -       - - -      ||  321   0.115    -        - - -
3931   0.000    -       - - -      ||  311   0.081    -        - - -
3941   0.000    -       - - -      ||  301   0.092    -        - - -
.........................................................................
.........................................................................

      Potential exons are listed in the following

      pos        strand    strand_prob    frame    quality      orf

1501 - 1671      f         0.66           1        good       1396 - 2299
2591 - 2721      f         0.89           3        excellent  2544 - 2829
1271 - 1321      r         0.61           3        good       1119 - 1395
3071 - 3171      f         1.00           2        excellent  2993 - 3677
```

FIGURE 8.17 Example of output from the GRAIL system for the HUMPEM sequence. Only part of the file is shown.

5.2.3 Testing the System

CRM was tested on a set of sequences from GenBank. The module revealed 90% of coding exons of 100 bp and more. CRM correctly identified 96% of 100 base sequence windows tested as coming from coding or non-coding DNA. The percentage of non-coding windows assigned as coding was 8%.

5.3 GeneID

GeneID (Guigo et al., 1992) is a hierarchical rule based computer system for prediction of genes in DNA sequences. Initiation codons, stop codons, acceptor splice sites and donor splice sites are identified using a number of different approaches and evaluated by a set of filters and rules. These elements are combined into higher-order gene elements (potential coding exons), then filtered and combined into potential genes, which are evaluated and ranked.

5.3.1 Input

GeneID is accessed as an e-mail service facility using "geneid@darwin.bu.edu". Before submitting a sequence you need to register you name by sending a line with the word "register", followed by your name and address. The sequence should be submitted in the FASTA format.

GeneID was originally designed for prediction of the exon/intron structure in full length mRNA. If the sequence does not contain first or last exons, then GeneID will try to predict first and last exons. The input sequence must be not less than 100 bp and not more than 20 kb.

The program is written in C and runs under the Unix operating system.

5.3.2 Algorithm

At the first step of analysis, sets of potential sites are revealed: initiation codons, stop codons, acceptor and donor splice sites by using the weight matrix. Then a set of potential first, internal and terminal coding exons are generated. A predicted first exon is a pair $(x1, x2)$, where $x1$ is an initiation codon and $x2$ is a donor site. The position of $x1$ is less than the position of $x2$ and there is no stop codon between $x1$ and $x2$ in the frame defined by $x1$. A predicted internal exon is a pair $(x1, x2)$ where $x1$ is an acceptor splice site and $x2$ is a donor site. The position of $x1$ is less than the position of $x2$ and there is at least one frame where no stop codons were found between $x1$ and $x2$. A predicted terminal exon is a pair $(x1, x2)$ where $x1$ is an acceptor splice site and $x2$ is a stop codon. The position of $x1$ is less than the position of $x2$ and there is no stop codon between $x1$ and $x2$ in the frame defined by $x2$. Predicted exons are filtered by a special set of rules. Series of variables are determined for each predicted exon. In accordance with the values of these variables, the potential exon may be rejected.

The goal is to reduce the size of the set of potential exons by discarding as many falsely predicted exons as possible without discarding those truly predicted. 24 different variables are computed for each predicted exon. These variables are:

- Variables 1 to 4. Fraction of nucleotides A, T, C and G in the exon sequence.

- Variables 5 to 8. Codon position correlations: chi-square statistics of correlation between the 3rd position of a codon and the first position of the next one and between the middle position of 2 consecutive codons have been found characteristic of coding sequences (Smith et al., 1983).

- Variables 9 to 16. Numerical derivatives of variables 1 to 8 at the beginning of the exon.

- Variables 17 to 24. Numerical derivatives of variables 1 to 8 at the end of the exon.

A discriminant function partially based on a neural network was derived for reducing the number of falsely predicted exons.

Finally, predicted genes are obtained as linear arrangements of exon classes. Each class consists of equivalent exons. Two exons are equivalent if they can occur in exactly the same potential gene (if they are completely interchangeable).

5.3.3 Output

An example of the output is shown in Figure 8.18. The lists of potential start codons, stop codons, donor splice sites, acceptor splice sites, first exons, internal exons, last exons and reconstructed genes are returned.

5.3.4 Testing the System

GeneID was tested on a set of sequences from GenBank. The percentage of nucleotides truly predicted as coding was 69%. The percentage of predicted coding nucleotides that are actually coding was 84%.

```
REPORT for sequence HUMPEM.SEQ, 4243 bases. Thu Jun 25 10:58:06 EDT 1992
1. potential START CODONS
     Position   Score   Sequence
        669     0.75    AGGAATGG
     . . . . . . . . . . . . . . . . . . . . . . . . .
       4164     0.81    CAGAATGT
2. potential STOP CODONS
     Position   Codon
        66      TGA
     . . . . . . . . . . . . . .
       4228     TGA
3. potential DONOR SITES
     Position   Score   Sequence
        16      0.68    CCCGGTCCGAG
     . . . . . . . . . . . . . . . . . . . . . . . . . . . .
       4220     0.62    GCGAGTTTGTT
4. potential ACCEPTOR SITES
     Position   Score   Sequence
        146     0.71    GTTCATCGGAGCCCAGG
     . . . . . . . . . . . . . . . . . . . . . . . . . . . . . . . .
       4239     0.71    TTGTTTGAGAAGCCAGG
5. potential FIRST EXONS (from startcodon to donor site)
   (Only exons upstream of 3'-most predicted last exon)
     Score   Frame   Start   Stop      Equivalent exons, if any
     1.09      2      1022    1032
     . . . . . . . . . . . . . . . . . . . . . . . . . . . . . . . . . . . .
     0.13      0      1232    1471
6. potential INTERNAL EXONS (Only exons downstream of 5'-most predicted
   first exon, and upstream of 3'-most predicted last exon)
     Score   Frame        Start   Stop     Equivalent exons, if any
     0.85    0 1 0 1       1409    2265     1472   2265       1418   2265
                          1445    2265
     . . . . . . . . . . . . . . . . . . . . . . . . . . . . . . . .
     0.31    0 1 0 1       3680    3903
7. potential LAST EXONS (from acceptor site to stopcodon)
   (Only exons downstream of 5'-most predicted first exon)
     Score   Frame   Start   Stop      Equivalent exons, if any
     0.65      2      1600    2036
     . . . . . . . . . . . . . . . . . . . . . . . . . . . . . . . . .
     0.30      0      2731    2850
8. potential GENES
   4026 gene models were analyzed and ranked according to likelihood
   The 20 most likely genes are
   Ranking scores List of exons(*) constituting gene (first, internal(s), last
     0.948  1.521    1022   1032     1600   2265     2570   2706    2851   2972
                     3053   3202     3535   3589     3735   3748
     . . . . . . . . . . . . . . . . . . . . . . . . . . . . . . . . . . . . . . . . . . .
     0.948  1.258    1022   1032     1600   2265     2570   2706    2851   2972
                     3221   3296     3735   3748
```

FIGURE 8.18 Text output of the GeneID system for the HUMPEM sequence of man. Only one part of the file is shown.

5.4   gm

Gene Modeller (gm) is a tool for exploratory analysis of the DNA sequences in different organisms (Fields and Soderlund, 1990; Soderlund et al., 1992).

The gm program reads from a file information about the sequence data, organism-specific consensus matrices, codon asymmetry tables and a set of parameters. It includes three components: a fully automated DNA sequence analysis program (gm) that identifies possible genes contained in a sequence, a menu-based program (menu) for running pattern analyses on sequences interactively, and an optional graphic interface (gmwin) that can be run on a workstation display under X-windows. The system is implemented in C, and is designed to run on Unix workstations.

5.4.1 Algorithm

The gm system includes several modules. The analysis may be performed automatically by using the default parameters or it is possible to change the parameters in order to get better results.

gm automates the following steps in DNA sequence analysis in order to find the candidate genes, each specified as a sequence of exons and introns that satisfy all evaluation criteria:

- Identification of all (ORFs.
- Identification of sequences matching consensus matrices for 5' and 3' splice sites.
- Evaluation of sequences between identified splice sites, using AT frequency and AT-containing dinucleotide frequency as criteria for intron sequences, and optional searches for which lariat branch formation sites are in frame, and which therefore may be exons.
- Evaluation of candidate exons using CG frequency and codon usage asymmetry as criteria.
- Identification of initiation contexts, polyadenylation signals, and promotors using consensus matrices.
- Translation of all in-frame exons of each candidate gene.

Some modules are based on methods which require consensus matrix files to specify splice sites, initiation contexts, splicing branch sites (optional), poly(A) sites, and promotor elements. Matched cut-off values must be chosen to be appropriate for each matrix used.

Consensus matrices are described in general by Stormo (1988); log likelihood matrices are described by Berg and von Hippel (1987).

5.4.2 Output

An example of the output is shown in Figure 8.19. gm outputs a set of models describing the structure of candidate genes in a sequence. The gm graphical output interface allows one to display the potential genes as schematic diagrams together with DNA and the translated amino acid sequence. gm also generates files with predicted amino acid sequences. The format of output is adapted for plsearch (a protein motif identification program) (Smith and Smith, 1990) and it is possible to analyse predicted amino acid sequences using this program.

```
Genes    --> Final_list  size 2
       --> GENE-1  size 7   length 1318
           --> TATAA Box
               --> BASE    336     TATAA
           --> EXON                (0.500,17)
               --> BASE    395     ATG
               --> BASE    556
           --> INTRON             (0.863,76.000)
               --> BASE    557
               --> BASE    658
           --> EXON               (0.637,15)
               --> BASE    659
               --> BASE    1335
           --> INTRON             (0.788,16.500)
               --> BASE    1336
               --> BASE    1387
           --> EXON               (0.551,19)
               --> BASE    1388
               --> BASE    1436    END
           --> AATAAA
               --> BASE    1654    AATAAA
       --> GENE-2  size 5   length 1318
           --> TATAA Box
               --> BASE    336     TATAA
           --> EXON                (0.500,17)
               --> BASE    395     ATG
               --> BASE    556
           --> INTRON             (0.863,76.000)
               --> BASE    557
               --> BASE    658
           --> EXON               (0.637,17)
               --> BASE    659
               --> BASE    1336    END
           --> AATAAA
               --> BASE    1654    AATAAA
Final Genes 2   Time: 0 min, 1 sec, 500000 microsec
```

FIGURE 8.19 Typical output of the gm system for a Human sequence.

5.5 GenView

GenView is a computing tool designed for the identification of the protein coding regions in human nucleotide sequences (Milanesi et al., 1993). GenView works in two modes: an automated and an interactive mode. The automated version allows one to accomplish the recognition by using the standard parameters and programs. In interactive mode it is possible to change the parameters and programs. A graphical interface has been provided for easy use of the programs and for visualization of the results of the analysis. This program is able to analyse sequence of length not less than 100 bp and not more than 30 kb. GenView is developed for PC DOS (Windows 3.1) and VAX/VMS.

5.5.1 Algorithm

The following procedures are involved in the algorithm predicting gene coding regions.

1. Identification of the potential splice sites.
2. Construction of a Potential Coding Fragment (PCF).
3. Estimation of the protein coding potential of the revealed PCF.
4. Best exons prediction.
5. Construction of potential genes and the choice of a set of genes having the maximal coding potential.

GenView is organized in different modules which are able to perform a series of individual tasks.

The first module compares the sequence under investigation with each set of donor or acceptor consensus for recognition of potential splice sites in human sequences (Rogozin et al., 1993).

A second module performs a verification of the recognized exon/intron structure of genes using an alternative technique based on weight matrices (Shapiro and Senapathy, 1987).

The third module finds all PCFs and estimates their protein coding potential by using a dicodon statistic derived from the k-tuple statistics (Claverie et al., 1990). The PCFs with a score of the coding potential P_i over 0 are selected for further analysis as potential fragments of the gene coding regions.

Two levels of significance for PCFs are used:

1. Prediction of "excellent" PCFs only. The comparison between real data and the computational results for this level showed that 58% of true exons were lost (under-prediction) and 3% false exons were found (over-prediction). For correctly predicted exons 3% of the total length was lost and 10% was over-predicted.

2. Prediction of all "good" PCFs. The probability of losing true exons is nearly 40%, but the probability that the chosen exon is false is about 6-8%.

The last module is able to construct a set of potential genes from the set of revealed PCFs. The aim is to design a limited set of genes that has maximal coding potential. The coding potential P_g of a gene G, consisting of m PCFs separated by m-1 introns, is calculated as a sum of all PCFs involved in this gene:

$$P_g = \sum_{i=1}^{m} P_i \qquad \text{(EQ 8.21)}$$

For two PCFs to be present in one gene and separated by an intron, they should satisfy the two following rules of compatibility:

- Non-overlapping rule. Two PCFs involved in one gene are not overlapping. Minimal intron length between two non-overlapping exons cannot be less than 60 bp.

- Rule of saving the translation frame. Let A and B be two sequential non-overlapping PCFs (PCF A being positioned upstream relative to B). After eliminating the separating intron, these two PCFs can form a longer fragment only on condition that they retain the same translation frame.

Due to the above rules for the set of N revealed PCFs one may design a matrix $Q = \{q(k, l)\}\, ; k, l = 1, ..., N$, which describes all possible variants for uniting two PCFs.

$$q(k, l) = \left(\begin{array}{c} 1, \text{ if } k\text{-}th \text{ and } l\text{-}th \text{ PCF satisfy the rules} \\ 0, \text{ otherwise} \end{array} \right) \qquad \textbf{(EQ 8.22)}$$

The problem of searching for a set of potential genes for a given region of the nucleotide sequence means a search for a path with a maximal weight through the non-oriented graph defined by the matrix Q. The weight is determined according to Equation 8.21. The computations produce not one but a number of paths with high weights. The path with the greatest weight is assumed to correspond to a real gene.

5.5.2 Output
The GenView system outputs the results of analysis in two ways:

1. Saving the results of the gene structure prediction in a text file (Figure 8.20).

```
=================================================================
Sequence length= 4243 Direct(0),Complementary(1) chain=0
=================================================================
Gene N 1 Number of exons = 5 Weight = 1151


POTENTIAL EXON  1 WITH ACC and DONOR SPLICE SITES:
Start  of exon  1 =     667
End    of exon  1 =     933
Weight of exon  1 =       9


.......................................................


POTENTIAL EXON  5 WITH ACC and DONOR SPLICE SITES:
Start  of exon  5 =    3745
End    of exon  5 =    3920
Weight of exon  5 =       7


=================================================================
BEGIN NONCODING REGION    :     1
Potential noncoding region: TACTCCTCTCCGCCCGGTCCGAGCGGCCCCTCAGCTTGCGCGGCC
.......................................................
Potential noncoding region: GTTGGTGAAAGGGGGAGGCCAGCTGGAGAACAAACGGGTAGTCAG
Potential noncoding region: GGGGTTGAGCGATTAGAGCCCTTGTACCCTACCCAG
END NONCODING REGION      :   666

BEGIN REST OF FIRST CODON :   667
Rest of first codon       : GA
END   REST  OF FIRST CODON :   668

  BEGIN  EXON  Nx  1       :   669
Potential exon Nx  1       : ATGGTTGGGGAGGAGGAGGAAGAGGTAGGAGGTAGGGGAGGGGGC
Amino acid sequence        :  M   V   G   E   E   E   E   E   V   G   G   R   G   G   G
Potential exon Nx  1       : GGGGTTTTGTCACCTGTCACCTGCTCGCTGTGCCTAGGGCGGGCG
Amino acid sequence        :  G   V   L   S   P   V   T   C   S   L   C   L   G   R   A
.......................................................
=================================================================
```

FIGURE 8.20 Example of output for the genes prediction of the HUMPEM sequence by GenView (Milanesi et al., 1993). Only the beginning of the file is shown.

2. Visualization of the results obtained by the automated analysis of the sequence by means of the graphic interface (Figure 8.21). In this mode the system permits refinement of the prediction.

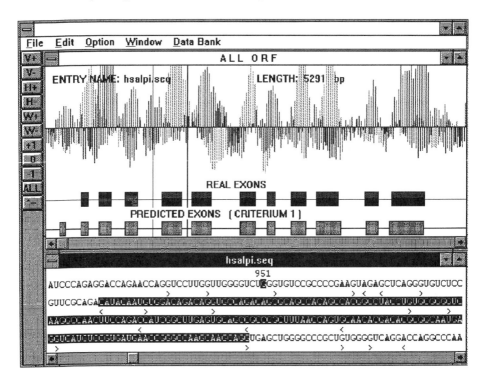

FIGURE 8.21 Graphic interface of the GenView system.

5.5.3 Testing the System

The comparison between real data and the computational results showed that 16% of true exons were lost (under-prediction) and 15% false exons were found (over-prediction).

For the correctly predicted exons 4% of the total length was lost and 13% was over-prediction. The control set included 110 exons in 18 genes, of total length 16,299 bp.

5.6 INTRON

INTRON is a computer program for predicting intronless subsequences in a cDNA sequence. It was developed by A. Glodek, M. Gorski and M. H. Polymeropoulos (1991).

5.6.1 Algorithm

For every input sequence INTRON performs three steps:

1. Finds all GG/CC pairs (possible former exon-intron splice sites).

2. Finds all stop codons in all three possible reading frames.

3. Eliminates the pairs that probably do not represent former splice sites: the pairs surrounded by stop codons in every reading frame, and the pairs where the distance between the closest to a pair at two surrounding stop codons from the same reading frame is not greater than a specified value ("distance", given by the input option).

All pairs that were not eliminated at Step 3 represent possible former exon-intron splice sites. They are listed on the output in lower-case. All eliminated GGs are listed in upper-case.

Every input strand is processed by the INTRON program twice. For the first processing, the program assumes that the input strand is the sense mRNA strand, and steps 1-3 are performed for every GG pair and stop codons: TAA, TGA, TAG. For the second processing, the program assumes that the input strand is an inverse complement of the sense strand, and steps 1-3 are performed for every CC pair and inverse complements of stop codons TAA, TGA, TAG: TTA, TCA, CTA.

5.6.2 Output

The INTRON output consists of two files:

1. lenfile.

   The output file "lenfile" contains a list of lengths of all upper-case subsequences found in the analysed sequence.

   The program writes the name of the sequence being analysed and the lengths of upper-case subsequences found in it, one subsequence per line. The same file may be used to store listings from different INTRON runs. New data will be appended to the existing file.

2. outfile.

The output file "outfile" contains a listing of all GG/CC pairs found and their positions in the input strand, all stop codons and inverse complements of stop codons found and their positions in the input strand. The input sequence is listed in upper-case, and all GG/CC pairs that are considered to be possible former exon-intron splice sites are listed in lower-case. All upper-case subsequences in the input strand probably do not include former splice sites and may be used for selection of polymerase chain reaction (PCR) primers.

The format of the "outfile" resembles the format of the input file, except for base pair numbers every 10 bp, and character substitutions in the sequence code. Figure 8.22 show an example of INTRON output.

```
; INTRON v. 1.1, 1991 (C) Anna Glodek, Mirek Gorski, Mihael Polymeropoulos
; Thu May 30 11:14:13 1991              <--- date and time of the run
;
; Input  file: t1.seq (sequence: T1)      <--- name of file and sequence
; Output file: t1.out                     <--- name of the output file
;                                             (input option "-o")
; Elimination rule distance= 1000 <--- distance used, (input option "-d")
; GG-frame #1,  5 stop codon(s):  <---- first reading frame, GG pairs
;       TAA          TGA          TAG          TAG          TAA
;       1            7            25           28           43
; GG-frame #2,  1 stop codon(s):  <---- second reading frame, GG pairs
;       TAG                       <---- stop codon found
;       32                        <---- position of the first base of
;                                       the stop codon
; GG-frame #3,  1 stop codon(s):  <---- third reading frame, GG pairs
;       TAA
;       39
; CC-frame #1,  2 stop codon(s):  <---- first reading frame, CC pairs,
;                                       inverse complement assumed
;       TCA          TTA          <---- inverse complements of stop codons
;       13           55
; CC-frame #2,  1 stop codon(s):  <---- second reading frame, CC pairs,
;                                       inverse complement assumed
;       TTA
;       38
; CC-frame #3,  0 stop codon(s):  <---- third reading frame, CC pairs,
;                                       inverse complement assumed
; All GG in a sequence. Lower-case gg - intron possible.
;       gg           gg           gg           gg           gg           gg
;       4            5            30           34           49           50
;       gg
;       60   <---- position of the first g in the pair in the sequence
; All CC in a sequence. Lower-case cc - intron possible.
;       cc           cc           cc           cc           cc
;       10           11           52           53           58
; The sequence:    <---- sequence is listed on the second page
T1   <---- name of the input sequence
     s                              w  <---- w replaced by 'A', s by 'G'
TAAgggTGAcccTCATTCGTACGATAGTAggTAggCATTAAATAAGATgggcccTTAccggTA1
     10        20        30        40        50        60
```

FIGURE 8.22 Example of the output of the INTRON program (Glodek et al., 1991).

5.7 GeneParser

GeneParser is a computer program for identification of coding regions in genomic DNA sequences (Snyder and Stormo, 1993). The current version has been tested on sequences of up to 73,000 nucleotides.

5.7.1 Algorithm

The program GeneParser uses dynamic programming for exon/intron prediction. It is based on several statistics: codon usage, local compositional complexity, length distributions of exons and introns, k-tuple frequencies, weight matrices for splice signals. Dynamic programming was integrated with training a neural network to maximize the number of correct predictions. The system was trained on a set of 56 human gene fragments.

5.7.2 Testing the System

GeneParser was tested using GeneID, SORFIND and GRAIL test sets analysing the entire sequence. The system has been trained on a set of 56 human gene fragments containing 150 exons in a total of 158,691 nucleotides. GeneParser is able to identify precisely 75% of the exons and correctly predict 86% of coding nucleotides. 13% of non-exon nucleotides were predicted to be coding.

6 Functional Motifs in Amino Acid Sequences

Every year, the families of sequenced proteins are expanded. Many newly discovered primary sequences are found to be structurally or functionally similar to those already known and may be inferred to represent evolutionary homologies to earlier investigated proteins. This situation is favourable for the study of isostructural or isofunctional types of protein molecules and their evolutionary families by means of the methods for multiple sequence and structure alignment. The most productive approach is the description of functional regions in groups of the aligned sequences with derivation of a set of statistically significant discriminating rules for the presence/absence within these regions of certain amino acid residues.

6.1 PROSITE Database of Motifs in Proteins

PROSITE is a database for sites and patterns in proteins that are structurally or functionally conservative (Bairoch, 1991).

This database consists of two basic and one additional ASCII (text) files. The last, PROSUSER.TXT is the user manual. It fully describes the format and the current state of the given release of PROSITE database. The files PROSITE.DAT and PROSITE.-DOC contain the database itself in computer readable and free native language formats, respectively.

Examples of the data written to the file PROSITE.DAT are given in Figures 8.23-8.25. From Figure 8.23 it is clear that recognition of the motif is possible by means of the formalized information about the consensus of the conserved protein regions contained in the field "PA". The less formalized logic rules from the field "RU" are shown in Figure 8.24. Results of testing for the given rules and consensuses on the current version for the Swiss-Prot database are all given in the field "DR" (see Figure 8.25). Other fields for the file PROSITE.DAT contain additional information about the protein sites, less significant from the viewpoint of computer recognition.

The file PROSITE.DOC, or textbook, repeats all the information from the file PROSITE.DAT in free format English language. Here are also contained descriptions and comments of the authors of the database regarding certain aspects of the information in the current version.

PROSITE can be obtained from the EMBL File Server via network, on magnetic tape or CD ROM.

```
//
ID    ASN_GLYCOSYLATION; PATTERN.
AC    PS00001;
DT    APR-1990 (CREATED); APR-1990 (DATA UPDATE); APR-1990 (INFO
UPDATE).
DE    N-glycosylation site.
PA    N-{P}-[ST]-{P}.
CC    /TAXO-RANGE=??E?V;
CC    /SITE=1,carbohydrate;
DO    PDOC00001;
//
```

FIGURE 8.23 An example from the file PROSITE.DOC.The field "PA" contains a good formalized consensus of N-glycosylation (the first site position always contains the N residue, for the second and fourth positions is typical of P and one the third are "either S, or T").

```
//
ID   SULFATATION; RULE.
AC   PS00003;
DT   APR-1990 (CREATED); APR-1990 (DATA UPDATE); APR-1990 (INFO
UPDATE).
DE   Tyrosine sulfatation site.
RU   (1) Glu or Asp within two residues of the tyrosine (typically
at -1).
RU   (2) At least three acidic residues from -5 to +5.
RU   (3) No more than 1 basic residue and 3 hydrophobic from -5 to
+5
RU   (4) At least one Pro or Gly from -7 to -2 and from +1 to +7 or
at least
RU       two or three Asp, Ser or Asn from -7 to +7.
RU   (5) Absence of disulfide-bonded cysteine residues from -7 to
+7.
RU   (6) Absence of N-linked glycans near the tyrosine.
CC   /TAXO-RANGE=??E??;
DO   PDOC00003;
//
```

FIGURE 8.24 An example from the PROSITE.DAT file. The field "RU" contains a set of 6 logic rules used for the recognition of the tyrosine sulphatation site in proteins. The information stored in "RU" is less formalized than that involved in "PA" (see Figure 8.23).

```
//
ID   PROKAR_LIPOPROTEIN; RULE.
............
DE   Prokaryotic membrane lipoprotein lipid attachment site.
PA   {DERK}(6)-[LIVMFSTAG](2)-[IVSTAGQ]-[AGS]-C.
RU   Additional rules:
RU   (1) The cysteine must be between positions 15 and 35 of the
RU       sequence in consideration.
RU   (2) There must be at least one charged residue (Lys or Arg)
RU       in the first seven residues of the sequence.
............
DR   P05372, 17K$RICRI , T; P16624, 17K$RICTY , T; P06548, BLA3$BACCE, T;
............
DR   P02938, MULI$SERMA, N;
............
DR   P11572, 19KD$MYCTU, ?; P11460, 40KD$VIBAN, ?; P15929, FLGH$SALTY, ?;
............
DO   PDOC00013;
//
```

FIGURE 8.25 An example from the PROSITE.DOC file. The field "DR" show the results of testing for the prokaryotic membrane lipoprotein lipid attachment site consensus in the Swiss-Prot database (where "T", "N" and "?" are "correct recognition of the known site", "non-recognition of the known site" and "recognition of the false site".

6.2 Programs for the Search for Motifs, Patterns and Profiles in Proteins

The problem of searching for protein functional motifs is very important. Application of such techniques make it possible to predict functions of human nucleotide sequences at the level of proteins. A requirement for these computing tools is flexibility to accommodate high complexity of the definition of motifs.

SCRUTINEER (Sibbald and Argos, 1990) is a computing tool with a wide range of basic capabilities. Various search criteria can be combined. The main functions of SCRUTINEER are:

- Searching an amino acid sequence for strings of amino acids as targets. As an example let us consider a string from Figure 8.23. In the PROSITE database it is written as N-{P}-[ST]-{P}, and for the search in the SCRUTINEER computing tool it should be transformed to NP[ST]P. The user should specify the number of mismatches and in this example either one or two mismatches should be allowed.

- Using an amino acid sequence alignment as the target and searching sequences for regions which are similar to the alignment.

- Using targets which consist minimally of frames. A frame has a minimum and maximum length. Adjacent to a frame may be located other frames as well as amino acids. An unlimited number of constraints may be put on a frame. These constraints are: (i) composition constraints (e.g. at least four amino acids must belong to the set [MGC]); (ii) position constraints (e.g. in position 3 must be G); (iii) interactive constraints (e.g. if the amino acid in position 4 belongs to the set [MGTS] then the amino acid in position 5 must belong to the set [YGT]); (iv) parametric constraints (e.g. the average helix propensity must be more than 0.7 and less than 3.0).

- Combining existing targets into new ones. For this purpose a variety of Boolean combinations ("and", "or", "not", etc) is used. Also, it is possible to define several targets that can occur in a certain order in the sequence from the N to C terminus.

It is also possible to search for titles or entries in amino acid sequence databases, to display on the screen in a variety of formats, and output to an external file results of the analysis for regions in a sequence which are compatible with the target.

SCRUTINEER was developed for the VMS operating system in the Pascal language.

The SCRUTINEER program and documentation are distributed freely. The source code can be obtained via e-mail (contact sibbald@embl-heidelberg.de).

A number of similar programs that perform some of the tasks performed in the SCRUTINEER computing tool have previously been described (Staden, 1988; Devereux et al., 1984).

For a systematic approach to protein identification see Hodgman (1992).

7   Acknowledgements

This work was supported by "Genetic Engineering" and "Bioinformatic" CNR projects, Russian National Human Genome Projects and Russian Ministry of the Higher School, Science and Technique Politics. This work benefitted from discussions at the "Recognizing Genes" workshop at the Aspen Center for Physics.

8   References

Ambrose C and Bina M (1990). Strategy for statistical-mapping of potential regulatory regions in the human genome. J. Mol. Biol. 216, 485-490.

Bairoch A (1991). PROSITE: a dictionary of sites and patterns in proteins. Nucleic Acids Res. 19 (suppl.), 2241-2245.

Beckmann JS, Brendel V and Trifonov E (1986). Intervening sequences exhibit distinct vocabulary. J. Biomol. Struct. Dyn. 4, 391-400.

Berg OG and von Hippel PH (1987). Selection of DNA binding sites by regulatory proteins. J. Mol. Biol. 193, 723-750.

Brinstiel ML, Busslinger M and Strub K (1985). Transcription termination and 3'-processing: the end is in the site. Cell 41, 349-359.

Bucher P (1989). The eukaryotic promotor database of the Weizmann Institute of Science. "EMBL Nucleotide Sequence Data Library Release 19", Postfach 10.2209, D-6900 Heidelberg.

Bucher P (1990). Weight matrix description of four eukaryotic RNA polymerase II promotor elements derived from 502 unrelated promotor sequences. J. Mol. Biol. 212, 563-578.

Bucher P and Trifonov NE (1988). CCAAT box revisited: bidirectionality, location and context. J. Biomol. Struct. Dyn. 6, 1231-1236.

Claverie J-M, Sauvaget I and Bougueleret L (1990). k-tuple frequency analysis: from intron/exon discrimination to T-cell epitope mapping. Methods Enzymol. 183, 163-180.

Conway L and Wickens M (1987). Analysis of mRNA 3' end formation by modification interference: the only modifications which prevent processing lie in AATAAA and the poly(A) site. EMBO J. 6, 4177-4184.

Devereux J, Haeberli P and Smithies O (1984). A comprehensive set of sequence analysis programs for VAX. Nucleic Acids Res. 12, 387-395.

Faisst S and Meyer S (1992). Compilation of vertebrate encoded transcription factors. Nucleic Acids Res. 20, 1-26.

Fickett JW (1982). Recognition of protein coding regions in DNA sequences. Nucleic Acids Res. 10, 5303-5318.

Fields CA and Soderlund CA (1990). GM: a practical tool for automating DNA sequence analysis. Comput. Applic. Biosci. 6, 263-270.

Gelfand MS (1989). Statistical analysis of mammalian pre-mRNA splicing sites. Nucleic Acids Res. 17, 6369-6382.

Gelfand MS (1990a). Global methods for the computer prediction of protein-coding regions in nucleotide sequences. Biotechnology Software 7, 3-11.

Gelfand MS (1990b). Computer prediction of the exon-intron structure of mammalian pre-mRNAs. Nucleic Acids Res. 18, 5865-5869.

Ghosh D (1990). A relational database of transcription factors. Nucleic Acids Res. 18, 1749-1756.

Gil A and Proudfoot NJ (1987). Position-dependent sequence elements downstream of AAUAAA are required for efficient rabbit b-globin mRNA 3' end formation. Cell 49, 399-406.

Glodek A, Gorski M and Polymeropoulos H (1991) "INTRON Version 1.1 Manual". Laboratory of Biochemical Genetics, The National Institute of Mental Health, Neuroscience Center at St Elizabeths, Washington DC.

Gough MN, Metcalf D, Gough J, Grail D and Dunn AR (1985). Structure and expression of the mRNA for murine granulocyte-macrophage colony stimulating factor. EMBO J. 4, 645-653.

Guigo R, Knudsen S, Drake N and Smith T (1992). Prediction of gene structure. J. Mol. Biol. 225, 141-157.

Hodgman TC (1992). Nucleic acid and protein sequence management. In "Microcomputers in Biochemistry: A Practical Approach" (ed. FA Boyce, pp. 131-158. IRL Press, Oxford.

Humphray T, Christofori G, Lucijanie V and Keller W (1987). Cleavage and polyadenylation of messenger RNA precursors in vitro occurs within large and specific 3' processing complexes. EMBO J. 6, 4159-4168.

Hutchinson GB and Hayden MR (1992). The prediction of exons through an analysis of spliceable open reading frames. Nucleic Acids Res. 20, 3453-3462.

Iida Y and Sasaki F (1983). Recognition patterns for exon-intron junctions in higher organisms as revealed by computer search. J. Biochem. Tokyo. 94, 1731-8.

Jackson RJ, Howell MT and Kaminski A (1990). The novel mechanism of initiation of picornavirus RNA translation. TIBS 15, 477-483.

Karlin M (1989). In "Tissue Specific Gene Expression" (ed. R Renkawitz), pp. 137-148. VCH Verlagsgesellschaft, D-6940 Weinheim (FRG).

Kolaskar AS and Reddy BVB (1985). A method to locate protein coding sequences in DNA of prokaryotic systems. Nucleic Acids Res. 13, 185.

Kolchanov NA, Rogozin IB, Kel AE, Ponomarenko MP, Likhachev J and Milanesi L (1991). Computer analysis and recognition of human splice sites. Genome Informatics Workshop II, Japan.

Kondrakhin YV, Shamin VV and Kolchanov NA (1993). Construction of generalized consensus matrix for recognition of vertebrate pre-mRNA 3'-terminal processing sites. Comput. Applic. Biosci. In Press.

Kozak M (1984). Compilation and analysis of sequences upstream from the translational start site in eukaryotic mRNAs. Nucleic Acids Res. 12, 857-872.

Kozak M (1987). An analysis of 5'-noncoding sequences from 699 vertebrate messenger RNAs. Nucleic Acids Res. 15, 8125-8132.

Kozak M (1989). The scanning model for translation: an update. J. Cell Biol. 108, 229-241.

Kudo M, Kitamura-Abe S, Shimbo M and Iida Y (1992). Analysis of context of 5'-splice site sequences in mammalian mRNA precursors by subclass method. Comput. Applic. Biosci. 8, 367-376.

Lapedes A, Barnes C, Burks C, Farber R and Sirotkin K (1990). Application of neural networks and other machine learning algorithms to DNA sequence analysis. In "Computers and DNA" (eds GI Bell and TG Marr), pp. 157-182. Addison-Wesley, New York.

Lancaster, CA, Peat N, Dihig T, Wilson D, Taylor-Papadimitrou J and Gendler SJ (1990). Structure and expression of the human polymorphic epithelial mucin gene: an expressed VNTR unit. Biochem. Biophys. Res. Commun. 173, 1019-1029.

Lewin B (1980). "Gene Expression" Vol. 2. John Wiley, New York.

Libermann TA, Leonardo M and Baltimore D (1990). Involvement of a second lymphoid-specific enhancer element in the regulation of immunoglobulin heavy-chain gene expression. Mol. Cell. Biol. 10, 3155-3162.

Lutcke HA, Chow KC, Mickel FS, Moss KA, Kern HF and Scheele GA (1987). Selection of AUG initiation codons differs in plants and animals. EMBO J. 6, 43-48.

McLauchlan J, Gaffney D, Whitton JL and Clements JB (1985). The consensus sequence YGTGTTYY located downstream from the AATAAA signal is required for efficient formation of mRNA 3' termini. Nucleic Acids Res. 13, 1347-1369.

Maniatis T and Reed R (1987). The role of small nuclear ribonucleoprotein particles in pre-mRNA splicing. Nature 325, 673-678.

Manley JL (1988). Polyadenylation of mRNA precursors. Biochim. Biophys. Acta 950, 1-12.

Milanesi L, Kolchanov NA, Rogozin IB, Ischenko IN, Kel AE, Orlov YL, Ponomarenko MP and Vezzoni P (1993). GenView: a computing tool for protein-coding regions prediction in nucleotide sequences. In "Proceedings of the Second International Conference on Bioinformatics, Supercomputing, and Complex Genome Analysis".

Montell C, Fisher EF, Caruthers MH and Berk AJ (1983). Inhibition of RNA cleavage but not polyadenylation by a point mutation in mRNA 3' consensus sequence AAUAAA. Nature 305, 600-605.

Mount SM (1982). A catalogue of splice junction sequences. Nucleic Acids Res. 10, 459-472.

Mural RJ, Einstein R, Guan X, Mann RC and Uberbacher EC (1992). An artificial intelligence approach to DNA sequence feature recognition. Trends Biotech. 10, 66-69.

Nakata K, Kanehisa M and DeLisi C (1985). Prediction of splice junctions in mRNA sequences. Nucleic Acids Res. 13, 5327-5340.

Nussinov R (1991). Signals in DNA sequences and their potential properties. Comput. Applic. Biosci. 7, 295-299.

Nussinov R (1992). The eukaryotic CCAAT and TATA boxes, DNA spacer flexibility and looping. J. Theor. Biol. 155, 243-270.

Penotti FE (1990). Human DNA TATA boxes and transcription initiation sites. A statistical study. J. Mol. Biol. 213, 37-52.

Prestridge DS (1991). SIGNAL SCAN: a computer program that scans sequences for eukaryotic transcriptional elements. Comput. Applic. Biosci. 7, 203-206.

Prestridge DA and Stormo G (1993). Signal Scan 3.0: new database and program features. Comput. Applic. Biosci. 9, 113-115.

Proudfoot NJ (1991). Poly(A) signals. Cell 64, 671-674.

Rogozin IB, Kolchanov NA and Milanesi L (1993). Classification of human splice sites. Int. J. Genome Res. 1, (in press).

Saenger W (1984). In "Springer Advanced Texts in Chemistry" (ed. CE Cantor). Springer-Verlag, New York.

Schmid CW and Shen C-KJ (1985). In "Molecular Evolutionary Genetics" (ed. RJ MacIntyre), p. 323. Plenum Press, New York.

Senapathy P, Shapiro MB and Harris NL (1990). Splice junctions, branch point sites, and exons: sequence statistics, identification and genome project. Methods Enzymol. 183, 252-278.

Shachmuradov IA, Kolchanov NA, Solovyev VV and Ratner VA (1986). Enhancer-like structures in moderate repetitive sequences of eukaryotic genomes. Genetika 22, 357-367 (in Russian).

Shapiro MB and Senapathy P (1987). RNA splice junctions of different classes of eukaryotes: sequence statistics and functional implications in gene expression. Nucleic Acids Res. 15, 7155-7174.

Sibbald PR and Argos P (1990). Scrutineer: a computer program that flexibly seeks and describes motifs and profiles in protein sequence databases. Comput. Applic. Biosci. 6, 279-288.

Smith TF, Waterman MS and Salder JR (1983). Statistical characterization of nucleic acid sequences functional domains. Nucleic Acids Res. 11, 2205-2220.

Smith R and Smith T (1990). Automatic generation of diagnostic sequence patterns from sets of related protein sequences. Proc. Natl Acad. Sci. USA 87, 118-122.

Snyder EE and Stormo G (1993). Identification of coding region in genomic DNA sequences: an application of dynamic programming and neural networks. Nucleic Acids Res. 21, 607-613.

Soderlund CA, Shanmugam P, White O, Fields C (1992). A tool for exploratory analysis of DNA sequence data. In "Proceedings of the Hawii International Conference on System Sciences, Biotechnology Computing Minitrack, January 7-10".

Staden R (1984). Measurements of the effect that coding for a protein has in DNA sequence and their use in finding genes. Nucleic Acids Res. 12, 551.

Staden R (1988). Methods to define and locate patterns of motifs in sequences. Comput. Applic. Biosci. 4, 53-60.

Staden R (1989). Method for calculating the probabilities of finding patterns in sequences. Comput. Applic. Biosci. 5, 89-96.

Staden R (1990). Finding protein coding regions in genomic sequences. Methods Enzymol. 183, 163-180.

Staden R and McLachlan AD (1982). Codon Preference and its use in identifying protein-coding regions in long DNA sequence. Nucleic Acids Res. 10, 141.

Steingrimsdottir H, Rowley G, Dorado G, Cole J and Lehmann AR (1992). Mutations which alter splicing in the human hypoxanthine guanine phosphoribosyltransferase gene. Nucleic Acids Res. 20, 1201-1208.

Stormo GD (1987). Identifying coding sequences. In "Nucleic Acid and Protein Sequence Analysis: A Practical Approach" (eds MJ Bishop and CJ Rawlings), pp. 231-258. IRL Press, Oxford.

Stormo GD (1988). Computer methods to locate signals in nucleic acid sequences. Ann. Rev. Biophys. Biophys. Chem. 17, 241-263.

Taya Y, Devos R, Tavernier J, Cheroutre H, Engler G and Fiers W (1982). Cloning and structure of the human immune interferon-gamma chromosomal gene. EMBO J. 1, 953-958.

Trifonov EN (1987). Translation framing code and frame-monitoring mechanism as suggested by the analysis of mRNA and 16S rRNA nucleotide sequences. J. Mol. Biol. 194, 643-652.

Wickens M (1990). How the messenger got its tail: addition of poly(A) in the nucleus. TIBS 15, 277-281.

Willard HF and Waye JS (1987). Hierarchical order on chromosome-specific human alpha satellite DNA. TIG 3, 192-198.

Wingender E (1988). Compilation of transcription regulating proteins. Nucleic Acids Res. 16, 1879-1900.

Wingender E, Heinemeyer T and Lincoln D (1991). Regulatory RNA sequences: predictability of their function. Adv. Mol. Genet. 4, 95-108.

Winnacker EL (1989). In "Tissue Specific Gene Expression" (ed. R Renkawitz), pp. 3-12. VCH Verlagsgesellschaft, D-6940 Weinheim (FRG).

APPENDIX 1 # Glossary of Computing Terms

Anonymous FTP

A mechanism for making files publicly available.

Archie

An index of files available by anonymous FTP.

ASCII - American Standard Code for Information Interchange

A method of representing characters in computers.

Bit

The smallest unit of computer memory containing either 0 or 1. Physically this is represented by a two state device.

Bulletin board

Electronic bulletin boards allow computer users to submit messages to a central location for viewing and response by others.

Byte

The smallest unit of computer memory which is directly addressable. Typically this is of 8 bits and is able to store a single ASCII character.

GUIDE TO HUMAN GENOME COMPUTING
ISBN 0-12-102050-9

CISC - Complex Instruction Set Computer

A CPU with a rich set of instructions working at a restricted clock speed.

CD ROM - Compact Disk Read Only Memory

An optical disk written with laser technology to store digital information. This type is written once and read many times.

Client-Server Computing

A model of sharing of computing resources.

CPU - Central Processing Unit

The part of the computer where instructions of the program are interpreted as logical or arithmetic operations on data.

CSMA/CD - Carrier Sense Multiple Access with Collision Detect

The physical basis of Ethernet.

DBA - Database Administrator

Person responsible for overall control of a database.

DBMS - Database Management System

Software to manage persistent data and to access and manipulate large amounts of data efficiently.

DDL - Data Definition Language

Language to define a conceptual schema in a DBMS.

DML - Data Manipulation Language

Language to manipulate data in a DBMS.

e-mail

Electronic mail is used for sending messages between computer users on a network.

Ethernet

A LAN technology with a bus structure of a single strand to which all nodes connect.

FAQ - Frequently Asked Questions

Introductory information relating to the subject of a Network News bulletin board.

FDDI - Fibre Distributed Data Interface

A LAN technology based on Token Ring.

File-store

> Computer memory which is not lost when the computer is switched off. Files are the units of storage for this kind of memory.

FTP - File Transfer Protocol

> An Internet protocol for transfer of files.

Gopher

> A worldwide hierarchical information system on the Internet.

GUI - Graphical User Interface

> Rather than typing commands, the user interacts with the computer via diagrammatical representations.

Internet

> A worldwide network of computers.

ISDN - Integrated Services Digital Network

> The networks providing both voice and digital data transmission on the same medium.

LAN - Local Area Network

> A computer network which spans a limited area such as one or a few buildings.

MAN - Metropolitan Area Network

> A computer network spanning the geographical area of a city.

Memory

> The information store of the computer.

Mouse

> Input device for pointing at the screen. Mouse movements and interactions by mouse buttons are tracked by programs.

Network News

> Electronic bulletin board of the Internet.

NFS - Network File System

> A distributed file system with transparent access irrespective of the physical location of the information.

Operating System

> A master control program which manages the functions of the computer and controls the running of application programs.

OSI - Open Systems Interconnection

A model for exchanging data over networks devised by the International Standards Organization.

PAD - Packet Assembler and Disassembler

Hardware and software interconverting the network representation and the computer representation of data.

Peripherals

Devices connected to a computer which are not essential for its function. Examples are printers, scanners and tape drives.

PSDN - Public Switched Data Network

The networks dedicated to digital data transmission.

PSTN - Public Switched Telephone Network

The networks used for telephone conversations.

RISC - Reduced Instruction Set Computer

A CPU with a core set of instructions from which complex operations may be built. This design allows high clock speeds.

RPC - Remote Procedure Call

A method of communication in client-server computing.

SEQUEL

Former name of SQL.

SMTP - Simple Mail Transfer Protocol

An Internet protocol for transfer of electronic mail.

SQL

A standard DML.

TCP/IP - Transmission Control Protocol/Internet Protocol

Network protocol used on the Internet.

Telnet

An Internet protocol for remote connections to provide a terminal session.

Token Ring

A circular network configuration with message passing, tokens, which nodes may examine for relevance.

Usenet

Electronic bulletin board of the Internet, also known as Network News.

VAN - Value Added Network

Services offered by an organization to customers on circuits owned by a separate telecommunications company.

WAIS - Wide Area Information Server

A facility to browse the contents of documents distributed around the world.

WAN - Wide Area Network

A computer network spanning a large geographical area such as the whole globe.

WIMPS - Windows, Icons, Mouse, Pull-down menus

A particular style of GUI.

X11

The implementation the X Window System, Version 11.

X.25

A low level network protocol for data exchange between computers.

X Terminal

Hardware and software to give a terminal session using the X Window protocol.

X Window System

Software definitions developed at the Massachussets Institute of Technology and used to implement GUIs.

APPENDIX 2   # Resources

AAtDB

An *Arabidopsis thaliana* Database, the genomic database for the plant thale cress. This database was built using software developed for ACeDB. Maintained by Mike Cherry (cherry@frodo.mgh.harvard.edu).

ACeDB

A *Caenorhabditis elegans* database, the genomic database for the nematode worm. You can ask to be placed on the e-mail list for ACeDB by contacting Richard Durbin (rd@mrc-lmb.cam.ac.uk) or Jean Thierry-Mieg (mieg@kaa.c-nrs-mop.fr).

The latest version of this program is available by ftp from several public file servers. In each case log in as user "anonymous" and give a user identifier as password. (1) lirmm.lirmm.fr (193.49.104.10) in France, directory genome/ acedb. (2) cele.mrc-lmb.cam.ac.uk (131.11.84.1) in England, in pub/acedb. (3) ncbi.nlm.nih.gov (130.14.20.1) in the USA, in repository/acedb.

aids-db

A collection of sequences from HIV and related viruses. Gerald Myers, LANL (glm@life.lanl.gov), Kersti MacInnes, LANL (kam@life.lanl.gov).

American Type Culture Collection

An on-line catalogue of clones, hosts, oligonucleotides, recombinant libraries and vectors is available for query via the IRX software. Accessible by telnet atcc.nih.gov; Login: search; Password: common. ATCC, 12301 Parklawn Drive, Rockville, MD 20852, USA. e-mail: help@atcc.nih.gov.

BIOSCI

The BIOSCI newsgroup network was developed to allow easy worldwide communications between biological scientists who work on a variety of computer networks. By having distribution sites or "nodes" on each major network, BIOSCI allows its users to contact people around the world without having to learn a variety of computer addressing tricks. Any user can simply post a message to his/her regional BIOSCI node and copies of that message will be distributed automatically to all other subscribers on all of the participating networks, including the Internet, USENET, BITNET, EARN, NET-NORTH, HEANET, and JANET. If you are located in the Americas or the Pacific Rim countries, please request that version of the BIOSCI information sheet by sending e-mail to the Internet address biosci@net.bio.net. The BIOSCI information sheet for Europe, Africa, and Central Asia is obtained from biosci@daresbury.ac.uk. If you have access to USENET news simply read and post to the newsgroups in the "bionet" newsgroup hierarchy using your USENET news software (e.g. readnews, rn, vnews, ANU-NEWS, postnews).

BISANCE

The CITI2 (Centre Inter-Universitaire de Traitement de l'Information) has been the French national computing resource for bio-molecular analysis since 1983 (Dessen et al., 1990). It provides on-line access to databases of nucleic and protein sequences, software for sequence retrieval and programs for sequence analysis. It has been the French node of EMBNET network since 1988. To register as a user of BISANCE write to BISANCE, CITI2, 45 rue des Saints Peres, 75270 PARIS Cedex 06, France. Tel: +33 1 42 96 24 89.

BLAST

To receive the current set of instructions on using the BLAST e-mail server, send a help message to the normal BLAST e-mail server address blast@-ncbi.nlm.nih.gov. Put the word "HELP" (without the quotes) on a single line in the body of the mail message. No subject line is needed. The BLAST program manual, which is appended to the help text, describes many BLAST program features and parameters. Only a subset of the program parameters are supported through the use of BLAST e-mail server directives. For answers to further questions not adequately explained in the help text in the BLAST

Manual, send a mail message with your question to NCBI staff at the address blast-help@ncbi.nlm.nih.gov. Do NOT send "HELP" requests for the documentation to this address.

BLITZ

BLITZ is an automatic electronic mail server for the MPsrch program of Shane Sturrock and John Collins, Biocomputing Research Unit, University of Edinburgh, Scotland. Send an electronic mail message to BLITZ@EMBL-Heidelberg containing the word "HELP" and the documentation will be automatically mailed to you. If you have any problems using the BLITZ service, or any questions, please send them to NETHELP@EMBL-Heidelberg.DE.

BLOCKS

BLOCKS is an aid to the detection and verification of protein sequence homology. There is a BLOCKS e-mail searcher, which compares a protein or DNA sequence to the current database of protein blocks. A detailed help file may be obtained by sending a blank e-mail message with the subject "help" to blocks@howard.fhcrc.org.

Cambridge Structural Database

The Cambridge Structural Database holds the atomic coordinates of small molecules. Produced by CCDC, University Chemical Laboratory, Lensfield Road, Cambridge CB2 1EW, U.K. Tel: +44 223-336409.

CarbBank

PC-based database and software system that contains information about the structure of complex carbohydrates. Includes the Complex Carbohydrate Structure Database (CCSD) and the CarbBank software system. Maintained by Dana Smith, Scott Doubet and Peter Albersheim (carbbank@uga.bitnet or 76424.1122@compuserve.com).

Cattle Genetic Map

Dr J. E. Womack, Texas Veterinary Medical Center, Texas A & M University, College Station, TX 77843-4467, USA. Tel: 409 845 2651. Fax: 409 845 9972.

chrominfo

An Apple Macintosh-based database system and associated software containing human chromosome map information. Maintained by Prakash Nadkarni (nadkarni-prakash@cs.yale.edu).

Chromosome Abnormality Database

Mrs M. Fitchett & Dr S. Mercer, Dept of Medical Genetics, Churchill Hospital, Old Road, Headington, Oxford, OX1 7LJ, UK.

Coriell Institute

An electronic catalogue will be available soon. Human Genetic Mutant Cell Repository, Coriell Institute for Medical Research, 401 Haddon Avenue, Camden, NJ 08103, USA.

CRI-Map

Dr Phil Green, Washington University, Box 8232, 4566 Scott Avenue, St Louis, MO 63110, USA.

DAPMAIL

DAPMAIL is a program that gives remote access to the Edinburgh University Biocomputing Research Unit (BRU) fast sequence database searching programs that runs on an Active Memory Technology Distributed Array Processor AMT DAP. To use DAPMAIL, send electronic mail to dapmail@uk.ac.ed. It is important for your system to be able to receive return mail from the Edinburgh system; please check initially by requesting "help" and verifying you can receive the message from Edinburgh. The output file may be quite big; check regularly that you have enough space in your system to receive a big (up to 100 KB) file. Currently the following commands are available:

prosrch - runs the protein database search program using a query sequence

ptnsrch - runs the protein database search program. using a query pattern

diasrch - runs the nucleic acid database search program using a query sequence

help - gets you the help file

news - gets you a file of current news about dap searches and available resources

DIMDI

Deutsches Institut für Medizinische Dokumentation und Information, Weisshaustrasse 27, D-5000 Koln 41, Germany. Tel: 49 221 47 241. Fax: 49 221 41 1429.

DKFZ

In 1990, the Commission of the European Communities launched the Human Genome Analysis Programme (HGA). Major parts are the genetic mapping of markers on a set of large families, establishment of an ordered library of DNA clones spanning the human genome, data handling and data analysis, scientific training, and study of ethical issues involved in genome research. In 1991, Deutsches Krebsforschungszentrum (DKFZ) in Heidelberg was appointed to serve as the data resource for the HGA programme.

The main goals of the Resource Centre are the data and analysis services, training of users, promotion of network communication, and new developments in database integration and interfacing.

The data and analysis services are centred around a collection of sequence and structure databases (PDB, EMBL, GenBank, SwissProt, PIR, etc.) to which mapping and disease databases have been added (OMIM and GDB). Users are provided with a friendly menu-guided environment in the UNIX operation system giving them database search options, a variety of analysis tools including the GCG package, support for graphical output, file editing options, and electronic communication. Off-line support, a telephone hot line, comprehensive manuals, and training courses are integral parts of the service.

Two major developments at the Resource Centre are HUSAR and IGD. HUSAR - the Heidelberg Unix Sequence Analysis Resources - is a sequence and structure analysis package based on a Unix implementation of the GCG programs. IGD - the Integrated Genomic Database - is a collaborative project aimed at integrating genome related data from multiple resource databases (EMBL, SwissProt, GDB, OMIM, RLDB, UK Probe Bank).

Mrs. Barbara Maier, European Data Resource for Human Genome Analysis, DKFZ/Molecular Biophysics, Im Neuenheimer Feld 280, D-6900 Heidelberg, Germany. Tel: +49 6221 42 2372. Fax: +49 6221 42 2333. e-mail: dok418@cvx12.dkfz-heidelberg.de.

DNA Data Bank of Japan

DDBJ is primarily concerned with covering DNA data produced in Japan and has close collaborative ties with GenBank and EMBL. DNA Data Bank of Japan, Laboratory of Genetic Information Analysis, National Institute of Genetics, Mishima, Shizuoka 411, Japan.

ECO2DBASE

The *Escherichia coli* gene-protein database, which links information about *E. coli* genes and their protein spots on two dimensional gels. Maintained by Frederick C. Neidhart (frederick_c._neidhardt@um.cc.umich.edu).

EMBL Data Library

EMBL seeks to collect, organize, document and make freely available the body of known nucleotide sequence data. EMBL Data Library, Postfach 10.2209, Meyerhofstrasse 1, D-6900 Heidelberg, Germany. Tel: +49 6221 387258. Fax: +49 6221 387519. e-mail: DataLib@EMBL-Heidelberg.DE.

EMBL Network Fileserver

You use the file server by sending one or more of the commands shown below as electronic mail to the address NETSERV@EMBL-Heidelberg.DE. The requested file(s) will then be returned to you by the file server.

Help - sends a general help file (this file)

Help <topic> - sends the help file and directory listing of <topic>

Get <filename> - sends the file <filename>

Dir <directory> - same as Help <directory>

Size <filesize> - change packet size of split files

The files accessible via the file server are organized into directories. The following directories exist:

Nuc - Nucleotide Sequence data from the EMBL and GenBank sequence databases.

Prot - The SwissProt Protein Sequence Database

ProteinData - Protein structure data

Prosite - Prosite Pattern Database

Blocks - Protein Blocks Database

PKCDD - Protein Kinase Catalytic Domain Database

ECD - *E. coli* Database

ENZYME - The ENZYME database

HLA - HLA sequence alignments

EPD - Eukaryotic Promotor Database

RepBase - Prototypic sequences for human repetitive DNA

LiMB - Listing of Molecular Biological Databases

REBASE - Restriction Enzyme database

RELIBRARY - Restriction enzyme lists for various software packages

FlyBase - Drosophila genetic map database

HaemB - Haemophilia B database

CpGIsle - Database of CpG islands in human genome

SmallRNA - Compilation of small RNA sequences

tRNA - tRNA database

Berlin - Berlin Databank of 5S rRNA and 5S rRNA gene sequences

rRNA - Compilation of small ribosomal subunit RNA sequences

Alu - Alu sequence database

CodonUsage - Codon usage tables

Align - DNA sequence alignments and consensus sequences

RefList - Bibliographies, Reference lists

DOS_Software - Free software for IBM PCs and clones

Mac_Software - Free software for the Apple Macintosh

VAX_Software - Free software for VAX/VMS

UNIX_Software - Free software for UNIX

Software - General software and software information

Doc - Documents with relevance to molecular biology (submission forms, technical documents, etc.)

CUTG - Compilation of codon frequencies tabulated from the GenBank nucleotide sequence database

3d_ali - Three dimensional protein alignment database

XRay - Information for crystallographers

EMBNET

This is an association of national EMBNET (European Molecular Biology network) national nodes as well as some specialized nodes listed by Stoehr and Omond (1991).

EMBASE

EMBASE (Excerpta Medica) seeks comprehensive coverage of the world bio-medical literature. Produced by: Elsevier Science Publishers BV, Excerpta Medica, Molenwerf 1, 1014 AG Amsterdam, The Netherlands. Tel: +31 20 5803 507. Fax: +31 20 5803 222.

Encyclopedia of the Mouse Genome

Dr J Nadeau, The Jackson Laboratory, Bar Harbor, ME 04609, USA.

enzyme

The Enzyme Data Bank, a database of information about enzymes, including names, catalytic activity, cofactors, and pointers to relevant entries in sequence databases. This directory also includes an ASN.1 encoding of the database. Maintained by Amos Bairoch (bairoch@cmu.unige.ch).

Eukaryotic Promotor Database (EPD)

The Eukaryotic Promoter Database, a collection of biologically functional, experimentally defined RNA POL-II promoters active in higher eukaryotes. Maintained by Philipp Bucher (philipp.bucher@isrec.arcom.ch).

European Collection of Animal Cell Cultures (ECACC)

PHLS Centre for Applied Microbiology & Research, Division of Biologics, Porton Down, Salisbury SP4 0JG, Wiltshire, UK.

European Human Cell Bank (EHCB)

Dr B. Bolton, PHLS Centre for Applied Microbiology & Research, Division of Biologics, Porton Down, Salisbury SP4 0JG, Wiltshire, UK.

FASTA

The program is available by anonymous ftp from uvaarpa.virginia.edu (128.143.2.7).

Mail-FASTA is based on the FASTA program developed by Pearson and Lipman as implemented in the GCG package. It allows you to perform fast and sensitive comparisons of your nucleic acid or protein sequences against various databases including the most recent EMBL entries. It answers the question: which entries in the database are similar to my sequence? Nucleotide sequence databases available: EMBL database, GenBank database, latest releases plus new entries, and individual divisions of EMBL. Protein sequence databases available: Swiss-Prot database, PIR/NBRF database, latest releases plus new entries. To obtain the help information send the message "help" to FASTA@EMBL-Heidelberg.DE.

FASTMAP, PEDRAW

Dr David Curtis, Academic Department of Psychiatry, St. Mary's Hospital, Praed Street, London W2 1NY, UK.

FlyBase

The Drosophila Genetic Database, the genomic database for the fruit fly *Drosophila melanogaster*. Maintained by Michael Ashburner. e-mail: ma11@phx.cam.ac.uk.

GBASE

The genetic database of the mouse at The Jackson Laboratory. Muriel T. Davisson, Donald P. Doolittle, Thomas H. Roderick, and Alan L. Hillyard, The Jackson Laboratory, 600 Main Street, Bar Harbor, ME 04609-0800, USA. Tel: 207-288-3371. Fax: 207-288-5079.

GCG Package

Dina Beers, GCG, University Research Park, 575 Science Drive, Suite B, Madison, WI 53711, USA. Tel: 608 231 5200. e-mail: help@gcg.com.

GenBank

GenBank is a US government sponsored, internationally available collection of all reported nucleotide sequences, catalogued and annotated with functional physical and administrative context distributed by the NCBI.

GeneID

GeneID is an Artificial Intelligence system for analysing vertebrate genomic DNA and prediction of exons and gene structure. It is implemented as an automatic e-mail response system (geneid@bir.cedb.uwf.edu).

Genethon

Genethon, Human Genome Research Centre, 1 rue de l'Internationale, BBP 60 - 91002, Evry, France.

Genome Data Base (GDB)

The goal of GDB is to provide a human genetic mapping and disease database to support the mapping and sequencing of the genome. GDB User Support, Welch Medical Library, Johns Hopkins University, Baltimore, MD 21205-2100, USA. Tel: 401 955 7058. e-mail: help@welch.jhu.edu.

GnomeView

Available by FTP from pnlg.pnl.gov (130.20.64.11) in the gnomeview directory. If the local machine runs Unix the FTP session must be given the command "quote site unix" because the remote machine runs VAX/VMS. The file named something like "GV_b1.2.get.ftp.full.1" contains a script for pulling all the other files over. Contact Richard Douthart, Life Sciences Center, Pacific Northwest Laboratory, Richland, WA 99352, USA. Tel: 509 375-2653. Fax: 509 375-3649. e-Mail: dick@gnome.pnl.gov.

GRAIL

To become a registered user send the following e-mail message to grail@ornl.gov (please make sure that the key word "Register" is on the first line of your message)"

Register

Your name

Your address

Your phone number

Your e-mail address

ICAtools

Dr. J Parsons, Dept. of Genetics, Washington University School of Medicine, St. Louis, MO 63110, USA. e-mail: jparsons@elegans.wustl.edu.

HOMOG

See LIPED.

Integrated Genomic Database (IGD)

IGD aims to provide access to constituent "working" databases, especially those associated with the EC and national European programmes. The project is run by the German Cancer Research Centre (DKFZ) in Heidelberg in collaboration with the Imperial Cancer Research Fund in London/Clare Hall and the UK HGMP-RC in Harrow. IGD is being designed as a network system on the client/server architecture. Dr O. Ritter, Deutsches Krebsforschungszentrum, Im Neuenheimer Feld 280, D-6900 Heidelberg, Germany.

INTERLAB/Ansaldo Network

Dr A. Manniello (Cell Line Data Base)

Dr B. Parodi (B Line Data Base)

Dr O. Aresu (Molecular Probe Data Base)

Interlab Project, Servizio tecnologie Biomediche, Instituto Nazionale per la Ricerca sul Cancro, Viale Benedetto XV, 10-16132 Genova, Italy.

kabat

A collection of sequences of immunological importance, including aligned protein and nucleic acid sequences in various formats. Compiled by Elvin Kabat (kabat@ncbi.nlm.nih.gov). Maintained by George Johnson (tt@immuno.esam.nwu.edu).

LINKAGE

Pascale Denayrouse, Fondation Jean Dausset - CEPH. Fax: (+33) 1 40 18 01 55.

LINKSYS, LINK2MAP, LINK2CRI

John Attwood, MRC Human Biochemical Genetics Unit, University College London, Wolfson House, 4 Stephenson Way, London NW1 2HE, UK.

LIPED, PC LINKAGE, HOMOG

Professor Jurg Ott, Columbia University,Box 58, 722 West 168 Street, New York, NY 10032, USA.

List of Molecular Biology Databases (LiMB)

The LiMB database (Lawton, Martinez and Burks, 1989) is available in hardcopy, PC floppy disk or via electronic mail. e-mail: limb%life@lanl.gov.

MAP

Professor Newton Morton, Department of Community Medicine, Southampton General Hospital, University of Southampton, Southampton SO9 4XY, UK.

MAPMAKER

Mapmaker Distribution, The Lander Lab, Whitehead Institute for Biomedical Research, Nine Cambridge Center, Cambridge, MA 02142, USA.

Marshfield Medical Research Foundation

Dr J. Weber, Marshfield Medical Research Foundation, 1000 North Oak, Marshfield, WI 54449, USA.

Martinsried Institute for Protein Sequences (MIPS)

MIPS serves as the European partner of PIR, improving accessibility for European researchers and attempting speedier processing of protein sequences submitted for publication. Produced by Martinsried Institute for Protein Sequences (MIPS), Max Planck Institute for Biochemistry, D-8033 Martinsried bei Muenchen, Germany.

MEDLINE

MEDLINE seeks comprehensive coverage of the world's biomedical literature. Produced by MEDLARS Management Section, 8600 Rockville Pike, National Library of Medicine, Bethesda, MD 20894, USA.

Mendelian Inheritance in Animals (MIA)

Dr Frank Nicholas, Department of Animal Science, University of Sydney, New South Wales 2006, AUSTRALIA. Tel: +61 2 692 2184. Fax: +61 2 692 2114.

metabolism

A collection of notes and datasets relating to intermediate metabolism. Maintained by Peter Karp (pkarp@ai.sri.com).

metproto

A database of metabolic reactions. Maintained by Ray Ochs. e-mail: rso2@-po.cwru.edu.

Mouse Backcross Database (MBX)

UK HGMP Resource Centre, Watford Road, Harrow, Middlesex HA1 3UJ, UK. Tel: +44 81 869 3446. Fax: +44 81 869 3807. e-mail: cbates@crc.ac.uk.

MRC Radiobiology Unit Databases

Databases of mouse genetics information. Dr J. Peters, MRC Radiobiology Unit, Chilton, Didcot, Oxfordshire OX11 0RD, UK. Tel: +44 235 834393. Fax: +44 834918.

National Centre for Biotechnology Information (NCBI)

The National Center for Biotechnology Information, National Library of Medicine, Bethesda, MD 20894, USA. Tel: 301 496 2475. e-mail: info@ncbi.nlm.nih.gov.

Microbial Strain Data Network (MSDN)

Access to MSDN is possible either by direct connection to the MSDN computer CGNET VAX/VMS or via Telecom Gold. In order to get an identification number and password and further information about services and possible charges contact: MSDN Secretariat, 307 Huntingdon Road, Cambridge, CB3 0JX, UK.

NFRES

Non-redundant Functionally Equivalent Sequences. A collection of non-redundant nucleic acid sequences from GenBank, separated into different functional classes (coding regions, exons, introns, etc.). Maintained by Andrzej Konopka. e-mail: konopka@fcrfv2.ncifcrf.gov.

Normalised Gene Designation Database (NGDD)

The following is a list of the organisms and the gene designations considered in this collection:

3. *Escherichia coli* (K-12) 1032 genes
4. *Salmonella typhimurium* 666 genes
5. *Bacillus subtilis* 537 genes
6. *Pseudomonas aeruginosa* 230 genes
7. *Caulobacter crescentus* 93 genes

Compiled by Yvon Abel (Centre de Recherches Mathematiques) and Robert Cedergren (Departement de Biochimie), Universite de Montreal, CP 6128, Succ "A", Montreal, Quebec, Canada, H3C 3J7. E-mail: cedergren@bch.umontreal.ca.

On-line Mendelian Inheritance in Man (OMIM)

OMIM is a database in the Johns Hopkins University School of Medicine maintained by Victor McKusick providing textual information on human genetic diseases. Produced by: Dr Victor McKusick, Blalock 10, Johns Hopkins Hospital, Baltimore, MD 21205, USA. Tel: 301 955 6641.

PC LINKAGE

See LIPED.

Pedigree/DRAW

Dr Jean W. MacCluer, Department of Genetics, Southwest Foundation for Biomedical Research, PO Box 28147, San Antonio, TX 78284, USA.

PedDraw

See FASTMAP.

PedPack

Dr Alun Thomas, School of Mathematical Sciences, University of Bath, Claverton Down, Bath BA2 7AY, UK.

PiGBASE

Dr Alan Archibald, AFRC Roslin Institute, Roslin, Midlothian, EH25 9PS, UK. Tel: +44 31 440 2726. Fax: +44 31 4440 0434.

pkinases

A non-redundant annotated collection of protein kinase sequences. Maintained by Anne Marie Quinn (quinn@salk-sc2.sdsc.edu).

Poultry Genome Database

Dr David W. Burt, AFRC Roslin Institute, Roslin, Midlothian, EH25 9PS, UK. Tel: +44 31 440 2726. Fax: +44 31 4440 0434.

PRIMER

PRIMER c/o The Lander Lab., Whitehead Institute/MIT, 9 Cambridge Center, Cambridge, MA 02142, USA. Also by anonymous ftp from genome.wi.mit.-edu in the directory distribution. e-mail to "primer@genome.wi.edu" (Internet) or "lander@mitwibr (Bitnet).

PROSITE

PROSITE is a compilation of biologically significant protein sequence patterns. Produced by Amos Bairoch, Department of Medical Biochemistry, CMU, University of Geneva, Switzerland. Tel. +41 22 361 84 92. e-mail: bairoch@cmu.unige.ch.

Protein Database (PDB)

PDB seeks comprehensive coverage of bibliographic, atomic coordinate and crystallographic structure factor data for biological macromolecules. Produced by: Chemistry Department, Brookhaven National Laboratory, Upton, NY 11973, USA. Tel: 516 282 4382, E-mail: pdb@bnlchm.bitnet.

Protein Identification Resource (PIR)

PIR collects data on completed sequence proteins, amino-terminal sequences and bibliographic citations for amino acid sequences. PIR also contains an auxiliary database for sequences in preparation and additional fragmentary and predicted sequences. Produced by: Protein Identification Resource (PIR), National Biomedical Research Foundation, 3900 Reservoir Road, NW, Washington, DC 20007, USA.

REBASE

Dr R. Roberts, Restriction Enzymes Database, New England Biolabs, 32 Tozer Road Beverly, MA 01915-5599, USA.

repbase

A collection of datasets of human repetitive DNA sequences. Maintained by Jerzy Jurka (jurek@jmullins.stanford.edu).

Reference Library Database (RLDB)

Dr H. Lehrach and Dr G. Zehetner, Imperial Cancer Research Fund Genome Analysis Laboratory, 44 Lincoln's Inn Fields, London WC2A 3PX, UK.

Science Citation Index

ISI (Science Citation Index), a machine readable version of the printed Science Citation Index with additional journal coverage from the Current Contents series of publications. Produced by: Institute for Scientific Information, 3501 Market St., Philadelphia, PA 19104, USA. Tel: 800 523 1850 ex 1483 or 215 386 0100.

SIGMA

System for integrated genome map assembly available by anonymous ftp from atlas.lanl.gov. Additional information may be obtained by sending the message "sigma-info" to bioserve@t10.lanl.gov. Contact is Michael J. Cinkosky, Theoretical Biology and Biophysics Group, Los Alamos National Laboratory, Los Alamos, NM 87545, USA. Tel: 505 665 0840.

Sequence Analysis Bibliographic Reference Data Bank (SEQANALREF)

SEQANALREF is a bibliographic reference databank relative to papers dealing with sequence analysis. This databank stores the references of articles from the expanding field of mathematical and computer analysis of biomolecular sequences. The majority of entries belong to one of the following categories:

- Algorithms for protein and nucleic acid sequence analysis: primary, secondary and tertiary structure analysis; pattern matching; similarity searches; alignments, etc.

- Algorithms for sequence-based phylogenetic analysis.
- Description of biopolymer data banks: nucleic acid, protein, tertiary structure, carbohydrates, etc.
- Description of software packages.
- Description of on-line services for molecular biologists.
- Compiled by Amos Bairoch, Department of Medical Biochemistry, CMU, University of Geneva, Switzerland. Tel. +41 22 361 84 92. e-mail: bairoch@cmu.unige.ch.

SCRUTINEER

This is a program for investigating protein motifs. It is available for VAX Pascal on the EMBL network fileserver. In case of problems contact sibbald@embl-heidelberg.de.

SEQNET

This is an on-line computing service for molecular biology. UK academics should send an e-mail request to uig@cxa.dl.ac.uk and ask for the SEQNET registration forms. You must supply your ordinary mail address so the forms can be sent out to you. The registration forms can also be obtained from: Program Enquiry Office, SERC Daresbury Laboratory, Warrington WA4 4AD, UK. Industrialists should contact: DRS, SERC Daresbury Laboratory, Warrington WA4 4AD, UK.

SheepMap

Dr G.W. Montgomery, Molecular Biology Unit, Dept of Biochemistry, University of Otago, PO Box 56, Dunedin, New Zealand. Tel: +64 3 479 7832. Fax: +64 3 477 5413.

Staden Package

Dr Rodger Staden, MRC Laboratory of Molecular Biology, Hills Road, Cambridge CB2 2QH, UK. e-mail: rs@mrc-lmba.cam.ac.uk.

SwissProt

SWISSPROT attempts to list all protein sequences and related data. Compiled by Amos Bairoch, Department of Medical Biochemistry, CMU, University of Geneva, SWITZERLAND Tel: +41 22 361 84 92. e-mail: bairoch@cmu.unige.ch.

TBASE

A computerized database for transgenic animals and targeted mutations (Woychik et al., 1993). Available via Gopher at Johns Hopkins University, connect your client to merlot.welch.jhu.edu, port 70.

t4phage

A genomic database for the T4 phage. Maintained by David Batts, Shane Peterson and Dr. Elizabeth Kutter (t4phage@milton.u.washington.edu).

Transcription Factor Database (TFD)

tfdhelp@ncbi.nlm.nih.gov, TFD-related technical help requests. tfdinfo@ncbi.nlm.nih.gov, messages or questions addressed to the TFD users community. tfdinfo-request@ncbi.nlm.nih.gov, requests for subscription to the TFDINFO users mailing list. Compiled by David Ghosh, National Center for Biotechnology Information. e-mail: ghosh@ncbi.nlm.nih.gov.

UK DNA Probe Bank

Mr S. Bryant and Dr N. Spurr, Human Genetic Resources, Imperial Cancer Research Fund, Clare Hall Laboratories, South Mimms, Hertfordshire, EN6 3LD, UK.

UK Human Genome Mapping Project Resource Centre (UK HGMP-RC)

The computing facility of the UK HGMP-RC is a client/server system designed to support molecular biology and genetics research in the UK and Europe (Rysavy et al., 1992). To register for biological materials or computing apply to UK HGMP Resource Centre, Watford Road, Harrow, Middlesex HA1 3UJ, UK. Tel: +44 81 869 3446. Fax: +44 81 869 3807. e-mail: cbates@crc.ac.uk.

Wessex Register of Chromosome Abnormalities

Mrs S. Youings and Dr P. Jacobs, Salisbury District Hospital, Odstock, Salisbury, Wiltshire, SP2 8BJ, UK.

XShell

Stephen P Bryant, Human Genetic Resources Laboratory, Imperial Cancer Research Fund, Blanche Lane, South Mimms, Potters Bar, Herts EN6 3LD, UK.
Tel: (+44) 707 644444
Fax: (+44) 707 646332
Internet: s.bryant@mahler.clh.icnet.uk

References

Dessen P, Fondrat C, Valencien C and Mugnier C (1990). BISANCE: a French service for access to biomolecular sequence databases. Comput. Applic. Biosci. 6, 355-356.

Lawton JR, Martinez FA and Burks CA (1989). Overview of the LiMB database. Nucleic Acids Res. 17, 5885-5899.

Rysavy FR, Bishop MJ, Gibbs GP and Williams GW (1992). The UK Human Genome Mapping Project online computing service. Comput. Applic. Biosci. 8, 149-154.

Stoehr P and Omond R (1991). EMBnet: European Molecular Biology Network. In "Genome Analysis: from Sequence to Function", (eds J Collins J and AJ Driesel), pp. 177-177. Huethig Buch Verlag, Heidelberg.

Woychik RP, Wassom JS and Kingsbury D (1993). TBASE: a computerised database for transgenic animals and targeted mutations. Nature 363, 375-376.

APPENDIX 3 | # User Desktop Devices: Hardware and Software

Francis Rysavy

Clinical Research Centre, Watford Road, Harrow,
Middlesex HA1 3UJ, UK
Internet: frysavy@crc.ac.uk

To access the networking services described in this book the desktop devices required are very dependent on the readers' local information technology (IT) infrastructure. Thus this account can serve only as guidance. IT systems are continually being developed and this information will quickly become out of date. Readers are recommended to contact their local computer centres for up to date information on product and service availability.

The national and international network services can be accessed in two ways (see Chapter 1, Section 2.3) either by using an IP service or by making an X29 call.

1   IP Service

The access may be performed from any network worldwide which connects to the INTERNET. One of the principal advantages of using the IP service is that X (X-windows graphical interface) applications can be run on remote hosts and displayed to an appropriately equipped desktop device.

Many of the databases of interest to molecular biologists and geneticists already have an X version, including such programs as "xrn" which provides a comfortable environment for reading network news bulletins, the X version of the Staden software, ACEDB the nematode genome database system, ENTREZ which provides access to nucleic acid and protein sequences and their references (including abstracts) and others.

The desktop device can be not only a UNIX workstation but also a personal computer (PC) or X terminal from a number of manufacturers. It must be equipped with appropriate networking and graphical display facilities. It has to be well integrated into the local IT infrastructure, which should be connected to a wide area computer network (WAN).

- A UNIX workstation, from manufacturers such as Sun, DEC, IBM, Hewlett-Packard, Silicon Graphics to name just a few, equipped with software which will allow it to perform as an X display server using the IP protocol. The terminal emulators discussed below should be also available. The workstation should have a colour screen of the highest quality, minimum size 17" and resolution 1024 by 768 pixels is recommended. To get a good performance not less than 16 Mbytes of memory is required. To interact with X a three button mouse is desirable.

- A PC configured so that it can support X applications and terminal emulations as the workstation above. The X display server "eXceed", recommended by the UK IUSC (Inter University Software Committee) Workstations working party is available for IBM compatible PCs via CHEST (Combined High Education Software Team) in the UK. There are many other products available on the market. "MacX" is the X display server for the Apple Macintosh. The screen of the PC should be sized as for the workstation. The more powerful the CPU and the more memory available, the better is the performance. The PC should have an appropriate graphics card, an Ethernet card, not less than an 80 Mbyte disk and a three button mouse.

- An X terminal from number of manufacturers. A large, high resolution colour screen (as above) would be an asset. The rest of the configuration will depend on the IT infrastructure to which the terminal is connected.

2 X29 Call Using a PAD

Access is possible to a variety of networks such as the UK JANET, the EuropaNet or the Public Data Networks . The desktop device used can be any PC or workstation running a terminal emulator or a terminal, which provides or has access to, a PAD.

If full screen editing is required the reader will need a terminal or a personal computer/workstation terminal emulator with full screen facilities such as a VT100. To perform graphical work a TEKTRONIX emulation is frequently used by applications programs. The DOS version of the Public Domain program KERMIT supports both VT100 and TEKTRONIX 4010 emulation. Similar emulations are available for the Apple Macintosh.

Index